MACMILLAN/McGRAW-HILL

Math

ESL
Activity Guide

Grade 5

- Unit Planners
- Read Together
- Hands-on Lessons
- Math Activities
- Multilevel Strategies

- Math Vocabulary
- Learning Resources
- Foldables
- Problem Solving
- Assessment

Macmillan McGraw-Hill

Building Math Concepts and Language Skills

The primary purpose of Macmillan/McGraw-Hill Math ESL is to provide differentiated instruction and support for both ESL and grade level math teachers. English language learners will master established math standards at the same time as they participate in the English language acquisition process.

Read Together

Sets the scene to build background and develop oral language by integrating:

- Math Objectives
- ESL Standards
- Reading Skills
- Vocabulary
- Multilevel Strategies

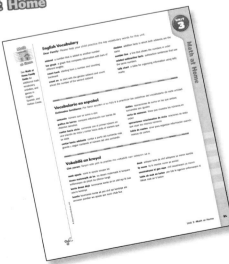

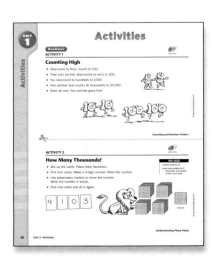

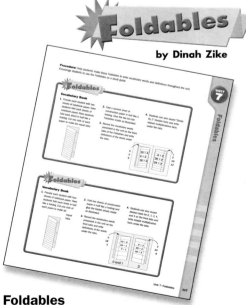

Foldables by Dinah Zike

Math at Home
Provides math vocabulary in 3 languages that students can review at home with their families.

Activities
Each unit contains engaging real-life activities that help English language learners develop and reinforce math concepts.

Foldables
Help students organize and summarize math content and vocabulary.

Lesson 4

🕐 45 minutes

▶ **Key Strategy**
Use visuals

▶ **Format**
Whole class and small groups

▶ **Math Vocabulary**
even, odd

▶ **Daily Vocabulary**
count by, pattern

▶ **Resources**
Learning Resource 22
Teacher Tool 12

Materials
• connecting cubes
• crayons
• index cards (per pair)

Assessment
Check children's mastery of the lesson vocabulary by observing them as they skip-count and color the hundred charts. See Assessment Checklist on page 93. Remind children to work on their Foldables.

Home Connection
Invite children to take a hundred chart home and choose a number to skip-count by with their family. Prompt children to share their experiences with the class.

Skip-Counting Patterns

Math Objectives
• Identify number patterns.
• Identify and extend skip-counting patterns.

ESL/TESOL Descriptors
• Engage in conversation.
• Connect new information to information previously learned.

Activate Prior Knowledge Give each child 40 connecting cubes. Instruct them to construct four 10-cube trains. Count the cubes. Remind children that they can count by tens. Demonstrate and have children repeat.

Hands-on Lesson Sit in a circle. Give each child an index card and crayon. Say: one; write it on your index card. Prompt children to count by ones around the circle, saying their number and adding it to the card. Go around once more, asking children to stand and show their card as they say the number. Challenge children to skip-count by twos, encouraging those children with cards 2, 4, 6, etc. to stand and count around the circle. Repeat, counting by three and fives.

• Divide the class into groups and assign each a number: 2, 3, 5, or 10. Distribute copies of Teacher Tool 12. Have groups use the chart to skip-count by their assigned number. Tell children to color the numbers they land on.

• Discuss **even** and **odd** numbers. Challenge children to identify whether their sequence includes all even numbers, all odd numbers, or both.

• Invite groups to share their hundred charts and verbally describe the number patterns they see. Challenge them to point to each number as they lead the class in skip-counting to 100. Distribute Learning Resource 22: Counting Patterns. Help children to complete it.

Challenge Invite groups to calculate how many numbers are included in their sequence when they count to 100. Ask them if there are more or fewer numbers when counting by a greater number.

Multilevel Strategies

❶ Preproduction
Write 2, 3, 5, and 10 on the board. Count aloud by one of these numbers and have children point to the number you are counting by.

Writing Have children illustrate the numbers in a sequence counted by twos.

❷❸ Early Production and Speech Emergence
Count aloud and ask: Am I counting by twos, threes, fives or tens?

Writing Point to 2, 3, 5, or 10 and have children write the numbers in that sequence.

❹❺ Intermediate and Advanced Fluency
Ask children to count by twos, threes, or fives.

Writing Have children write these numbers using number words.

Learning Resource 22

Name _____

Counting Patterns

Fill in the blanks. Count by threes.
Circle all the even numbers.

3 | 6 | 9 | | 15 | | | 24 | 27 |

| 33 | | 39 | 42 | | | 51 | 54 | 57 |

Fill in the blanks. Count by fives.
Draw a box around the odd numbers.

5 | 10 | 15 | 20 | | 30 | | 45 |

| | 65 | | | 80 | 85 | 95 |

© Macmillan/McGraw-Hill

Lessons

• Each lesson introduces math concepts by activating prior knowledge

• Modeling opportunities that help students to build math background, master key concepts, and develop thinking skills

• Multilevel strategies, both oral and written, are complemented with a reproducible learning resource

---

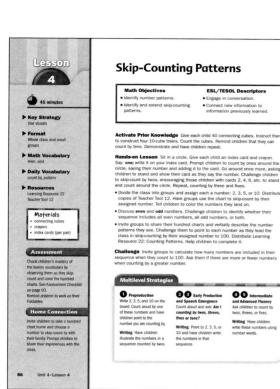

Math at Home
Includes math vocabulary, math-problem practice, and games; in 3 languages.

Math Center Cards
Students come together at the math center and engage in real-life problem-solving situations.

Math Rhymes and Songs CDs
Help develop math concepts and vocabulary and strengthen students' auditory and listening skills.

Overhead Manipulatives
Provide teachers with additional resources to model concepts and activities.

MACMILLAN/McGRAW-HILL
Overhead Manipulative Kit
Grades K–3
Math

• Attribute Blocks
• Base Ten
• Bills Set
• Clock Dials
• Cubes
• Connecting Cubes
• Counters, Two Colors
• Fraction Strips
• Pattern Blocks

Macmillan McGraw-Hill
ISBN 0021044678

Assessment

• Unit assessment checklist helps teachers monitor and evaluate students' progress

• Foldables provide an additional informal assessment opportunity

Problem Solving

• Lessons use the 4-step heuristic: Read, Plan, Solve, and Look Back

• Mathematical problem-solving models

• Embedded reading skills and math strategies that build reasoning skills

---

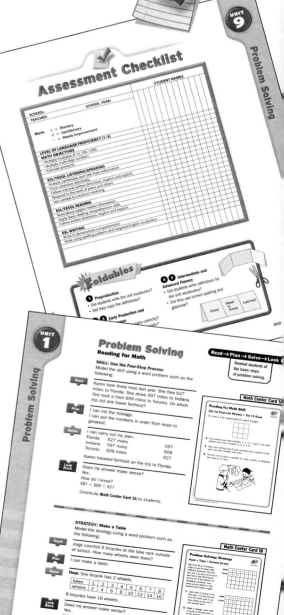

Assessment Checklist

Problem Solving
Reading for Math

SKILL: Use the Four-Step Process
Model the skill using a word problem such as the following:

Karen took three trips last year. She flew 627 miles to Florida. She drove 597 miles to Indiana. She took a train 609 miles to Toronto. On which trip did she travel farthest?

STRATEGY: Make a Table
Model the strategy using a word problem such as the following:

Jorge counted 8 bicycles at the bike rack outside of school. How many wheels were there?

LOG ON
www.mmhmath.com provides ESL teachers with additional math resources, such as printable vocabulary cards and ESL appropriate Web-linked activities.

Building Math Concepts and Language Skills

Sally Blake, Ph.D. and Josefina Villamil Tinajero, Ed. D.
The University of Texas at El Paso

The Mathematics Challenge

School teachers are still facing a mathematical problem that is causing great concern: how to teach basic mathematical concepts to the increasing numbers of English Language Learners (ELLs) (Mather & Chiodo, 1994). Most teachers in public schools and colleges are white and female, yet 35% or more of their students are minorities, a growing number of them ELLs. The United States is growing increasingly diverse. The Hispanic population grew more than seven times as fast as other parts of the country between 1980 and 1990 and is projected to double from the year 2010 to 2050, from 39.3 million to 80.7 million (U.S. Census Bureau: 1993).

While some gains in scores of ELLs are evident with national mathematics tests, there still remains a large gap between groups according to scores from *The Nation's Report Card* (NCES 2001). The problem becomes more transparent in the light of international studies. Recent data from the Third International Mathematics and Science Study (TIMSS, 1996, and TIMMS-R, 1999) indicate that US students seldom explore key concepts in mathematics in-depth, that underlying themes and principles are either not identified or simply stated but not developed, and that students spend more time practicing routine procedures than in conceptual mathematical thinking. This problem becomes more pronounced when working with children starting with limited communication skills in the English language.

With this significant and growing percentage of American school children coming from families whose primary language is not English, mainstream classroom teachers must grapple with a much wider range of language development and skill levels than in the past. Finding ways to address the needs of students is an ever-increasing concern, particularly in mathematics, where students experience great difficulty understanding concepts and expressing and exploring their thinking in English. In order to be successful, teachers must pay special attention to methods used to teach second-language learners as well as the methods used in the process of teaching mathematics. A school with adequate resources, including teachers, technology, and support staff may succeed well with students whose values and experiences harmonize with the school. However, these schools may be far less successful if the school is dismissive of education that is consistent with students' cultural background (Ginorio & Huston, 2002).

Helping All Children Learn Mathematics

The world is becoming more mathematical, and children need more mathematics to survive daily living and to develop job skills for more sophisticated technology. Career advancements and educational opportunities often depend on mathematics achievement. As technology increases, the use of mathematics becomes more important for all people and a part of a social process which people need to understand. The interactions of mathematics and technology and the various fields with human social systems and the values that society applies can influence how children learn and apply mathematics (Johnson, 1989). Answers to mathematics learning questions can no longer be ignored; mathematics is too important a subject to consider unteachable for any child. Mathematics is no longer a subject reserved for afternoons in classrooms—it is a vital part of life and survival for the modern population. All children must become highly proficient in mathematics.

To become mathematically literate, children must know more than arithmetic. They must acquire knowledge of such important concepts as measurement, geometry, statistics, probability, and algebra (Standards, 2000). Educators of children must prepare them for the world in which they will live, one where mathematics is an everyday occurrence, not a score on a worksheet. They need opportunities to use number concepts and skills to explore, discover, and solve meaningful problems (Gestwicki, 1995).

While English acquisition and literacy development are viewed by teachers as primary goals for ELLs, an equally important objective is engaging students in challenging work in mathematics. Cultural attitudes in the United States make it socially acceptable, even trendy, to lack mathematical knowledge (Deitte & Howe, 2003). This is reinforced when teachers see mathematics as an objective of lesser importance than other subjects. All teachers must subscribe to the notion that all students are capable of and expected to acquire a high level of serious scholarship in mathematics and must offer the core curriculum to all students, regardless of their English language proficiency. In order to accomplish this, teachers must be equipped with the knowledge and skills needed to provide excellent educational experiences for ELLs in math while developing students' language proficiency.

Integrating Language Development with Content Learning

Moreno-Armella, A. & Block, D. (2003) provide evidence that in order to incorporate the immense scientific and technological developments of the past decades for successful school experiences, students must develop the cognitive and academic skills required for learning academic subject matter. Mathematics understanding for children involves many elements. It is a way of solving real problems and of having an understanding of number which includes operations on number, functions and relations, probability and measurement (Brewer, 1995). Students must also acquire high levels of English language proficiency, including the cognitive academic language proficiency needed to manipulate abstract concepts in mathematics (Collier, 1995). To achieve these goals, teachers must integrate language development with content teaching, make use of learners' experiences, and focus on higher-level cognitive skills. Instead of seeing language merely as a means of communication, teachers need to see language as a medium of learning (Mohan, 1986).

The challenge for teachers is to identify effective ways in which language instruction and academic content instruction in mathematics can be successfully combined, so as to introduce children to a new language and a new set of cultural experiences simultaneously. The challenge is to adapt the language of instruction without watering down the content and to use materials that follow the core curriculum, but are adapted or supplemented for students acquiring English (Crandall and Willetts, 1986). In order to meet these challenges, teachers must be knowledgeable and skilled at integrating a variety of strategies and techniques that facilitate language growth across the stages of language acquisition while focusing on teaching mathematical concepts. Depth versus breadth is an important teaching component of mathematics. Teaching a few topics well is more cognitively sound than teaching many concepts with little understanding. The integration process is important and founded on the following concepts for teaching language and mathematics.

1. The process of doing mathematics/science is not less important than its result.
2. Conceptual learning leads procedural development.
3. It's better to solve one problem by three methods than three problems by one method.
4. The purpose of math/science activity is not to get the right answer but to promote students' thinking. Giving right answers to students is to do their thinking for them.

5. It doesn't matter if you know how to solve 100 problems; it does matter how you approach the rest of them.
6. Do not be afraid of making mistakes, but be afraid of repeating them.
7. Fun is a derivative of challenge.
8. What we assess is what we value. (Tchoshanov, Blake & Duval, 2002).

A Conceptually Rich Instruction Sequence is important for all children when learning mathematics. The following sequence is recommended by the Third International Mathematics and Science Study (TIMSS, 1999).

A. Posing a problem/experiment
B. Individual work on the problem
C. Work in pairs and small groups
D. Presentation of the group's solution
E. Whole class discussion
F. Extension and overview of the problem/experiment

This sequence of instruction is also a way to develop language skills and build confidence in presenting ideas. The process helps students focus on their internalization of concepts, uses discourse with others, and allows reflection.

Facilitating Language Growth Across Stages of Language Acquisition

When working with students acquiring English, it is important to keep in mind that, as individuals, they are at different levels of English and mathematics proficiency. Thus, when planning activities for them, teachers must be aware of the levels of receptive and productive language they bring to the learning task as well as mathematical concepts and skills. There may be some children who are not ready to begin producing oral English. They may be experiencing the "silent period" of language learning during which they listen to rather than produce language although students may have a strong background in mathematics in their native language. The teacher needs to provide conceptual identification activities to more accurately identify children's level of thinking mathematically. Since children's receptive language skills develop earlier than their productive ones (Rice, 1989), it is important to keep in mind that language learning is taking place during this time (Evans, 1990). Children don't always need to respond in order to learn new language skills. They can and do benefit greatly from the opportunity to absorb the conversations of others (Rice, 1989).

Use of Multilevel Strategies. The level of participation and responses required of students during a math lesson can be tailored to address the specific needs of students who may be at different levels of language proficiency. These strategies are known as multilevel strategies. The unique combination of grade-level content plus multi-level teaching strategies can facilitate access to the core curriculum. These multilevel interpretations occur in mathematical thinking and need the same approach as language learners. A pupil's mental development is determined by the content of what he/she is learning (El'koniin & Davydov, V.V., 1975).

Helping Children Move Through The Stages. Students move through a series of predictable stages as they progress towards native-like fluency in English and develop mathematics concepts. Though the stages themselves are predictable, individual language acquisition will vary as students develop at their own pace. Progress along a pathway to fluency is not always signaled by forward movement alone. Rather, students who show growth spurts in acquiring new vocabulary, for example, may exhibit less control in using it grammatically. Such spurts and lags in language development are highly individual and are a normal part of the language acquisition process (Tinajero & Schifini, 1997).

Teachers can create language growth across the stages by using the instructional strategies and techniques discussed below.

Organizing Curriculum for English Language Learners

Teachers must provide English Language Learners with access to the core curriculum in order to help them learn the cognitively demanding and often abstract content in mathematics. Too often ELLs are placed in tracks that do not address the core or main ideas in mathematics necessary for future success. The ESL activities in this guide use the grade-level mathematics content as the vehicle for language development. The multilevel strategies integrated throughout the program facilitate language and content learning. Providing access to a quality mathematics core curriculum is important for several reasons.

1. The core curriculum is consistent with current recommendations from professional societies and research on how children learn. The NCTM Standards, for example, include topics such as estimation, measurement, number, problem solving, spatial sense, patterns, and communication.
2. The core curriculum addresses a broad range of content that is relevant, engaging, and meaningful to all students. This content can be made comprehensible to LEP students through a wide variety of learning experiences, materials and equipment, and ESL instructional strategies.
3. The core curriculum allows for focus on important mathematical topics while integrating cross-curricular areas through thematic/project-type planning.
4. The core curriculum emphasizes reasoning, problem solving, and decision making essential to success in mathematics.
5. The core curriculum builds the children's sense of competence and an enjoyment of learning.

Maximizing Learning in Mathematics for English Language Learners

The strategies and techniques outlined below are used throughout the ESL Activity Guide to adapt, simplify, and supplement the core mathematics textbook in order to make learning more comprehensible and meaningful to students. By incorporating these strategies and techniques, the mathematics content can be presented in a way that is more comprehensible by: (1) contextualizing abstract mathematical problems and activities, (2) effectively combining language instruction and academic content instruction, (3) presenting the mathematics grade-level content instead of watering down the academic program, and (4) incorporating activities and examples that relate mathematics concepts to the native culture and experiences of students.

Address children's learning from their cultural perspective. Each child comes to school with different backgrounds and beliefs. Children from different cultures and backgrounds should be accepted and appreciated. Activities from other cultures should be integrated with mathematics every day. Teachers must model acceptance of differences and encourage each child to be proud of his or her accomplishments. To increase teachers' awareness of the manner in which they interact with children during the course of the day, videotaping might be used to provide data for self-evaluation of their daily interactions with students.

Provide background experience and personalize lessons. The more knowledge and experience the student has of the language and content of a lesson, the easier it will be to understand it. To make lessons more comprehensible, integrate the following ideas:

- draw examples from the experiences of students as the basis for teaching new concepts
- use analogies to relate the teaching of new math concepts to experiences in the students' backgrounds, homes, and neighborhoods
- personalize the content by using the names of people and places familiar to students
- use students' names and familiar objects in word problems
- allow students to write their own word problems
- use context or themes with which students are familiar to generate mathematical problems and activities
- encourage students to explain solutions to problems to other students with stronger command of both languages
- simplify English word problems, write short sentences, maintain active voice, and use present tense
- elicit experiences and activities that relate to the native culture of the students.

Facilitating Language Growth Across the Stages

When planning lessons or activities, teachers must be aware of students' varied levels of receptive and productive language.

Stage	Students' Behaviors	Teachers' Behaviors	Questioning Techniques
① Preproduction			
▪ Students are totally new to English ▪ Generally lasts 1–3 months	▪ Points to or provides other nonverbal responses ▪ Actively listens ▪ Responds to commands ▪ Understands more than can produce	▪ Gestures ▪ Language focuses on conveying meanings and vocabulary development ▪ Does not force students to speak ▪ Shows visuals and real objects	▪ Point to the __. ▪ Find the __. ▪ Put the __ next to the __. ▪ Do you have the __? ▪ Is this a __? ▪ Who wants the __?
② Early Production			
▪ Students are "low beginners" ▪ Generally lasts several weeks	▪ One or two word utterances ▪ Uses short phrases and simple sentences related to social, everyday events ▪ Listens with greater understanding	▪ Asks questions that can be answered by yes/no ▪ Ask either/or questions ▪ Models correct responses ▪ Ensures supportive, low anxiety environment ▪ Does not overtly call attention to grammar errors ▪ Asks short "WH" questions	▪ Yes/no (Did you like the story?) ▪ Either/or (Is this a pencil or a crayon?) ▪ One-word responses (What am I holding in my hand?) ▪ General questions which encourage lists of words (What do you see in the book bag?) ▪ Two-word responses (Where did I put the pen?)
③ Speech Emergence			
▪ Students are "beginners" ▪ May last several weeks or months	▪ Participates in small group activities ▪ Demonstrates comprehension in a variety of ways ▪ Speaks in short phrases and sentences ▪ Begins to use language more freely	▪ Focuses content on key concepts ▪ Provides frequent comprehension checks ▪ Uses performance-based assessment ▪ Asks open-ended questions that stimulate language production	▪ Why? ▪ How? ▪ How is this like that? ▪ Tell me about __. ▪ Talk about __. ▪ Describe __. ▪ What is in your book bag?
④ ⑤ Intermediate and Advanced Fluency			
▪ Students are "high beginners, intermediate, or advanced" May require several years to achieve nativelike fluency in academic settings	▪ Participates in reading and writing activities to acquire new information ▪ Demonstrates increased levels of accuracy and correctness and is able to express thoughts and feelings ▪ Produces language with varied grammatical structures and vocabulary ▪ May experience difficulties in abstract, cognitively demanding subjects	▪ Fosters conceptual development and expanded literacy through content ▪ Continues to make lessons comprehensible and interactive ▪ Teaches thinking and study skills ▪ Continues to be alert to individual differences in language and culture	▪ What would you recommend/suggest? ▪ How do you think this story will end? ▪ What is this story about? ▪ What is your favorite part of the story? ▪ Describe/compare __. ▪ How are these similar/different? ▪ What would happen if __?

Use manipulative materials and hands-on activities. ELLs need to be supported with hands-on activities that make abstract concepts in math language real to them. Manipulative materials and hands-on activities will help students understand complex and abstract concepts. Concrete materials used in a variety of ways help children represent mathematical ideas. Manipulatives and hands-on activities help students move from understanding simple, concrete concepts to understanding more difficult and abstract concepts. Activities that involve students actively in solving problems through experimentation, measuring, cutting, charting, and weighing are particularly good. Learning centers which provide manipulative materials for exploration and discovery are very effective, as are multimedia materials for learning content and processes.

Plan and organize the classroom to encourage active child involvement and maximize interaction. The most favorable environment for English acquisition is a natural, language-rich setting where students interact with each other and feel comfortable to experiment with language for meaningful communication—much like the context in which they acquired their first language. Students need countless opportunities to hear and use English in small groups and in pairs and to take risks as they try out their developing knowledge of the language and acquire math concepts.

As students complete math assignments, provide them with opportunities to practice their English by increasing the frequency and variety of interactions among students. Pair them with proficient English speakers for math activities such as solving a story problem. Group them with students of varying proficiencies for activities such as measuring, weighing, or cutting.

Cooperative learning activities also increase the frequency and variety of second-language practice through different types of interaction. Such activities also provide students with opportunities to act as resources for each other and thus assume a more active role in learning.

One of the most important elements associated with successful mathematics learning is the creation of a "risk free" environment where children are allowed to make mistakes without criticism but provided helpful guidance from adults and peers. The children should be encouraged to keep trying, and incorrect answers should be regarded as important steps toward learning.

Utilize a variety of teaching methods. Variety addresses not only the needs of children but the nature of mathematics. Set up engaging learning centers with multilevel activities to address children with different developmental stages and learning styles. Encourage small group work that focuses on cooperative learning to allow for socialization and discourse as recommended by Vygotsky and build confidence in each child's ability to

perform mathematical tasks successfully. The teacher plays an important role in this interaction as a guide for developing and extending knowledge. Learning leads development in mathematics. Encourage peer tutoring— children helping children—to facilitate mathematical understanding. Try team teaching with a bilingual or ESL teacher to increase effectiveness in learning mathematical concepts as well as developing higher levels of language proficiency. Try creative classroom arrangements which encourage talking, writing, modeling, and acting out mathematics ideas. Utilize open-ended activities in which children solve real-life problems.

Develop partnerships with parents and other family members. Outside the classroom, enlist the assistance of parents. Help parents to feel confident that their efforts in the home will help their children do better in school. The home provides the first learning experiences for a child and will serve as reinforcement for what is taught at school. Parents or other family members can encourage mathematics development after school hours and provide valuable background information for the teacher. Helping parents understand how to help children learn mathematics is an important role for the teacher. Techniques such as welcoming parents into the classroom and encouraging their participation in the school program, visiting in the home to establish mutual respect, and communicating with the family help develop home-school relationships. Monthly Mathematics Nights can be planned by teachers.

Integrate the curriculum to build connections between mathematics topics and other subject areas. One way to achieve this is to teach through interdisciplinary projects or broad thematic units. Literature-based units lend themselves to integrated curriculum planning. Some children's mathematics texts, for example, help teachers integrate literature with other curriculum areas.

Allsopp, Lovin, Green, & Savage-Davis (2003) make the following key points concerning learning mathematics.

Teaching in authentic and meaningful contexts. When mathematics makes sense to students or when they see a reason to use mathematics, they retain higher levels of learning. This is more important with students struggling with two languages. Making sense of mathematics is a key element in mathematical learning.

Directly modeling both general problem-solving strategies and specific learning strategies using multisensory techniques. The teachers' use of problem-solving strategies and the direct communication of this process with students as the teacher uses it help students to understand thinking and identify useful stages.

Giving students opportunities to use their language to describe their mathematical understanding. It is emphasized again how important it is for students to be able to use their own natural language to internalize mathematical concepts. False language can develop misconceptions, which may stay with students throughout their school career. The internalization of concepts **must** start in the children's natural language.

Providing multiple opportunities to help students use their developing mathematical knowledge and build proficiency. Practice is vital to understanding and gaining confidence in mathematics. Students who may be insecure with their language skills need confidence in their ability to succeed across all learning.

Providing the Right Support with Macmillan/McGraw-Hill's Math ESL

The goal of any mathematics program is to enable children to use math through exploration, discovery, and solving meaningful problems based on conceptual knowledge. Macmillan/McGraw-Hill MATH program focuses on these three strategies. The ESL activities help teachers support the teaching of mathematics to LEP students by providing highly interactive and fun whole-class activities that also address the unique needs and experiences of students. In these activities, ELLs are not isolated from their non-ELL classmates; rather, learning is a cooperative venture. The teacher does not have to teach the same lesson twice to different groups.

Teaching for understanding and enhancing the process of learning involve holistic skills instruction (Brophy, 1995). In the ESL Activity Guide for Macmillan/McGraw-Hill's MATH, skills are taught to ELLs as strategies adapted to situations, with emphasis on modeling the cognitive components. At the same time, the activities support language development. The suggested activities incorporate a greater range of tasks incorporated in the core mathematics curriculum. As in the core program, the ELL activities allow students to construct their own knowledge in purposeful activities requiring decision making, problem solving, and judgments.

Finally, the integrated approach in Macmillan/McGraw-Hill's MATH allows ELL students to experience cooperative work with others, and provides time to enhance personal strengths, self knowledge, and competencies in all areas of development. Integrated units in the core program address individual learning levels and adhere to the constructivists' theories of learning. As in the core program, the ESL activities allow children to learn from experiences, those encountered at random and those to which they are introduced deliberately, allowing students to incorporate their own language and cultural experiences.

References

Allsopp, L.L., Green, G. & Savage-Davis, E. (2003). *Why students with special needs have difficulty learning mathematics and what teachers can do to help. Mathematics Teaching in the Middle School.* Vols. 8, 6, pp. 308-315.

Brophy, Jere. "Probing the Subtleties of Subject-Matter Teaching." *Contemporary Issues in Curriculum.* (Ornstein and Behar, Eds.). Needham Heights, MA: Allyn and Bacon, 1999.

Clune, William H. (2000) *The National Standards in Math and Science: Developing Consensus, Unresolved Issues, and Unfinished Business.*

Collier, V. (1995). "Acquiring a Second Language for School." *Directions in Language and Education. National Clearinghouse for Bilingual Education* 1(4) (1995): 1-12.

Deitte, J.M. & Howe, R. M. (2003). *Motivating students to study mathematics. Mathematic Teacher.* V. 96,4,pp. 278-286.

Ginorio, A. & Huston, M. (2001). *Latinas in School. ¡Sí, se puede! Yes, We Can!* Washington, DC: AAUW Educational Foundation.

Kamii, C. and Kamii, M. *Negative Effects of Achievement Testing in Mathematics.* Washington, DC: NAEYC, 1990.

Mather, J.R.C. and Chiodo, J. J. (Spring 1994). A mathematical problem: How do we teach mathematics to LEP elementary students?

The Journal of Educational Issues of Language Minority Students. Vol. 13, pp. 1-12. Boise State University.

Mohan, B. A. (1986). Language and content learning: finding common ground. *ERIC/CLL News Bulletin.* Clearinghouse on Language and Linguistics, Vol. 9, No. 2, pp. 1,8.

Moreno-Armella, L. & Blaock, D. (2003). *Democratic access to powerful mathematics in a developing country.* In *Handbook of International Research in Mathematic Education* (English, L.D., ed.) Mahwah, NJ: Lawrence Erlbaum Associates.

National Board for Professional Teaching Standards (2000). *What Teachers Should Know How to Do.* http://ww.nbpts.org/nbpts/standards/intro.html.

National Council for Accreditation of Teacher Education (2000). *NCATE 2000 Unit Standards.*

National Science Foundation. *Women, Minorities, and Persons with Disabilities in Science and Engineering:* 1998. Arlington, VA, 1999.

Reys, R., Reys, B., Lapan, R., Holliday, G., & Wasman, D. (2003). *Teaching and learning mathematics for social justice in an urban, Latino school.* Journal for Research in Mathematics Education. Vols. 34, 1 pp. 37-73.

Rice, M. (1990). Children's language acquisition. *American Psychologist.* Volume 4, February, pp. 149-156

Suter, L.E.(ed.) National Science Foundation (NSF), 1996. *The learning curve: What we are discovering about U.S. science and mathematics education.* A prefatory report of the National Science Foundation's indicators of science and mathematics education. 1995. (NSF 96-53). Washington, D.C.

Tchoshanov, M. Blake, S. & Duval, A. (2002). Preparing Teachers for a New Challenge: Teaching Calculus Concepts in Middle Grades. International Conference on the Teaching of Mathematics Proceedings. Athens, Greece. July 2002.

Tinajero, J. V. and Schifini, A. (1997). *Into English! Teacher's Guide.* Carmel, CA: Hampton-Brown Books.

U.S. Department of Education (2001). The Nation's Report Card: Mathematics 2000. Washington, DC: Office of Educational Research and Improvement.

Willoughby, Stephen S. *Mathematics Education for a Changing World.* Alexandria, Virginia: Association for Supervision and Curriculum Development, 1990.

Contents

How To Use   Language-Free Math Inventory

The **Language-Free Math Inventory** assesses the mathematical ability of incoming students at the previous grade level and is taken independently by each student. The purpose of this tool is to focus on mathematics knowledge without involving language. The Inventory assists the teacher in identifying English language learners who are behind cognitively, either because they have not had the opportunity to attend school or have not received specially designed academic instruction while learning English.

The items included in the **Language-Free Math Inventory** are based on mathematics standards for students at the previous grade level. The results will reveal which students may need remediation. For example, if a student inaccurately responds to or skips two or three sections, you will know where he or she needs help. If a student is unable to complete accurately more than half of the items, you might want to engage him or her in remediation, according to your school's or district's philosophy.

The **Language-Free Math Inventory** is taken independently by each student. All English language learners can complete the inventory at the same time as you monitor them without giving assistance. So that students do not feel overwhelmed, it is suggested that you have them complete one page at a time with breaks in between or over a period of days. As students begin the Inventory, explain that you do not expect them to know how to do all the items and that you will use the results to teach them what they need to know. Try to make students feel that it is okay if they do not know how to do a section; they can skip it. If possible, you might consider communicating the purpose of the Inventory to older students through a bilingual student or parent.

Name _____   **Date** _____

Math Inventory

A. Write Whole Numbers to 1,000,000

999,994	999,995	999,996	999,997	999,998	999,999	
79,997	79,998	79,999		80,001	80,002	
699,997	699,998		700,000		700,002	700,003

B. Write Decimals

63.1	63.2	63.3	63.4		63.6	63.7		63.9	
	5.43	5.44		5.46	5.47	5.48	5.49		5.51

C. Compare Whole Numbers and Decimals

$<$ $=$ $>$

127,643 $\bigcirc$ 127,644   131,584 $\bigcirc$ 131,584

500,300 $\bigcirc$ 530,000   640,000 $\bigcirc$ 604,000

55 $\bigcirc$ 5.5   82.03 $\bigcirc$ 82.3

2.71 $\bigcirc$ 27.01   4.28 $\bigcirc$ 428

Name _____ **Date** _____

Math Inventory

D. Order Whole Numbers, Fractions, and Mixed Numbers on a Number Line

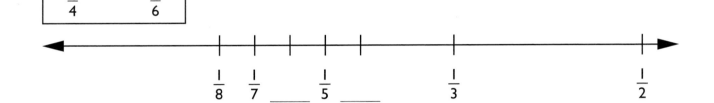

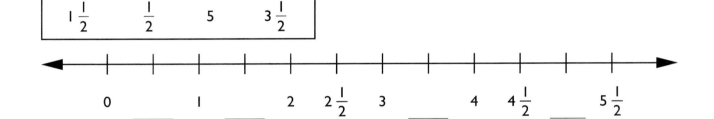

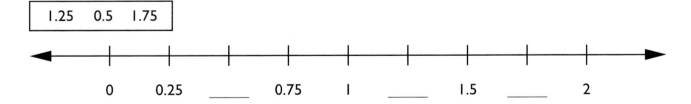

E. Add, Subtract, Multiply, and Divide Whole Numbers

5,433	52,231	65,843	167,502	349,786
+ 2,162	+ 7,456	+ 6,248	+ 24,689	+ 60,248

7,579	59,751	44,662	65,041	225,603
− 2,244	− 6,531	− 6,584	− 38,724	− 64,728

Name _____ **Date** _____

Math Inventory

$$\begin{array}{r} 513 \\ \times\ 23 \\ \hline \end{array} \qquad \begin{array}{r} 323 \\ \times\ 52 \\ \hline \end{array} \qquad \begin{array}{r} 42{,}313 \\ \times\ 22 \\ \hline \end{array} \qquad \begin{array}{r} 75 \\ \times\ 64 \\ \hline \end{array}$$

$$\begin{array}{r} 269 \\ \times\ 43 \\ \hline \end{array} \qquad \begin{array}{r} 823 \\ \times\ 58 \\ \hline \end{array} \qquad \begin{array}{r} 3{,}595 \\ \times\ 65 \\ \hline \end{array} \qquad \begin{array}{r} 25{,}261 \\ \times\ 37 \\ \hline \end{array}$$

_____

$3\overline{)39{,}696}$ $\qquad\qquad$ $2\overline{)64{,}244}$ $\qquad\qquad$ $4\overline{)33{,}528}$ $\qquad\qquad$ $6\overline{)65{,}238}$

_____

F. Evaluating Expressions

$(36 - 14) - 8 =$ _____ $\qquad\qquad$ $(25 - 10) - 6 =$ _____

$36 - (14 - 8) =$ _____ $\qquad\qquad$ $25 - (10 - 6) =$ _____

_____

$(2 \times 12) - (16 \div 4) + 5 =$ _____ $\qquad\qquad$ $(10 \times 3) - (24 \div 8) + 6 =$ _____

_____

$(12 + 16) \div 7 + 8 =$ _____ $\qquad\qquad$ $(8 + 8) \div 4 + 10 \times 2 =$ _____

$(22 + 11) \div 3 + 7 =$ _____ $\qquad\qquad$ $(13 + 17) \div 6 + 5 \times 3 =$ _____

Name _____ **Date** _____

Math Inventory

G. Graphing Equations

$y = 2x + 3$

x	y
2	7
3	
5	
8	

$x \div 5 = y$

x	y
15	
25	
40	
100	

H. Solving Equations

$6 + 4 = (2 \times 3) +$ _____

$0 + 7 = (8 - 8) +$ _____

$x - 3 = 5$

$x =$ _____

$8 \times 2 = (4 + 4) \times$ _____

$5 \times 5 = (2 + 3) \times$ _____

$7x = 35$

$x =$ _____

I. Prime Numbers

2	3	5	7	11

___2___ × ___2___ × ___3___ = 12

_____ × _____ = 33

_____ × _____ × _____ = 28

_____ × _____ = 15

_____ × _____ × _____ × _____ = 24

Name _____   **Date** _____

Math Inventory

J. Graphing Coordinates

$y = x - 2$

x	y
2	0
3	1
7	5

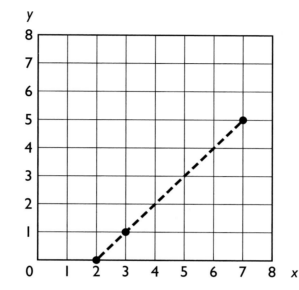

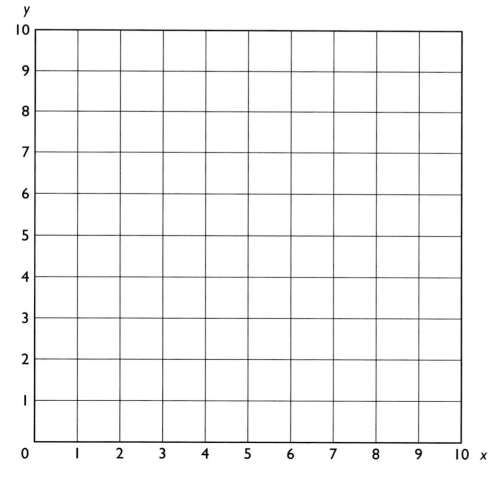

$y = 2x$

x	y
1	
2	
3	
4	
5	

Planner

Place Value: Add and Subtract Whole Numbers and Decimals

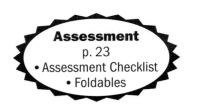
 **LOG ON** Visit **www.mmhmath.com**

Unit Activities		
• **Activity 1** (Readiness) Counting Zeros, p. 10		• **Activity 3** Making Decimal Models, p. 11
• **Activity 2** Great Numbers, p. 10		• **Activity 4** Subtract Using Mental Math, p. 11

Lessons	Key Objectives	Vocabulary	Materials	Resources
READ TOGETHER "Bushy-Tailed Mathematicians" by Betsy Franco, pp. 8–9	**Math:** Use place value to read and write whole numbers and decimals. **ESL/TESOL:** Goal 2, Standard 2. Goal 1, Standard 3.	amount, ball, bushy-tailed, favorite, giant, jar, leaf, saving, several, squirrels, walnuts		
UNIT WARM-UP Understanding Place Value p. 12	**Math:** Use place value to read and write whole numbers and decimals. **ESL/TESOL:** Goal 1, Standard 3.	expanded form, place, standard form, value		Teacher Tool 2
LESSON 1 Benchmark Numbers pp. 14–15	**Math:** Estimate quantities using benchmarks. **ESL/TESOL:** Goal 2, Standard 2. Goal 1, Standard 3.	benchmark, estimate	beans, 2 identical glass jars	Learning Resource 1
LESSON 2 Place Value pp. 16–17	**Math:** Use place value to read and write whole numbers and decimals. **ESL/TESOL:** Goal 2, Standard 2.	decimal, fraction, place, value, whole number	pencils	Learning Resource 2 Teacher Tools 1 and 3
LESSON 3 Properties of Addition pp. 18–19	**Math:** Add and subtract whole numbers and decimals. Identify and use the properties of addition. **ESL/TESOL:** Goal 2, Standard 2.	Associative Property, Commutative Property, equivalent decimal, Identity Property	large index cards	Learning Resource 3
LESSON 4 Compensation pp. 20–21	**Math:** Add and subtract whole numbers and decimals. **ESL/TESOL:** Goal 2, Standard 2.	compensation, round	calculator	Learning Resource 4
PROBLEM SOLVING p. 22 • Skill: Use the Four-Step Process • Strategy: Find a Pattern	Use skills and strategies to solve problems.			**Math Center Cards 1A, 1B**

See **Math at Home Family Guide** for additional math vocabulary, activities, and games in English, Spanish, and Haitian Creole.

English Vocabulary

Dear Family: Please help your child practice the key vocabulary words for this unit.

benchmark a point of reference from which other measurements may be estimated

decimal a number with one or more digits to the right of the decimal point, such as 8.37 or 0.05

equivalent decimals decimals that name the same number

estimate to find a number that is close to the exact answer without calculating an exact answer

expanded form a way of writing a number as the sum of the values of its digits

fraction a number that names part of a whole or part of a group

period each group of three digits in a place-value chart

place the position of a digit in a number

standard form the usual or common way to write a number

value the product of a digit multiplied by its place

whole number any one of the numbers, 0, 1, 2, 3, and so on

Vocabulario en español

Estimados familiares: Por favor ayuden a su hijo/a a practicar las palabras del vocabulario de esta unidad.

referencia punto de relación a partir del cual se estiman otras medidas

decimal número con uno o más dígitos a la derecha del punto decimal, como 8.37 ó 0.05

decimales equivalentes decimales que expresan el mismo número

estimar hallar un número que se aproxime al resultado exacto sin calcular un resultado exacto

forma desarrollada forma de escribir un número como la suma de los valores de sus dígitos

fracción número que representa una parte de un todo o de un grupo

periodo cada grupo de tres dígitos en una tabla de valor posicional

posición ubicación de un dígito en un número

forma estándar manera común de escribir los números

valor producto de un dígito multiplicado por su posición

número entero cualquiera de los números 0, 1, 2, 3, y así sucesivamente

Vokabilè an kreyòl

Chè paran: Tanpri ede pitit la pratike mo vokabilè nan seksyon sa a.

referans de baz yon pwen referans ou ka sèvi pou estime lòt ka

desimal yon nimewo ak youn osnon plizyè chif a dwat pwen desimal la, pa egzanp 8.37 o 0.05

desimal ki menm desimal ki eksprime menm nimewo an

estimasyon pou ka jwenn yon nimewo ki pre repons egzak la san–w pa kalkile yon repons egzak

fòm dekonpoze yon fason pou ekri yon nimewo tankou sòm valè chif li yo

fraksyon yon nimewo ki eksprime tout ou byen yon pati

seksyon chak gwoup twa chif nan tablo vale a

ran pozisyon yon chif

fom nòmal fason yo touou ekri yon nimewo

valè pwodui yon chif ou miltipliye pa ran li

yon nimewo antye nenpot nan nimewo sa yo, 0,1, 2, 3 elatriye

Bushy-Tailed Mathematicians

by Betsy Franco

 25 minutes

Math Objective
- Use place value to read and write whole numbers and decimals.

ESL/TESOL Descriptors
- Listen to, speak, read, and write about subject matter information.
- Listen to and imitate how others use English.

Reading Skill
- Sequence of Events.

Vocabulary
amount, ball, bushy-tailed, favorite, giant, jar, leaf, saving, several, squirrels, walnuts

Before Reading

Build Background/Oral Language
Discuss the title and illustrations. Ask students to predict what the poem is about.

Point to the squirrel, say the word, and have the class repeat. Describe the squirrel and its habits (bushy tail, climbs trees, eats nuts, etc.). Have students repeat words and pantomime. Ask questions about squirrels and have students answer with words they have just learned.

During Reading

- Read the poem through once without stopping as students track text.
- Reread, asking students to repeat each line after you. Encourage students to ask questions about new or difficult words.
- Read poem in unison.

Phonological/Phonemic Awareness
Point out the words that include *ou,* such as *count, grouped,* and *hours.* Say these sounds and words and have students repeat them. Draw three columns on the board. Write *group, hour,* and *count* at the top of each column. Underline *ou* in each and have students repeat the sound and the words. Brainstorm other words that can go in each column with the same spellings. *(group: bouquet, soup, toupee; hour: our, sour, flour; count: pouch, mouse)*

After Reading

Ask students what happened in the poem. Draw groups of ten nuts on the board. Count and have class repeat. Draw on the board the flow chart, Sequence of Events. Elicit the sequence of events, using words such as *first, next,* and *last.*

Art Invite students to illustrate a verse of the poem. Have them label their illustration.

Assessment

Observe fluency as students read the poem aloud. See Assessment Checklist on page 23.

Multilevel Strategies

1 **Preproduction**
Say: *Point to the word group.*

Writing Encourage students to draw a group of ten walnuts and label it.

2 **3** **Early Production and Speech Emergence**
Ask: *If the squirrels had 100 nuts, how many groups of ten did they make?*

Writing Have students draw groups of ten nuts and label them.

4 **5** **Intermediate and Advanced Fluency**
Ask: *What did the squirrels do in the poem?*

Writing Invite students to write about something they like to collect.

Bushy-Tailed Mathematicians

by Betsy Franco

Here is a story about some very busy squirrels. They spend all their time grouping and counting their walnuts and never get around to eating them.

The squirrels kept their walnuts
in a giant saving jar,
When the jar was full, they counted
all the walnuts saved so far.

First they grouped them all by tens
and then they counted one and all,
Though it took them several hours,
all the squirrels had a ball.

When the walnuts were all counted,
then the squirrels used a pen,
wrote the total on a leaf and
put them in the jar again.

They decided not to eat them
though they had a large amount,
'cause their favorite thing with walnuts
is to group by tens and count.

© Macmillan/McGraw-Hill

UNIT 1

Readiness

ACTIVITY 1

PARTNERS

Counting Zeros

- **Player 1:** Write a 5- or 6-digit number, such as 301, 070. Then read the name of the number—*three hundred one thousand, seventy*—to your partner.

- **Player 2:** Use mental math to find the number of zero digits in the number. Tell your partner if there are no zeros.

- Player 2 gets 1 point if correct. Take turns and play again. The first player to get 10 points wins.

- Players can also name the place value of every 0 digit in the number.

Find Place Value

 -

PARTNERS

ACTIVITY 2

Great Numbers

YOU NEED

magazines, newspapers, or books

1. Look for magazines, newspapers, or books with five 7-, 8-, or 9-digit numbers. Copy the sentence or headline with an example of each number.

2. Take turns reading a number. Your partner writes that number in word and expanded forms.

3. Check each other's work.

City Population Passes 1,500,000

State Budgets $43,695,708

2,082,354 Pennies Collected for the Homeless

Whole Numbers

ACTIVITY 3

PARTNERS

Making Decimal Models

- Draw a 10 cm-by-10 cm square.

- If the whole square equals 1, what decimal does one row of squares equal? What decimal does one small square equal? Discuss your answers with your partner.

Now take turns.

- Write a decimal with tenths or hundredths. Do not let your partner see it. Then show the number by shading a 10 cm-by-10 cm square.

- Your partner says and writes the decimal your drawing shows.

- Score one point for each correct answer. The first player to get five points wins.

YOU NEED

centimeter graph paper

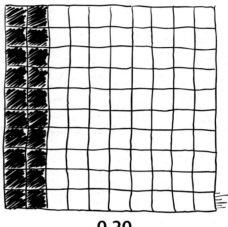

0.20

Find Decimal Place Value

ACTIVITY 4

PARTNERS

Subtract Using Mental Math

Make a poster that shows mental math techniques, for example:

- the left–to–right method of subtracting

  Example: $682 - 392 =$

- or the equal-additions method of subtracting.

  Example: $682 - 300 = 382 + 82 =$

Use any of these problems.

YOU NEED

construction paper
markers or crayons
scissors
tape

1. 515	**2.** 682	**3.** $7.45	**4.** 953
−297	−392	− 2.98	−693

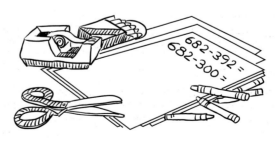

Your poster must show the steps to follow in both methods.

Step 1. You and your partner choose which problem you will show. Then each of you agree which methods you will use. Use a different method each time.

Step 2. Make a drawing for each problem. Then trade and look at your partner's drawing.

Step 3. Choose a final design for your poster. Display for class to study.

See answers on p. 291.

Estimate Differences

Understanding Place Value

 25 minutes

▶ **Key Strategy**
Use visuals

▶ **Format**
Whole class and small groups

▶ **Math Vocabulary**
expanded form, place, standard form, value

▶ **Daily Vocabulary**
almanac, dinosaur, encyclopedia, extinction, population

▶ **Resource**
Teacher Tool 2

Math Objectives	ESL/TESOL Descriptors
■ Use place value to read and write whole numbers and decimals. ■ Compare and order whole numbers and decimals.	■ Listen to and imitate how others use English. ■ Explore alternative ways of saying things.

Activate Prior Knowledge Ask students to think of large numbers, such as the population of the United States, the distance from Earth to the sun, or the number of years since the extinction of the dinosaurs. Invite students to look up the numbers in an almanac or encyclopedia and write them on the board.

Hands-on Lesson Distribute Teacher Tool 2: Place-Value Charts and have students recite the periods. Say: *Each period has ones, tens, and hundreds.* Then, invite students to copy the large numbers onto the Place-Value Charts. Point to each digit and say its **place** and **value.**

- Write this number: 376,284. Say: *This is the number of kilometers from Earth to the moon in* **standard form.** Then write: 300,000 + 70,000 + 6,000 + 200 + 80 + 4, and say: *This is the* **expanded form** *of the number.* Invite students to come to the board and point out the corresponding digits between the two forms. Give more examples of standard and expanded form.

- Ask a volunteer to look up the U.S. Census Bureau's "Population Clock" on the Internet. Write the number on the board. On May 1, 2003, the world's population was projected to be 6,289,299,109. Say: *As of May 1, 2003, the population of Earth was six billion, two hundred eighty-nine million, two hundred ninety-nine thousand, one hundred nine.*

- Invite 10 students to the front of the class to represent this number, each holding up a large index card with one of the digits. Invite three more students to write a comma on an index card and stand between the "periods." Say: *There is a comma after the billions period, a comma after the millions period, and a comma after the thousands period.*

Multilevel Strategies

❶ Preproduction
Have students point to the periods as you say them.

❷❸ Early Production and Speech Emergence
Encourage students to name each period.

❹❺ Intermediate and Advanced Fluency
Invite students to say the place value of each digit.

 LOG ON Visit **www.mmhmath.com** to find printable **Vocabulary Cards** that help build academic language.

Procedure: Help students make these Foldables to write vocabulary words and definitions throughout the unit. Encourage students to use the Foldables as a study guide.

 by Dinah Zike

Two-Tab Book

1. Provide each student with a sheet of paper. Have your students fold the paper lengthwise, almost in half, leaving a 1" tab uncovered. Label the tab *Place Value*.

2. Students can now fold in half in the other direction and cut up the fold of the top flap to make two tabs. Label one tab *Whole Numbers* and the other *Decimals*.

3. As students work through the unit, have them record notes, main ideas, vocabulary, and solution steps under the appropriate tabs.

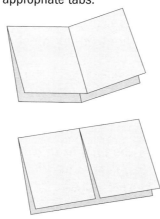

Labels may include:

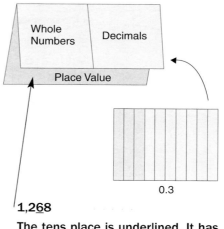

Place Value

0.3

1,2**68**

The tens place is underlined. It has a value of 60.

A whole number is any one of the numbers 0, 1, 2, 3, and so on.

 by Dinah Zike

Two-Tab Book

1. Provide each student with two sheets of paper. Have your students fold the sheets lengthwise, almost in half, leaving a 1" tab uncovered. Label one tab *Whole Numbers* and the other *Decimals*.

2. Students can now fold in half in the other direction and cut up

the fold of the top flap to make two tabs. On each Two-Tab Book, label the left tab + and the right tab − .

3. As students work through the unit, have them record notes, main ideas, vocabulary, and solution steps under the appropriate tabs.

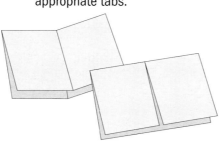

Labels may include:

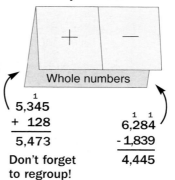

Whole numbers

$$\begin{array}{r} \overset{1}{5},345 \\ +\ \ 128 \\ \hline 5,473 \end{array}$$
Don't forget to regroup!

$$\begin{array}{r} 6,2\overset{1}{8}\overset{1}{4} \\ -\ 1,839 \\ \hline 4,445 \end{array}$$

Decimals

$$\begin{array}{r} \overset{2\ 1\ 2}{2}.995 \\ 0.867 \\ +0.929 \\ \hline 4.791 \end{array}$$

$$\begin{array}{r} \overset{3\ 1}{7}54.41 \\ -730.80 \\ \hline 23.61 \end{array}$$

Lesson 1

 45 minutes

▶ **Key Strategy**
Use visuals

▶ **Format**
Whole class and student pairs

▶ **Math Vocabulary**
benchmark, estimate

▶ **Daily Vocabulary**
basketball, identical, stadium

▶ **Resource**
Learning Resource 1

Materials
- beans
- 2 identical glass jars

Assessment

Check students' understanding of benchmark numbers as they complete the lesson. See Assessment Checklist on page 23. Remind students to work on their Foldables.

Home Connection

Have students explain to family members how they could use a benchmark number to estimate the number of people in a movie theater. Invite them to share their experiences with the class.

Benchmark Numbers

Math Objectives	ESL/TESOL Descriptors
▪ Estimate quantities using benchmarks.	▪ Compare and contrast information.
▪ Use skills and strategies to solve problems.	▪ Use context to construct meaning.

Activate Prior Knowledge Ask students to recall times they have been to a concert or sports event where a great many people were present. Ask: *Have you ever tried to figure out how many people were there?* Invite students to tell of different ways they may have tried to estimate a crowd.

Hands-on Lesson Place a clear glass jar on your desk and fill it with beans as students watch. Ask them to guess how many beans are in the jar and write the number down on a piece of paper.

- Lead a discussion about how to find the number of beans in the jar. Say: *I can count every bean in the jar, but that would take a long time. If I counted out a smaller number of beans and put them in another jar, maybe I could use that number to estimate the total.*

- Ask a volunteer to count out 25 beans and put them in the bottom of an identical jar. Hold up the container and ask students to observe how full it is. Say: *This jar has 25 beans in it. 25 is our benchmark number. I think the other jar holds about 10 times as much.* Write: $10 \times 25 = 250$. Say: *Using a benchmark number of 25, I estimate there are 250 beans in the jar.* Have students display the number they wrote down and compare it with this estimate.

- Divide the class into pairs of fluent and nonfluent speakers and distribute Learning Resource 1. Have them estimate the number of seats in the arena.

Cultural Link Worldwide, soccer events attract the largest following of any sport. Have students research the size of the biggest soccer stadium in their native country. Encourage them to explain how they could use a benchmark number to estimate the attendance at a soccer game.

Multilevel Strategies

❶ Preproduction
Say: *Point to the benchmark number on the board.*

Writing Invite students to write this number in expanded form.

❷❸ Early Production and Speech Emergence
Ask: *What was your benchmark number?*

Writing Encourage them to write the benchmark number and the estimate.

❹❺ Intermediate and Advanced Fluency
Ask: *How did you use the benchmark number to estimate?*

Writing Challenge them to write how to use a benchmark number to estimate.

Name _____

Basketball Benchmark

Estimate the number of seats.

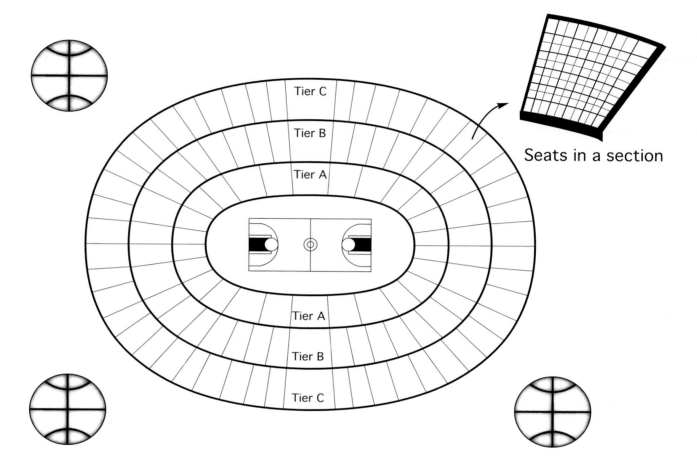

Seats in a section

1. How many sections are in Tier A? _____

2. How many sections are in Tier B? _____

3. How many sections are in Tier C? _____

4. How many sections are in all? _____

5. About how many seats are in a section? _____

6. How many people can this basketball arena hold?

_____

© Macmillan/McGraw-Hill

Lesson

2

  45 minutes

▶ **Key Strategy**
Use visuals

▶ **Format**
Whole class and student pairs

▶ **Math Vocabulary**
decimal, fraction, place, value, whole number

▶ **Daily Vocabulary**
names of U.S. coins

▶ **Resources**
Learning Resource 2
Teacher Tools 1 and 3

Materials
• pencils

Assessment

Check students' mastery of decimals and place value as they complete the lesson. See page 23 for Assessment Checklist.
Remind students to work on their Foldables.

Home Connection

Send a supermarket flyer home. Encourage students to look at the flyer and explain the place values of the different dollar amounts to family members. Invite students to report their experiences to the class.

Place Value

Math Objectives	ESL/TESOL Descriptors
■ Use place value to read and write whole numbers and decimals.	■ Select, connect, and explain information.
■ Compare and order whole numbers and decimals.	■ Analyze, synthesize, and infer from information.

Activate Prior Knowledge Review U.S. currency with students. Distribute Teacher Tools 1: Coins and 3: Bills. Have students say the coin names and their **values** aloud. Write the coin and its amount on the board: 1 penny, 1 cent = $0.01; 1 nickel, 5 cents = $0.05; 1 dime, 10 cents = $0.10; 1 quarter, 25 cents = $0.25; 1 half dollar, 50 cents = $0.50; 1 dollar, 100 cents = $1.00; 5 dollars, 500 cents = $5.00.

Hands-on Lesson Write $5.25 on the board and ask a volunteer to say the amount. Say: *Money is a good model for* whole numbers *and* decimals. Point to the decimal point and say: *The decimal point separates the dollars and the cents.* Hold up a dollar and say: *The dollars are whole numbers. The cents are less than whole numbers.*

• Ask: *How many pennies are in one dollar?* (*100*) Say: *Each penny is one hundredth of a dollar.* Write the **fraction** $\frac{1}{100}$ and say: *Here's one way to write one hundredth. This is a fraction. Who can show me another way?* Encourage a volunteer to write .01. Point to the two numbers and say: *These numbers are the same. Each means one hundredth.*

• Distribute Learning Resource 2. Have students read the headings across the top. Say: *These are the* **places**. *Write 3 in the ones place. Three is the value of the ones place. Write 2 in the tenths pace. Write 5 in the hundredths place. What do these numbers to the right of the decimal point mean?* (*They are less than one.*) Have students work in pairs to complete the Learning Resource.

Cultural Link Invite students to bring coins and bills from other countries. Encourage them to use the currency to make up whole numbers and decimals.

Multilevel Strategies

① **Preproduction**
Challenge students to point to place values as you say them.

Writing Say a money amount, such as $3.25, and have students write it.

②③ **Early Production and Speech Emergence**
Say: *Name the place values on the chart.*

Writing Have students write the decimal amounts of U.S. coins.

④⑤ **Intermediate and Advanced Fluency**
Say: *Explain how to write a number on a place value chart.*

Writing Encourage students to write a sentence about the value of a penny.

Name _____

Astounding Decimals

Write the values of each item in the chart.

100 THOUSANDS	THOUSANDS	HUNDREDS	TENS	ONES	.	TENTHS	HUNDREDTHS
					.		
					.		
					.		
					.		

Value: $3.25

Value: $149.95

Value: $19,395.75

Draw your own!

Value: _____

 45 minutes

▶ **Key Strategy**
Use visuals

▶ **Format**
Whole class and student pairs

▶ **Math Vocabulary**
Associative Property, Commutative Property, equivalent decimal, Identity Property

▶ **Daily Vocabulary**
line up

▶ **Resource**
Learning Resource 3

Materials
• large index cards

Assessment

Check students' mastery of decimals as they complete the lesson. See page 23 for Assessment Checklist. Remind students to work on their Foldables.

Home Connection

Have students take home copies of the Learning Resource and play the game with family members. Encourage them to report their experiences to the class.

Properties of Addition

Math Objectives	**ESL/TESOL Descriptors**
■ Add and subtract whole numbers and decimals.	■ Represent and interpret information visually.
■ Identify and use the properties of addition.	■ Demonstrate knowledge through application in a variety of contexts.

Activate Prior Knowledge Write *0.2; 0.20; 0.200; 0.2000*; and so on. Say: *These* equivalent decimals *represent the same amount.* Have volunteers come to the board and write other equivalent decimals. Ask: *Would the value of this number change if I put one hundred zeros after it?* (*No.*)

Hands-on Lesson Explain that adding and subtracting decimals is similar to adding whole numbers, but you have decimal points to line up and decimal values to add and subtract. Demonstrate decimal addition and subtraction on the board.

• On seven large index cards write the following decimals and symbols: *1.1, 3.2, 4.3, 6.6, +, +, =*. Invite seven volunteers to hold the cards in front of the class and form an addition sentence. (*1.1 + 3.2 + 4.3 = 6.6*) Have two "addends" change places. Ask: *Is the addition sentence still true?* (*Yes.*) Say: *This is the* **Commutative Property.** *These numbers "commute," or move, from one place to another, but the sum is still the same.*

• Demonstrate the **Associative Property** by making your hands into "parentheses" around the first and second "addends." Then put "parentheses" around the second and third addends. Elicit that the sum is the same.

• Make another index card with *0* on it and invite a volunteer to demonstrate the **Identity Property.** Say: *When a number is added to 0, the sum is that number.*

• Distribute Learning Resource 3 to pairs and help them play "Tic-Tac-Decimal." As they play the game, encourage them to say which addition property they could demonstrate with each problem.

Challenge Students can make up more difficult problems and a game board for "Challenge Tic-Tac-Decimal."

Multilevel Strategies

❶ Preproduction
Challenge students to point to the cards and symbols as you name them.

Writing Have students write an addition sentence.

❷❸ Early Production and Speech Emergence
Say: *Say the names of the numbers and symbols as I point to them.*

Writing Have students write an example of one of the Addition Properties.

❹❺ Intermediate and Advanced Fluency
Ask: *Explain the Commutative Property.*

Writing Invite students to write a sentence about an Addition Property.

Name _____

Tic-Tac-Decimals

Solve the problems. Cut them out and put them upside down in a pile. Take turns. Pick up a problem and place it where it belongs on the game board. Mark it with an *X* or an *O*. The first player to get 3 in a row wins.

15.993	**148.5**	**55.625**
23.97	**10.13**	**0.46**
111.1	**9.35**	**4.98**

Left column cards:

$$14.45 - 5.10$$

$$10.13 + 0$$

$$54.375 + 1.250$$

Right column cards:

$$128.3 + 20.2$$

$$12.453 + 3.540$$

$$0.66 - 0.20$$

Bottom row cards:

$$8.40 - 3.42$$

$$25.35 - 1.38$$

$$135.65 - 24.55$$

Lesson 4

 45 minutes

▶ **Key Strategy**
Use manipulatives

▶ **Format**
Whole class and student pairs

▶ **Math Vocabulary**
compensation, round

▶ **Daily Vocabulary**
compensate, decrease, increase, regrouping

▶ **Resource**
Learning Resource 4

Materials
• calculator

Assessment

Check students' understanding of addition and subtraction as they complete the lesson. See page 23 for Assessment Checklist.
Remind students to work on their foldables.

Home Connection

Have students use beans or pasta to demonstrate compensation to family members. Encourage them to report their experience to the class.

Compensation

Math Objectives	ESL/TESOL Descriptor
▪ Add and subtract whole numbers and decimals. ▪ Estimate sums and differences of whole numbers and decimals.	▪ Understand and produce technical vocabulary and text features according to content area.

Activate Prior Knowledge Write this addition problem: 198 + 227 = ___.
Ask a volunteer to solve the problem by regrouping 15 ones as one ten and 5 ones. Then ask: *Is there another way to solve this problem? Can you think of a way to do this so you don't have to regroup?*

Hands-on Lesson Distribute Learning Resource 4 and work together with students to complete the addition problems in Section A. Ask: *Do you see a pattern in these problems? What do you think the next sum will be? (420)*
Say: *The sums are all the same. In each problem one of the addends increases by 1; the other decreases by 1. One gets larger; one gets smaller. The sum is the same.* Point to the last problem in the section. Ask: *Can you add 200 and 220 mentally, without regrouping?* Elicit that numbers that are rounded to the nearest 10 or 100 are easy to add.

• Explain that **compensation** is a way of changing the addends to make them easier to add. You add a number to one of the addends to make it a **round** number, and subtract the same number from the other addend.

• Point out the subtraction problems in section C and invite students to find a pattern. Say: *The differences are the same. In each problem both numbers decrease by 1. Compensation can help you add or subtract.*

• Pair students and have them complete the Learning Resource.

Cultural Link In English, Spanish, and Haitian Creole the term *compensation* implies reward or give-and-take. Encourage children to look up the word, using an English dictionary or a dictionary of their native language, and discuss its significance.

Multilevel Strategies

❶ Preproduction
Have students point to the steps of rounding as you name them.

Writing Have students write a 2-digit number and then round it to the nearest ten.

❷❸ Early Production and Speech Emergence
Say: *I'm adding two numbers. I add 4 to one number and subtract 4 from the other. How does the sum change?*

Writing Students write four addition problems that have the same sums.

❹❺ Intermediate and Advanced Fluency
Ask: *How can I add 599 and 38 without regrouping?*

Writing Encourage students to write a sentence about compensation.

Name _____

Compensation Roundup

Do the addition and subtraction problems. Look for the pattern. Then make up addition and subtraction problems that have similar patterns.

ADDITION

A	B
196 + 224 = _____	_____ + _____ = _____
197 + 223 = _____	_____ + _____ = _____
198 + 222 = _____	_____ + _____ = _____
199 + 221 = _____	_____ + _____ = _____
200 + 220 = _____	_____ + _____ = _____

SUBTRACTION

C	D
204 − 89 = _____	_____ − _____ = _____
203 − 88 = _____	_____ − _____ = _____
202 − 87 = _____	_____ − _____ = _____
201 − 86 = _____	_____ − _____ = _____
200 − 85 = _____	_____ − _____ = _____

Problem Solving

Problem Solving
Reading for Math

SKILL: Use the Four-Step Process
Model the skill using a word problem such as:

 Read

The U.S. Immigration Service says that by 1995 5,069,181 people had come here from Great Britain; 5,424,543 from Italy; and 5,378,882 from Mexico. Show Mexico, Great Britain and Italy on the map. Which country did the most immigrants come from?

 Plan

I can use the information in the problem to answer the question. I can make a list.

 Solve

Think: In all three numbers the number in the greatest place is 5 million, so I look to the next greatest place. I can put the numbers in order from least to greatest.

5,069,181	Great Britain
5,378,882	Mexico
5,424,543	Italy

The most immigrants came from Italy.

 Look Back

How can I check my answer? I look at the numbers in the hundred thousand place. $0 < 3 < 4$

Distribute **Math Center Card 1A** to students.

Math Center Card 1A

Reading for Math Skill PARTNERS

USE THE FOUR-STEP PROCESS • HOW MUCH MONEY?

Look at the table and answer the questions below. Work with a partner. Do you think there are as many $5 bills as $1 bills? Which kind of bill in the United States has the greatest circulation? Which has the least circulation?

This table shows the number of each kind of bill in circulation.

Kind (Denomination)	Number of Bills in Circulation
$1 bills	6,253,758,057
$2 bills	548,577,377
$5 bills	1,468,874,833
$10 bills	13,338,391,336
$20 bills	4,093,739,605
$50 bills	932,552,370
$100 bills	2,640,194,345

Source: *The World Almanac for Kids, 1999*

1. What do you know?

2. What do you need to find?

3. Which kind of bill has the greatest number in circulation? Which kind of bill has the least number?

4. List the number of each kind of bill from the greatest to the least.

Math Center Card, Grade 5, Unit 1, 1A

STRATEGY: Find a Pattern
Model the strategy using a word problem such as:

 Read

Penny trained for the marathon. She ran 3 miles a day in June. She ran 6 miles a day in July. She ran 9 miles a day in August. She ran 12 miles a day in September. If she keeps the same pattern, how many miles a day will she be running in December?

 Plan

I can list the numbers and figure out the pattern of increase. I can list the months to find out how many months to December.

 Solve

The pattern of increase is 3, 6, 9, 12…
Think: Each number is 3 more than the number before. I can extend the pattern 3 more to find the answer. 3, 6, 9, 12, 15, 18, 21. In December she will be running 21 miles a day.

 Look Back

Does my answer make sense? Yes. If the pattern continues as it started she will be running 21 miles a day in December. $3 \times 3 = 9$. $12 + 9 = 21$.

Distribute **Math Center Card 1B** to students.

Math Center Card 1B

Problem Solving: Strategy INDIVIDUAL

FIND A PATTERN • TOO MANY SIT-UPS

Ricky wanted to do sit-ups. He decided to do the following:
- on the first day, 20 sit-ups
- on the second day, 3 more sit-ups than on the first day
- on the third day, 5 more sit-ups than on the second day
- on the fourth day, 7 more sit-ups than on the third day.

If this pattern of adding the next odd number of sit-ups continues, how many sit-ups will he do on the tenth day?

1. What do you know?

2. What do you need to find?

3. How many sit-ups will Ricky do on the tenth day?

4. Does Ricky's pattern make sense? Explain.

5. What is another pattern that Ricky can use?

JUNE

Math Center Card, Grade 5, Unit 1, 1B

Assessment Checklist

	STUDENT NAMES											
SCHOOL:												
TEACHER: **SCHOOL YEAR:**												
Mark: + = Mastery ✓ = Satisfactory − = Needs Improvement												
LEVEL OF LANGUAGE PROFICIENCY (1–5)												
MATH OBJECTIVES												
• Use place value to read and write whole numbers and decimals.												
• Estimate quantities using benchmarks.												
• Compare and order whole numbers and decimals.												
• Identify and use the properties of addition.												
• Add and subtract whole numbers and decimals.												
ESL/TESOL LISTENING/SPEAKING												
Analyze, synthesize, and infer from information.												
Listen to and imitate how others use English.												
Use context to construct meaning.												
Select, connect, and explain information.												
Understand and produce technical vocabulary and text features according to content area.												
ESL/TESOL READING												
Read about subject matter information.												
Apply basic reading comprehension skills.												
Follow written directions, implicit and explicit.												
ESL WRITING												
Write to demonstrate comprehension.												
Write using spelling patterns and targeted English vocabulary.												

  **by Dinah Zike**

1 **Preproduction**
- Did students write the unit vocabulary?
- Did they copy the definitions?

2 **3** **Early Production and Speech Emergence**
- Did students label the tabs correctly?
- Did they write the vocabulary words?
- Did they copy the definitions?

4 **5** **Intermediate and Advanced Fluency**
- Did students write definitions for the unit vocabulary?
- Did they use correct spelling and grammar?

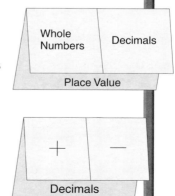

UNIT 2

Planner

Multiply Whole Numbers and Decimals

Assessment
p. 41
• Assessment Checklist
• Foldables

LOG ON Visit **www.mmhmath.com**

Unit Activities
• **Activity 1** (Readiness) Multiplication Story, p. 28
• **Activity 2** Multiplication Squares, p. 28
• **Activity 3** So Many Games! p. 29
• **Activity 4** No Nines! p. 29

Lessons	Key Objectives	Vocabulary	Materials	Resources
READ TOGETHER "Hindu Lattice Multiplication," pp. 26–27	**Math:** Multiply whole numbers and decimals. **ESL/TESOL:** Goal 2, Standard 3.	complicated, diagonals, Hindu, lattice, mathematician, method, removable, twelfth century		
UNIT WARM-UP Understanding Multiplication p. 30	**Math:** Multiply whole numbers and decimals. Estimate products of whole numbers and decimals. **ESL/TESOL:** Goal 2, Standards 2, 3.	array, Associative Property, Commutative Property, factor, product	base-ten set, counters	**Overhead Manipulatives**
LESSON 1 Multiply Whole Numbers pp. 32–33	**Math:** Multiply whole numbers. **ESL/TESOL:** Goal 2, Standard 2.	Distributive Property	counters, crayons or markers	Learning Resource 5 Teacher Tool 7
LESSON 2 Multiply Decimals pp. 34–35	**Math:** Multiply whole numbers and decimals. **ESL/TESOL:** Goal 1, Standard 3.	factor, product	number cube	Learning Resource 6 Teacher Tool 4
LESSON 3 Multiply Whole Numbers and Decimals pp. 36–37	**Math:** Multiply whole numbers and decimals. **ESL/TESOL:** Goal 2, Standards 1, 3.	clustering, factor, product		Learning Resource 7 Teacher Tools 4 and 5
LESSON 4 Exponents pp. 38–39	**Math:** Express products as powers and evaluate exponential expressions. **ESL/TESOL:** Goal 2, Standard 2.	base, exponent, power, square number	calculators	Learning Resource 8
PROBLEM SOLVING p. 40 • Skill: Estimate or Exact Answer? • Strategy: Guess and Check	Use skills and strategies to solve problems.			**Math Center Cards 2A, 2B**

See **Math at Home Family Guide** for additional math vocabulary, activities, and games in English, Spanish, and Haitian Creole.

English Vocabulary

Dear Family: Please help your child practice the key vocabulary words for this unit.

array a group of objects separated into rows and columns

base the number that is to be raised to a given power

clustering a way to estimate a sum by changing the addends that are close in value to one common number and multiplying by the number of addends

Distributive Property the property of distributing one operation over another with the results staying the same

exponent the number that tells how many times a base is used as a factor

factor a number that is multiplied to give a product
Example: In 3×5, 3 and 5 are factors.

power a number obtained by raising a base to an exponent

product the answer in a multiplication problem

Vocabulario en español

Estimados familiares: Por favor ayuden a su hijo/a a practicar las palabras del vocabulario de esta unidad.

arreglo objetos o símbolos ordenados en hileras y columnas

base número que se eleva según indica el exponente para dar una potencia

agrupación método de estimación usado cuando todos los sumandos se aproximan a un mismo número; consiste en multiplicar la cantidad de sumandos por ese número

Propiedad distributiva la propiedad de distribuir una operación sobre la otra sin alterar el resultado

exponente número que indica cuántas veces se usará la base como factor

factor número que se multiplica para obtener un producto.
Ejemplo: En *3 3 5*, 3 y 5 son factores.

potencia número obtenido al elevar la base a un exponente

producto resultado de la multiplicación

Vokabilè an kreyòl

Chè paran: Tanpri ede pitit la pratike mo vokabilè nan seksyon sa a.

koleksyon yon gwoup bagay ki separe e ranje ak kolòn

baz yon nimewo ki dwe transfome pou'l rive nan yon lòt nivo piwo.

gwoupman se yon fason pou'w kalkile yon sòm; lè ou chanje nimewo pou ajoute ki preske gen menm valè yo, fè yo vinn yon sèl epi miltipliye'l pa kantite nimewo oute gen pou ajoute yo

kalite distribitif miltipliye yon adisyon pa yon nonb egal menm operasyon lè w miltipliye chak manm adisyon an pa menm nonb la

ekspozan nimewo ki di konbyen fwa yon baz itilize kòm faktè

faktè yon nimewo ou itilize pou ba ou yon pwodui.
Egzanp: Nan *3 3 5*, 3 e 5 se faktè.

pisans nimewo ou jwenn nan lè-w ogmante yon baz pa yon ekspozan

pwodui repons yon miltiplikasyon

Hindu Lattice Multiplication

Math Objective
- Multiply whole numbers and decimals.

ESL/TESOL Descriptors
- Use context to construct meaning.
- Connect new information to information previously learned.

Reading Skill
- Compare and Contrast.

Vocabulary
complicated, diagonals, Hindu, lattice, mathematician, method, removable, sand, twelfth century

Before Reading

Build Background/Oral Language
Show visuals to preteach vocabulary. Point to the title of the story. Draw a lattice of diagonal lines that crisscross into diamonds. You may wish to explain that lattices are commonly used to support climbing plants. Draw a time line from the year A.D. 1000 to the present. Circle A.D. 1100, which is the twelfth century.

During Reading
- Read the story through once without stopping as students track text.
- Reread the story, pausing often to encourage students to ask questions about new or difficult words. Encourage students to use self–stick notes to mark them.
- Ask volunteers to read sentences from the story.

Phonological/Phonemic Awareness
Write the words *mathematician* and *multiplication* on the board. Underline *-tion* and *-cian* in the words and have students repeat. Elicit that they sound the same. Explain that *-cian* often means someone who does something, and the ending *-tion* often turns a verb into a noun. List and explain some other examples, such as *musician, physician, optician, ignition,* and *definition*.

After Reading
Have students fold a piece of paper in half to make a two-column chart and ask them to label the columns *Same* and *Different*. Compare and contrast twelfth-century math to modern-day methods.

Art Invite students to make their own lattice multiplication problem as an art piece for their portfolios. Have them show how they solved the problem.

Assessment
Assess lesson objectives and descriptors by observing groups' participation in the reading activity. See Assessment Checklist on page 41.

Multilevel Strategies

1 Preproduction
Say: *Point to the word lattice.*

Writing Ask students to label the lattice on the multiplication problem.

2 3 Early Production and Speech Emergence
Point to the multiplication lattice problem and ask: *What is this?*

Writing Ask students to label their art with the words *grid, diagonal,* and *lattice.*

4 5 Intermediate and Advanced Fluency
Ask: *How does lattice math work?*

Writing Encourage students to write what they learned about 12th-century math methods.

Hindu Lattice Multiplication

Although today most mathematicians use calculators for complicated multiplication, in the twelfth century Hindu mathematicians used the lattice method.

The lattice is a grid with diagonals. Lattices were usually drawn on blackboards with white removable paint or etched into boards covered with sand or flour.

Here is the lattice method used to multiply 876 by 5:

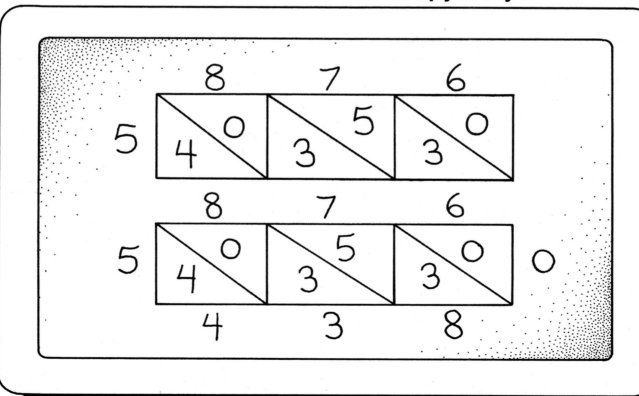

Activities

Readiness

ACTIVITY 1

PARTNERS

Multiplication Story

• **Each Partner:** Use these sentences to write word problems. Choose one sentence from each group. Trade problems with your partner. Solve.

• **First Sentence:**

"Marcos has 5 boxes of marbles."
"Paulo has 9 boxes of pencils."
"Sheila buys 4 packages of toothpicks."
"Mrs. Clark buys 8 cases of canned fruit juice."

• **Second Sentence:**

"Each case has 8."   "Each package has 7."
"Each case has 4."   "Each package has 6."
"There are 4 in each case."   "There are 5 in each box."
"There are 3 in each box."

• **Third Sentence:**

"How many are there in all?"

Multiply Whole Numbers

ACTIVITY 2

INDIVIDUAL

Multiplication Squares

1. Copy the multiplication square below.

5	4	0.6
6	1	2
0.4	3	10

• Find the product of each row and column.

• What do you see?

2. Now make another square. Multiply each number in the original square by 10, using place-value models to help you. Write the product in your new square.

• Find the product of each column of your square.

• What do you see?

YOU NEED

calculator
place-value models

See answers on p. 291.

Multiply Whole Numbers and Decimals

Game Zone

PARTNERS

So Many Games!

- Each player spins the spinner to get a number. Multiply by $10 or $20 to get a total budget.

- Each player gets to spend their budget on games from The Game Store.

- You want to buy as many games as you can for yourself and as gifts for friends.

- List the games you can buy and show your total. Have your partner check your answers.

YOU NEED

spinner (0-9)

THE GAME STORE	
Game Prices	
Match Your Price	$25.89
Hit the Deck	$10.25
Fan Fare	$8.49
Roll and Spell	$12.85
Stock Exchange	$20.99

Multiply Whole Numbers

INDIVIDUAL

No Nines!

Help! SOS! The 9 key on your calculator is not working.
How can you find the following products on your calculator?

1. $9 \times 447 = ?$

2. $9 \times 186 = ?$

3. $9 \times 400 = ?$

Hint: The distributive property will help you. Write more problems like this one to share with your friends.

YOU NEED

calculator

See answers on p. 291.

Use Distributive Property

© Macmillan/McGraw-Hill

Understanding Multiplication

 25 minutes

▶ **Key Strategy**
Use manipulatives

▶ **Format**
Whole class and groups

▶ **Math Vocabulary**
array, Associative Property, Commutative Property, factor, product

▶ **Daily Vocabulary**
chair, legs, multiply, switch

▶ **Resources**
Overhead Manipulatives:
Base-Ten Set, Counters

▶ **Materials**
base-ten set, counters

Math Objectives	ESL/TESOL Descriptors
■ Multiply whole numbers and decimals. ■ Estimate products of whole numbers and decimals.	■ Analyze, synthesize, and infer from information. ■ Focus attention selectively.

Activate Prior Knowledge Remind students that they have learned to round numbers and estimate. Write $15 + 93 + 62 = \_\_$; $173 - 52 = \_\_$; $6,032 - 542 = \_\_$; $4,123,999 + 200,097 + 573 = \_\_$ Ask students to solve each problem mentally through rounding and estimation. Then have volunteers solve the problems by regrouping. Remind students to think about place value when regrouping.

Hands-on Lesson Tell students they will multiply whole numbers using items in the classroom. Write: *There are 5 chairs and each chair has 4 legs. How many legs are there?* Ask a volunteer to explain how to solve the problem.

• Distribute counters and base-ten sets. Write 13×16 on the board. Ask students to use their counters or base-ten sets to display the numbers in an **array,** or separated in rows and columns. You may want to use Base Ten and Counters from **Overhead Manipulatives** to model. Ask them to switch numbers around to show the **Commutative Property.** Finally, have them round to the nearest tens place and estimate an answer. *(10 × 20 = 200)* Explain that in multiplication the numbers being multiplied are **factors.** The answer is the **product.**

• Write $7 \times 6 \times 5$ on the board. Ask students to use their counters or sets to display the numbers and demonstrate the **Associative Property.** Remind them that the way the factions are grouped doesn't change the product.

• Write 13×2.5. Have students round and estimate. Remind them that in multiplying decimals they will round to the nearest whole number. *(10 × 3 = 30)* Ask volunteers to explain their work.

• Write more problems on the board using multiples of 10, 100, and 1,000, and have students round and estimate with and without models.

Multilevel Strategies

1 Preproduction
Ask students to model 14×15 with the base-ten set.

2 3 Early Production and Speech Emergence
Use the base-ten set to model 14×15 and ask students to tell you the equation.

4 5 Intermediate and Advanced Fluency
Ask students to explain the Commutative Property.

 Visit **www.mmhmath.com** to find printable **Vocabulary Cards** that help build academic language.

Procedure: Help students make these Foldables to write vocabulary words and definitions throughout the unit. Encourage students to use the Foldables as a study guide.

 **by Dinah Zike**

Pocket Book

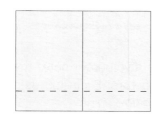

1. Provide each student with a sheet of paper. Have students fold a 2" tab along the long edge. Help them fold the folded paper in half like a hamburger to form a Pocket Book.

2. Glue or staple the ends of the pockets closed. Have students label their pockets *Things I Know* and *Need to Know*.

3. Students can take notes on 3" × 5" index cards or quarter-sheets of paper. Have them store their note cards in the appropriate pockets.

Note cards may include:

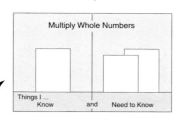

A factor is a number multiplied.

The result of multiplying factors is a product.

$3 \times 5 = 15$

factor   factor   product

How do I multiply a 3-digit number by a 2-digit number?

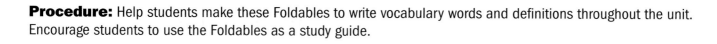 **by Dinah Zike**

Pocket Book

1. Provide each student with a sheet of paper. Have students fold a 2" tab along the long edge. Help them fold the folded paper in half like a hamburger to form a Pocket Book.

2. Glue or staple the ends of the pockets closed. Have students label their pockets *Things I Know* and *Need to Know*.

3. Students can take notes on 3" × 5" index cards or quarter-sheets of paper. Have them store their note cards in the appropriate pockets.

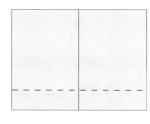

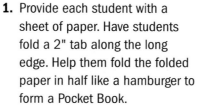

Note cards may include:

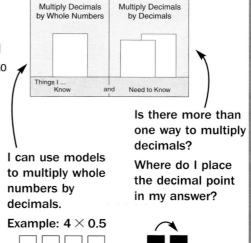

Is there more than one way to multiply decimals?

Where do I place the decimal point in my answer?

I can use models to multiply whole numbers by decimals.

Example: 4×0.5

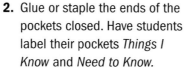

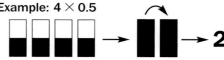

⏱ **45 minutes**

▶ **Key Strategy**
Use manipulatives

▶ **Format**
Whole class and individual

▶ **Math Vocabulary**
Distributive Property

▶ **Daily Vocabulary**
regroup

▶ **Resources**
Learning Resource 5
Teacher Tool 7

Materials
- counters
- crayons or markers

Assessment

Check students' mastery of multiplication as they complete the lesson. See Assessment Checklist on page 41. Remind students to work on their Foldables.

Home Connection

Distribute a clean copy of Teacher Tool 7 for students to take it home. Ask them to show family members what they are learning.

Multiply Whole Numbers

Math Objective	**ESL/TESOL Descriptors**
■ Multiply whole numbers.	■ Select, connect, and explain information. ■ Respond to the work of peers and others.

Activate Prior Knowledge Write $3 \times 4 \times 2$. Have a volunteer solve the problem. Then ask another volunteer to rearrange the factors. Elicit that using a different order does not change the product. *(Associative Property)*

Hands-on Lesson Distribute Teacher Tool 7: 10×10 Grid. Have students count boxes horizontally and vertically to show that there are 100 or 10×10. Elicit that you would shade the entire box to show the product of 10×10.

- Write 4×12. Have students shade their grid paper to reflect the equation and count the number of shaded boxes. *(48)* Then invite students to make arrays with their counters to solve the problem: $4 \times (10 + 2)$; $4 \times 10 = 40$; $4 \times 2 = 8$. $40 + 8 = 48$. *(4 rows of 10 counters, 4 rows of 2 counters)* Explain that this is called the **Distributive Property.** Invite students to write similar problems on the board and solve them together.

- Write 12×15 and guide students in solving a 2-digit multiplication problem: $(10 \times 15) + (2 \times 15) = 150 + 30 = 180$. Invite students to write similar problems on the board and solve them together.

- Distribute Learning Resource 5: Distributive Property. Encourage students to use arrays as they complete the worksheet.

- When students have completed the sheet, ask them to exchange papers with another student to check their answers.

Challenge Ask students how the product of 8×17 is different from the product of 80×17 or 800×17.

Multilevel Strategies

❶ Preproduction
Write 4×12. Ask students to solve, then point to or say the product.

Writing Encourage students to write the factors in a different order and solve.

❷❸ Early Production and Speech Emergence
Write 4×12. Ask students to read it aloud, solve, and name the factors and product.

Writing Have students write an equation that shows the Distributive Property.

❹❺ Intermediate and Advanced Fluency
Write 4×12. Ask students to say the steps for showing the Distributive Property.

Writing Invite students to write an explanation of the Distributive Property.

Name _____

Distributive Property

Use the Distributive Property to find the product.

PROBLEM	DISTRIBUTIVE PROPERTY
8 × 17	
12 × 15	
9 × 13	
7 × 17	
Make up your own problem here.	

Lesson

2

▶ **Key Strategy**
Use manipulatives

▶ **Format**
Whole class and pairs

▶ **Math Vocabulary**
factor, product

▶ **Daily Vocabulary**
estimate, number cube, round, toss

▶ **Resources**
Learning Resource 6
Teacher Tool 4

Materials
• number cube (optional)

Assessment

Check students' mastery of multiplication as they complete the lesson. See page 41 for Assessment Checklist. Remind students to work on their Foldables.

Home Connection

Ask students to find examples of how decimals are used in magazines or flyers and report their findings to the class.

Multiply Decimals

Math Objective	ESL/TESOL Descriptors
■ Multiply whole numbers and decimals.	■ Learn and use language "chunks." ■ Use context to construct meaning.

Activate Prior Knowledge Write 9×83. Ask students what they recall about rounding to estimate **products.** Invite students to estimate the product.

Hands-on Lesson Explain that multiplying decimals is similar to multiplying whole numbers. Model multiplying 1.7×2.19. Ask students to round and estimate. $(2 \times 2 = 4)$ Then multiply as if the decimals were whole numbers: $17 \times 219 = 3,723$. Use the estimate to put the decimal point in the correct place. The estimate was 4, so the product will be 3.723.

● Model this problem: 0.04×0.05. First, multiply as if these decimals were whole numbers: $4 \times 5 = 20$. To find place value, count the places to the right of the decimal point of each number. The 4 and 5 in 0.04 and 0.05 are both 2 places to the right: $2 + 2 = 4$ places. The answer is 0.0020; it has 4 places to the right of the decimal point.

● Distribute Learning Resource 6: Multiplyimg Decimals and Teacher Tool 4: Number Cube Patterns, to pairs of students. Ask partners to toss the number cube three times and write the numbers on Learning Resource 6. This is one **factor.** Next, have them toss the number cube two times to create the second factor. Students then complete the number sentence.

Cultural Link Decimals are indicated by a period in English, and by a comma in many other languages.

Challenge Ask students to write and solve a multiplication problem with decimals in the thousandths and ten-thousandths places.

Multilevel Strategies

❶ Preproduction
Ask students to point out where the decimal should go in the examples.

Writing Encourage students to write a multiplication problem with a decimal.

❷❸ Early Production and Speech Emergence
Ask students to name the product of a multiplication problem.

Writing Ask students to write a multiplication problem and label the factors and product.

❹❺ Intermediate and Advanced Fluency
Ask students to compare multiplying whole numbers and multiplying decimals.

Writing Invite students to write an instruction card that tells how to multiply decimals.

6

Name _____

Multiplying Decimals

Choose Strategy 1 or Strategy 2 to solve. Follow the steps to place the decimal point in the correct place.

	Multiply	Step 1	Step 2	Step 3
STRATEGY 1	Roll the number cube three times, then two. Write the numbers below.	Round each number and make an estimate.	Multiply the decimals as if they were whole numbers.	Use your estimate from Step 1 to place the decimal point.
	__.__ __ × __.__			
	__ __.__ × __.__			

	Multiply	Step 1	Step 2	Step 3
STRATEGY 2	Roll the number cube three times, then two. Write the numbers below.	Multiply the decimals as if they were whole numbers. Put a decimal point to the right of the number.	Count the places each factor has to the right of the decimal point. Add them to get a total.	Use the total of Step 2. Move the decimal point this number of places to the left. Fill empty places with zero(s).
	__ __.__ × __.__			
	__ __.__ × __.__			

⏱ **45 minutes**

▶ **Key Strategy**
Use manipulatives

▶ **Format**
Whole class and small groups

▶ **Math Vocabulary**
clustering, factor, product

▶ **Daily Vocabulary**
diagonally, horizontally, tic-tac-toe game, toss, turn, vertically

▶ **Resources**
Learning Resource 7
Teacher Tools 4 and 5

Assessment

Check students' mastery of unit pricing as they complete the lesson. See page 41 for Assessment Checklist. Remind students to work on their Foldables.

Home Connection

Invite students to take home a copy of the Learning Resource game to play with family members. Ask them to share their experience with the class.

Multiply Whole Numbers and Decimals

Math Objectives	**ESL/TESOL Descriptors**
▪ Multiply whole numbers and decimals.	▪ Negotiate and manage interaction to accomplish tasks.
▪ Estimate products of whole numbers and decimals.	▪ Focus attention selectively.

Activate Prior Knowledge Say: *Imagine we want to donate books to a school overseas: It costs $1.23 per lb. to ship the books. If we collect 230.5 lbs. of books, how much will the shipping cost?* Point out that problems involving money use decimals. Have volunteers come to the board to show how they could use estimation and the Distributive Property to help solve the problem.

Hands-on Lesson Distribute materials and Learning Resource 7. Tell students that they will play a game solving word problems. Divide the class into groups of 4 or 6 students, with each group splitting into two teams.

● The first team tosses the number cube (Teacher Tool 4) for the number of the problem they must solve. Then both teams work out the same problem separately. The first team to find the correct answer places a counter on the corresponding number on the game sheet. Both teams must agree that the answer is correct.

● The team that solved the problem correctly tosses the cube first for the next round. Groups continue playing until one team fills in 3 squares in a row vertically, horizontally, or diagonally. (*Answers*: 1. $8.75, 2. 47.25 hours, 3. 22.5 miles, 4. 42 letters, 5. $27.59, 6. 12 minutes, 7. $325.50, 8. $306.10, 9. $5.90) When the game is over, discuss what the groups learned from playing. Ask them to share any shortcuts they used to solve a problem.

● Use the unit Foldables to review the vocabulary word **clustering.**

Challenge Invite students to make up a new version of the word problems that can be solved by multiplying decimals and whole numbers.

Multilevel Strategies

1 Preproduction
Ask students to point to or say the decimal number in one of the problems in the game.

Writing Ask students to write out a problem as a number sentence.

2 3 Early Production and Speech Emergence
Point to one of the decimal numbers and ask students to say it.

Writing Have students write a sentence with the answer to a problem.

4 5 Intermediate and Advanced Fluency
Ask students to explain how to play the game.

Writing Invite students to write an instruction rule card for the game.

Name _____

Decimal Tic-Tac-Toe

Win the game by solving three problems in a row, in any direction.
Put a counter on each box your team solves first.

1. Five friends each ordered a slice of pizza. The pizza was $1.75 a slice. How much did the friends spend altogether? _____	**2.** Sami practices the piano 2.25 hours a day every day. How many hours does she practice in three weeks? _____	**3.** Jung rides 4.5 miles to school every day. How many miles does he travel in a school week? _____
4. Chris wrote three letters each day for two weeks. How many letters did Chris write? _____	**5.** A pen costs $0.89. The teacher buys a pen for each of the 31 students in her class. How much does the teacher spend? _____	**6.** A mouse can run through a maze in 1.5 minutes. How long would it take for the mouse to run through the maze 8 times? _____
7. Joe worked 42 hours this week. If he makes $7.75 an hour, how much did he earn this week? _____	**8.** Keiko spent $900 on a 3-day trip to Puerto Rico. Her expenses included $45 a day for taxis, $28.40 for gifts, and $143.50 a day for food and hotels. Airfare was her only other expense. What was the cost of the airfare? _____	**9.** Oscar sent 4 airmail letters that cost $0.80 each. He also sent 6 postcards at $0.45 each. How much did he spend on stamps? _____

Lesson 4

 45 minutes

▶ **Key Strategy**
Use visuals

▶ **Format**
Whole class and pairs

▶ **Math Vocabulary**
base, exponent, power, square number

▶ **Daily Vocabulary**
cubed, scientific notation, squared

▶ **Resource**
Learning Resource 8

Materials
• calculators

Assessment

Check students' mastery of exponents as they complete the lesson. See page 41 for Assessment Checklist. Remind students to work on their Foldables.

Home Connection

Ask students to draw an array made with items at home and share it with the class.

Exponents

Math Objective	**ESL/TESOL Descriptors**
▪ Express products as powers and evaluate exponential expressions.	▪ Interpret information presented visually.
	▪ Understand and produce technical vocabulary.

Activate Prior Knowledge Write 10×10. Ask: **What is the product?** Repeat with 100×10 and 1000×10. Tell students that this lesson will help them to learn more about multiplying a number by itself.

Hands-on Lesson Explain that when you multiply tens together, the product demonstrates the **power** of 10. Write $10 \times 10 = 10^2 = 100$. Explain that 10 is the **base** number, and the ^{2} superscript is the **exponent** or **power.** This number tells how many times the base is used as a factor.

• Write 10^3 and have a student write the equation $(10 \times 10 \times 10)$. Elicit that the power, or the exponent ^{3}, gives the number of times 10 is a factor. You can also count the zeros following the number to tell the power of 10.

• Explain we can write very large numbers with exponents in scientific notation. For example, the number 7,000,000 is written as 7×10^6. Tell students that exponents and bases are also used to express other numbers. For example, numbers to the power of ^{2}, such as 2^2, are **squared numbers;** and numbers to the power of ^{3}, such as 7^3, are cubed numbers. All numbers can be raised to any power.

• Distribute Learning Resource 8: Match It! and calculators. Before students begin their work on the sheet, ask them to take turns reading numbers from the columns to practice saying exponents. (Answers: 1. c; 2. i; 3. b; 4. g; 5. f; 6. d; 7. j; 8. h; 9. a; 10. e)

Challenge Ask students to research Earth's population (6.3 billion) and write it in scientific notation.

Multilevel Strategies

❶ Preproduction
Have students point to exponents on the Learning Resource as you say them.

Writing Ask students to write numbers as you say them.

❷❸ Early Production and Speech Emergence
Ask students to say exponential numbers as you point to them.

Writing Ask students to write numbers you say in squared or cubed form.

❹❺ Intermediate and Advanced Fluency
Ask students to explain exponents.

Writing Ask students to write an instruction card for writing numbers with exponents.

Name _____

Match It!

Draw a line from the number in the left column to the correct answer in the right column.

1. 10^7 a. 135

2. 6^4 b. 20

3. 5×2^2 c. 10,000,000

4. 10^2 d. 343

5. 8×10^4 e. 100,000

6. 7^3 f. 80,000

7. 4^2 g. 100

8. 3×10^2 h. 300

9. 5×3^3 i. 1,296

10. 10^5 j. 16

Problem Solving
Reading for Math

Read → Plan → Solve → Look Back

Remind students of
the basic steps
of problem solving.

SKILL: Estimate or Exact Answer?
Model the skill using a word problem such as:

 Read

250 tiles weigh a pound. Marco uses 556 tiles in his mosaic. Jenny uses 875 tiles in her mosaic. About how many pounds did they use together?

 Plan

I can estimate the total number of tiles each used. I can add to find the total. Then I can divide to find how many pounds.

 Solve

556 is about 600 tiles. 875 is about 900 tiles.
$600 + 900 = 1,500$ tiles.
Together they used about 1,500 tiles.
$1500 \div 250 = 6$.
Together they used about 6 pounds of tiles.

 Look Back

Does my answer make sense? Yes. Is my estimate more or less than the exact answer? I rounded both 556 and 875 up to the nearest hundred. The estimate is greater than the exact answer.

Distribute **Math Center Card 2A** to students.

Math Center Card 2A

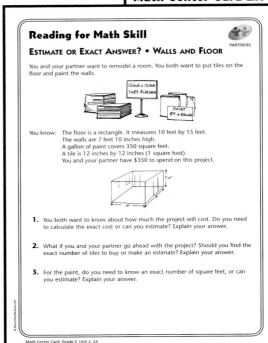

STRATEGY: Guess and Check
Model the strategy using a word problem such as:

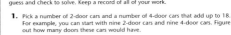

 Read

Bianca bought juice for the day camp. About half the campers like apple juice best and the others prefer orange juice. Bianca bought 63 juice boxes in all. The apple juice came in packs of 3 boxes. The orange juice came in packs of 2 boxes. How many apple and orange juice packs did she buy?

 Plan

I can guess and check to find the answer.

 Solve

Think: I can try 10 of each.
$10 \times 3 = 30$ $10 \times 2 = 20$
$30 + 20 = 50$ No.
Think: I can try 12 of each.
$12 \times 3 = 36$ $12 \times 2 = 24$
$36 + 24 = 60$ I need only one more 3-pack.
Bianca bought 12 packs of orange juice and 13 packs of apple juice.

Look Back

Does my answer make sense? Yes.

Distribute **Math Center Card 2B** to students.

Math Center Card 2B

Assessment Checklist

	STUDENT NAMES										
SCHOOL:											
TEACHER:　**SCHOOL YEAR:**											
Mark:　+ = Mastery　√ = Satisfactory　– = Needs Improvement											
LEVEL OF LANGUAGE PROFICIENCY (1–5)											
MATH OBJECTIVES											
• Multiply whole numbers and decimals											
• Estimate products of whole numbers and decimals.											
• Express products as powers and evaluate exponential expressions.											
ESL/TESOL LISTENING/SPEAKING											
Analyze, synthesize, and infer from information.											
Focus attention selectively.											
Respond to the work of peers and others.											
Select, connect, and explain information.											
Understand and produce technical vocabulary.											
ESL/TESOL READING											
Read about subject matter information.											
Apply basic reading comprehension skills.											
Follow written directions, implicit and explicit.											
ESL WRITING											
Write to demonstrate comprehension.											
Write using spelling patterns and targeted English vocabulary.											

 **by Dinah Zike**

1 **Preproduction**
- Did students write the unit vocabulary?
- Did they copy the definitions?

2 **3** **Early Production and Speech Emergence**
- Did students label the tabs correctly?
- Did they write the vocabulary words?
- Did they copy the definitions?

4 **5** **Intermediate and Advanced Fluency**
- Did students write definitions for the unit vocabulary?
- Did they use correct spelling and grammar?

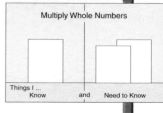

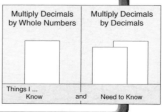

Planner

Divide Whole Numbers and Decimals

LOG
ON Visit **www.mmhmath.com**

Unit Activities		
• **Activity 1** Readiness The Sky Is the Limit, p. 46		• **Activity 3** Rolling for Zeros, p. 47
• **Activity 2** Math Marketing, p. 46		• **Activity 4** Division Signs, p. 47

Lessons	Key Objectives	Vocabulary	Materials	Resources
READ TOGETHER "The Doorbell Rang" by Pat Hutchins, pp. 44–45	**Math:** Divide whole numbers by 1-digit numbers. **ESL/TESOL:** Goal 2, Standards 2, 3.	cookies, cousins, doorbell, enormous, Grandma, makes, plenty, smell, starving		Graphic Organizer 5
UNIT WARM-UP Understanding Division p. 48	**Math:** Multiply whole numbers. Divide whole numbers by 1-digit numbers. **ESL/TESOL:** Goal 1, Standard 3.	dividend, divisor, quotient	counters	**Overhead Manipulatives**
LESSON 1 Exploring Division pp. 50–51	**Math:** Divide whole numbers by 1-digit and 2-digit numbers. Divide by 10, 100, and 1,000. **ESL/TESOL:** Goal 2, Standard 2.	dividend, divisor, fact family, quotient	counters, small paper cups	Learning Resource 9
LESSON 2 Estimate Quotients pp. 52–53	**Math:** Estimate quotients of whole numbers. **ESL/TESOL:** Goal 2, Standard 3. Goal 3, Standard 3.	compatible numbers	number cubes, pencils	Learning Resource 10 Teacher Tool 4
LESSON 3 Divide Decimals pp. 54–55	**Math:** Divide whole numbers by 2-digit numbers. Divide whole numbers and decimals. **ESL/TESOL:** Goal 1, Standard 3.	dividend, divisor, quotient, remainder	calculator, paper and pencils, scissors	Learning Resource 11 **Overhead Manipulatives**
PROBLEM SOLVING p. 56 • Skill: Interpret the Remainder • Strategy: Work Backward	Use skills and strategies to solve problems.			**Math Center Cards 3A, 3B**

See **Math at Home Family Guide** for additional math vocabulary, activities, and games in English, Spanish, and Haitian Creole.

English Vocabulary

Dear Family: Please help your child practice the key vocabulary words for this unit.

compatible numbers numbers that can be easily added, subtracted, multiplied, or divided mentally

dividend a number to be divided

divisor the number by which a dividend is divided

fact family a group of related facts using the same numbers

quotient the answer to a division problem

remainder in division, the number left after the quotient is found

---

Vocabulario en español

Estimados familiares: Por favor ayuden a su hijo/a a practicar las palabras del vocabulario de esta unidad.

números compatibles números que son fáciles de sumar, restar, multiplicar y dividir mentalmente

dividendo número que se divide

divisor número entre el cual se divide el dividendo

familia de operaciones grupo de operaciones relacionadas que usan los mismos números

cociente resultado de la división

residuo en una división, es el número que queda después de que se halla el cociente

---

Vokabilè an kreyol

Chè paran: Tanpri ede pitit la pratike mo vokabilè nan seksyon sa a.

nonb ki mache ansanm nimewo ki ka adisyone, retire, miltipliye, divize fasilman nan tèt ou

dividand nonb pou divize a

divizè nonb ki pou divize dividand lan

solisyon fanmi yon gwoup solisyon ki an rapò e ki sèvi ak menm nonb yo

kosyan repons yon divizyon

rès nan divizyon, sa ki rete lè w fin jwenn kosyan an

© Macmillan/McGraw-Hill

The Doorbell Rang

by Pat Hutchins

 25 minutes

Math Objective
- Divide whole numbers by 1-digit numbers.

ESL/TESOL Descriptors
- Use context to construct meaning.
- Retell information.

Reading Skill
- Cause and effect.

Vocabulary
brother, cookies, cousins, doorbell, enormous, Grandma, makes, plenty, share, smell, starving, stared

Before Reading

Build Background/Oral Language
Look at the title and illustrations. Pantomime knocking on a door and then ringing a doorbell. Write the word *cookie* on the board. Say: **I like chocolate chip cookies.** Ask students to repeat, and have volunteers say what kinds of cookies they like.

During Reading

- Read the story. The first time the words *the doorbell rang* appear, make a doorbell sound *(Bing bong!).* Then encourage students to chime in with the doorbell sound each time they hear the phrase in the story.

- Ask for volunteers to read the parts of different characters.

Phonological/Phonemic Awareness
Write *starving, share, smell* on the board. Say the words aloud and have students repeat and pantomime. Underline *st-, sh-,* and *sm-* and say them aloud. Draw three columns on the board and brainstorm words that start with the consonant clusters. (*story, steam; short, shampoo; smile, small*)

After Reading

Have students find the words *the doorbell rang* on the page. Ask volunteers why the share of cookies gets smaller each time the doorbell rings. Invite students to create a series of division sentences that show the effect of more visitors. Distribute Graphic Organizer 5: Cause and Effect Table to students and help them complete it. Ask students to retell the story.

Drama Invite students to role-play the story with props including a dozen paper cookies.

Assessment

Observe students as they read the poem aloud in their groups. See Assessment Checklist on page 57.

Multilevel Strategies

① Preproduction
Say: **Point to the picture of the cookies.**

Writing Have students write how many children visited Sam and Victoria.

② ③ Early Production and Speech Emergence
Ask: **Did Sam and Victoria's share of cookies get bigger or smaller when the visitors came?**

Writing Have students write the division sentence that shows the share of cookies before the visitors came.

④ ⑤ Intermediate and Advanced Fluency
Ask: **What happened to Sam and Victoria's share of cookies when the doorbell rang?**

Writing Have students write a sentence telling how the story ended.

The Doorbell Rang

by Pat Hutchins

"**I**'ve made some cookies for tea," said Ma.

"Good," said Victoria and Sam, "We're starving."

"Share them between yourselves," said Ma. " I made plenty."

"That's six each," said Sam and Victoria.

"They look as good as Grandma's," said Victoria.

"They smell as good as Grandma's," said Sam.

"No one makes cookies like Grandma," said Ma as the doorbell rang.

It was Tom and Hannah from next door.

"Come in," said Ma. "You can share the cookies."

"That's three each," said Sam and Victoria.

"They smell good as your Grandma's," said Tom.

"And they look as good," said Hannah.

"No one makes cookies like Grandma," said Ma as the doorbell rang.

It was Peter and his little brother.

"Come in," said Ma. "You can share the cookies."

"That's two each," said Victoria and Sam.

"They look as good as your Grandma's," said Peter.

"And smell as good."

"Nobody makes cookies like Grandma," said Ma as the doorbell rang.

It was Joy and Simon with their four cousins.

"Come in," said Ma. "You can share the cookies."

"That's one each," said Sam and Victoria.

"They smell as good as your Grandma's," said Joy.

"And look as good," said Simon.

"No one makes cookies like Grandma," said Ma as the doorbell rang and rang.

"Oh dear," said Ma as the children stared at the cookies on their plates. "Perhaps you'd better eat them before we open the door."

"We'll wait," said Sam.

It was Grandma with an enormous tray of cookies.

"How nice to have so many friends to share them with," said Grandma. "It's a good thing I made a lot!"

"And no one makes cookies like Grandma," said Ma as the doorbell rang.

Activities

ACTIVITY 1

INDIVIDUAL

The Sky Is the Limit

- The numbers in the balloons are quotients.
- The numbers in the kites are divisors.
- The numbers below are dividends.

  23.8, 28.32, 23.55, 15.12, 34.96

- Match a divisor with a dividend and quotient so that you have five true division sentences.

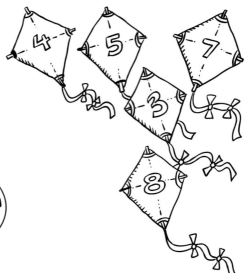

 See answers on p. 291.

One-Digit Divisors

ACTIVITY 2

PARTNERS

Math Marketing

Super-Duper Discount Market sells special packages called SalePAKS. The chart shows data about how the market makes SalePAKS.

YOU NEED

place-value models
calculators

- **Each Student:** Copy the table and use different calculation methods to complete the table. Use estimation, place-value models, paper and pencil, and a calculator. Take turns at each method. Compare your answers.

Item	Cans Per Case	Cans Per SalePAK	SalePAKS From 1 Case	Cans Left
tomato soup	48	3 cans		
tuna fish	64	5 cans		
apple juice	128	6 cans		
olives	250	4 cans		

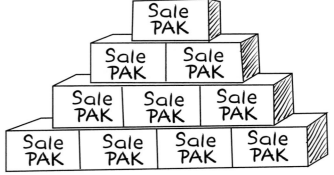

See answers on p. 292.

Two-Digit Divisors

Game Zone

ACTIVITY 3

SMALL GROUP

Rolling for Zeros

Each player follows these steps:

YOU NEED

number cube (1–6)

- Write a multiplication fact. Toss the number cube. Write that number of zeros after the product. Write a zero after one factor.

- Use the numbers to write a division problem.

- Find the quotient. Keep a total of your quotients.

- Take turns. Each player does this 5 times. Check each other's work as you play. The player with the greatest sum after five turns wins.

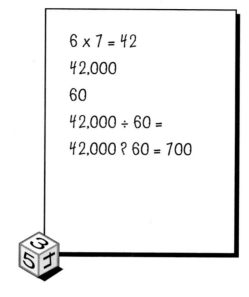

$6 \times 7 = 42$

42,000

60

$42,000 \div 60 =$

$42,000 \; ? \; 60 = 700$

Relate Multiplication and Division

ACTIVITY 4

INDIVIDUAL

Division Signs

Use all of the digits shown to create a whole number divisor and a dividend that is a decimal. (Hint: The divisor is a 1-digit number at all times.) Write the numbers on cards to move them around. You may have zero as the "whole-number" of the decimal.

YOU NEED

calculator

index cards

- Arrange the digits to get the greatest quotient possible.

- Arrange the digits to get the least quotient possible.

- Arrange the digits to get a quotient between 10 and 15.

$$2 \quad 3$$
$$4 \quad 5$$
$$.$$

$$4\overline{)23.5} \qquad 3\overline{)45.02}$$

$$5\overline{)3.42}$$

See answers on p. 292.

Divide Decimals by Whole Numbers

Understanding Division

25 minutes

▶ **Key Strategy**
Use manipulatives

▶ **Format**
Whole class and individual

▶ **Math Vocabulary**
dividend, divisor, quotient

▶ **Daily Vocabulary**
donuts, juice, ounces, share

▶ **Resource**
Overhead Manipulatives:
Counters

▶ **Materials**
counters

Math Objectives	ESL/TESOL Descriptors
▪ Multiply whole numbers. ▪ Divide whole numbers by 1-digit numbers.	▪ Use context to construct meaning. ▪ Select, connect, and explain information.

Activate Prior Knowledge Write 3×6 on the board. Ask: *How can I write this another way?* *(6 × 3)* Remind students that they can use the Commutative Property to multiply factors in any order, and the product will still be the same. Ask: *What is the product of each multiplication sentence?*

Hands-on Lesson Say: *We have just solved multiplication problems. Now let's look at how multiplication is related to division. They are inverse, or opposite, operations.* On the board, show two ways to write a division problem.

$$18 \div 3 = 6 \quad \text{or} \quad 3\overline{)18}^{\,6}$$

Point out that the numbers in the division problem are the same as in the multiplication problems 6×3 and 3×6. Label the **divisor** *(3)*, the **dividend** *(18)*, and the **quotient** *(6)*. Point out that in division the answer is called the quotient.

● Distribute counters. Say: *Seven children have 14 donuts. If they share the donuts equally, how many will each get? What do you need to find out?* *(14 ÷ 2)* Point out that students can use their knowledge of multiplication to answer the problem: *What number times seven equals fourteen?* *(2)* Write: $2 \times 7 = 14$. Then write: $14 \div 7 = 2$. You may want to use Counters from **Overhead Manipulatives** to model the problem. Then have students use their counters to show the problem.

● Explain that division can tell you the number of shares. Ask: *What if you want to know how many 8-oz. glasses there are in a 120-oz. container? How would you find out how many glasses of juice are in the container?* Elicit that you can use your knowledge of multiplication to find the answer. Encourage students to use their counters to make an array. Elicit the answer to $8 \times ? = 120$. *(15)*

Cultural Link You can ask students to show division procedure used in most Spanish-speaking countries.

Multilevel Strategies

1 Preproduction
Have students point to the dividend, the divisor, and the quotient as you name them.

2 3 Early Production and Speech Emergence
Encourage students to name the dividend, divisor and quotient as you point to them.

4 5 Intermediate and Advanced Fluency
Invite students to explain the terms of division.

LOG ON Visit **www.mmhmath.com** to find printable **Vocabulary Cards** that help build academic language.

Procedure: Help students make these Foldables to write vocabulary words and definitions throughout the unit. Encourage students to use the Foldables as a study guide.

 **by Dinah Zike**

Bound Book

1. Have students fold two sheets of paper in half and make a 1" margin at each end of the fold.

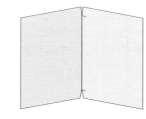

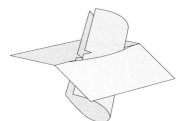

2. Cut one sheet along the fold from the ends, stopping at the margin marks. Cut the other sheet between the margins.

3. Roll up the first sheet and slip it halfway through the cut in the second sheet. Open it and fold the pages to make a Bound Book. Write the title *Divide Whole Numbers* on the front.

4. Now students can label each page with a lesson title from the unit and record main ideas,

vocabulary, and notes as they work through the unit.

Labels may include:

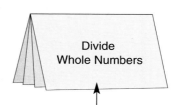

Divide Whole Numbers

Estimate Quotients
Compatible numbers are those that can easily be added, subtracted, multiplied, or divided mentally.

 **by Dinah Zike**

Bound Book

1. Have students fold two sheets of paper in half and make a 1" margin at each end of the fold.

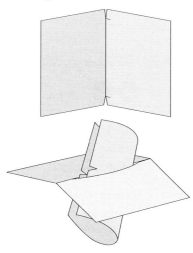

2. Cut one sheet along the fold from the ends, stopping at the margin marks. Cut the other sheet between the margins.

3. Roll up the first sheet and slip it halfway through the cut in the second sheet. Open it and fold the pages to make a Bound Book. Write the title *Divide Whole Numbers and Decimals* on the front.

4. Now students can label each page with a lesson title from the unit and record main ideas,

vocabulary, and notes as they work through the unit.

Labels may include:

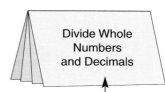

Divide Whole Numbers and Decimals

Choose the Method: Division

1 **I can use paper and pencil.**

2 **I can use a calculator.**

3 **I can use mental math.**

▶ **Key Strategy**
Use manipulatives

▶ **Format**
Whole class and small groups

▶ **Math Vocabulary**
dividend, divisor, fact family, quotient

▶ **Daily Vocabulary**
pattern

▶ **Resource**
Learning Resource 9

Materials
- counters
- small paper cups

Assessment

Check students' mastery of division concepts by observing them as they complete the lesson. See Assessment Checklist on page 57. Remind students to work on their Foldables.

Home Connection

Have students use materials they find at home (beans, elbow pasta) to create and solve a division problem to share with family members. Students can report their experience to the class.

Exploring Division

Math Objectives	**ESL/TESOL Descriptors**
■ Divide whole numbers by 1-digit and 2-digit numbers.	■ Select, connect, and explain information.
■ Divide by 10, 100, and 1,000.	■ Use context to construct meaning.

Activate Prior Knowledge Review how division and multiplication are inverse operations. Write: $6 \times 5 = 30, 5 \times 6 = 30$. Ask students what division sentences they can write using the same numbers. Write them on the board. ($30 \div 5 = 6$; $30 \div 6 = 5$)

Hands-on Lesson Point out to students that the two multiplication and division sentences on the board make up a **fact family.** They are the fact family for the numbers 6, 5, and 30.

- Say: *Knowing related facts helps you divide.* Write $42 \div 7$. Ask: *What number times 7 equals 42?* (6) Write $42 \div 7 = 6$. Use the division sentence to point to and define **dividend, divisor,** and **quotient.**

- Next, model a division pattern by adding zeros to the dividend: $300 \div 6 = 50$, $3,000 \div 6 = 500$. Elicit that adding a zero each time results in the same number of additional zeros in the quotient.

- Write $300 \div 60$. Point out that you can cross out the same number of zeros in the dividend and divisor, and then divide. Ask: *What is 30 divided by 6?* (5)

- Write $70 \div 10$; $800 \div 100$; $8,000 \div 100$; $8 \div 100$. Invite volunteers to cross out the same number of zeros in the dividend and divisor in each division sentence and solve each problem.

- Distribute Learning Resource 9. Have small groups work on their sheets together.

Challenge Tell students to imagine that they earn $10 a week. Ask *How many weeks will it take to earn $100? $1,000?* (10 weeks, 100 weeks)

Multilevel Strategies

1 Preproduction
Have students point to a fact family.

Writing Ask students to write a fact family of their own.

2 3 Early Production and Speech Emergence
Have students say a fact family aloud.

Writing Encourage students to write a phrase about what a fact family is.

4 5 Intermediate and Advanced Fluency
Have students explain how fact families help with division.

Writing Challenge students to write a sentence about fact families.

Name _____

Fact Families

Write the fact family for each group of numbers. Then solve the problems. You can use counters and cups to help you.

Example: 2, 6, 12. Look at the greatest number, 12. Use 12 counters. Use 2 cups. Divide 12 counters into 2 cups. $12 \div 2 = 6$, $2 \times 6 = 12$. Then divide 12 counters into 6 cups. $12 \div 6 = 2$, $6 \times 2 = 12$.

3, 5, 15	4, 5, 20	3, 7, 21
3, 3, 9	54, 6, 9	6, 1, 6
2, 8, 16	9, 5, 45	7, 10, 70

▶ **Key Strategy**
Use manipulatives

▶ **Format**
Whole class and groups

▶ **Math Vocabulary**
compatible numbers

▶ **Daily Vocabulary**
number cube

▶ **Resources**
Learning Resource 10
Teacher Tool 4

Materials
• number cubes
• pencils

Assessment

Check students' mastery of the lesson concepts as they complete the lesson. See Assessment Checklist on page 57. Remind students to work on their Foldables.

Home Connection

Have students take home their number cubes and solve division problems with family members. Ask them to share their experiences with the class.

Estimate Quotients

Math Objective	**ESL/TESOL Descriptors**
■ Estimate quotients of whole numbers.	■ Observe and model how others speak and behave in a particular situation or setting.
	■ Use context to construct meaning.

Activate Prior Knowledge To prepare students for estimating quotients, review estimating products. Remind students that when estimating, you don't need an exact answer. Write 19×22. Ask: **What can you do to estimate?** Elicit that the factors can be rounded: 19 can be rounded up to 20, and 22 can be rounded down to 20. Ask: **What is 20 × 20?** Say: **So 19 × 22 is about 400.**

Hands-on Lesson Tell students they can estimate quotients, too. Write $32 \div 7$. Point out that each number can be rounded to find **compatible numbers.** Tell students that compatible numbers are easier to divide. 32 can be rounded to 30. Ask: **What number close to 7 is compatible with 30?** (6) Write $30 \div 6 = 5$. Say: **So 32 ÷ 7 is about 5.**

• Divide students into groups of different levels of English proficiency. Distribute Teacher Tool 4: Number Cube Patterns to each student. Have each student cut out, color, assemble, and tape a cube.

• Have students take turns tossing the cubes three times. The first and second numbers tossed become the dividend, the third the divisor. Have them write the numbers on Learning Resource 10: Compatible Numbers.

• Ask groups to estimate using compatible numbers, draw a picture showing the problem, then divide to solve. Monitor the groups, making sure that the pictures match the problem and the quotients are correct.

• Ask group volunteers to present their picture solutions to the class.

Challenge Ask students to write examples of the use of compatible numbers in addition and subtraction. *(Pair addends with sums of 10; find numbers that are easy to subtract.)*

Multilevel Strategies

1 Preproduction
Ask students to point to the numbers on the cubes as you say them.

Writing Ask students to write the compatible numbers.

2 3 Early Production and Speech Emergence
Ask students to name the cube numbers.

Writing Encourage them to write a phrase about compatible numbers.

4 5 Intermediate and Advanced Fluency
Ask students to read aloud a division problem.

Writing Challenge them to write a sentence defining compatible numbers.

Name _____

Compatible Numbers

Use compatible numbers to estimate the quotient.

ROLL 2 NUMBERS	ROLL 1 NUMBER	SUBSTITUTE:	DRAW A:	WRITE AND SOLVE AN:
Dividend	Divisor	Compatible Numbers	Picture (use dots)	Equation

 45 minutes

▶ **Key Strategy**
Use manipulatives

▶ **Format**
Whole class and pairs

▶ **Math Vocabulary**
dividend, divisor, quotient, remainder

▶ **Daily Vocabulary**
dime, nickel, penny, quarter

▶ **Resources**
Learning Resource 11
Teacher Tools 1 and 3
Overhead Manipulatives:
Base-Ten Set

Materials
- calculator
- pencils
- scissors

Assessment

Check students' mastery of dividing decimals by observing them as they complete the lesson. See Assessment Checklist on page 57. Remind students to work on their Foldables.

Home Connection

Have students take home the Learning Resource to share with a family member. Invite students to report their experience to the class.

Divide Decimals

Math Objectives	**ESL/TESOL Descriptors**
▪ Divide whole numbers by 2-digit numbers.	▪ Practice new language.
▪ Divide whole numbers and decimals.	▪ Use context to construct meaning.

Activate Prior Knowledge Write *16 ÷ 4*. Remind students how to divide using fact families. Ask: ***What number times 4 equals 16?*** *(4)* ***What is 4 × 4?*** *(16)*

Hands-on Lesson Write *427 ÷ 4*. Use Base-Ten Set from **Overhead Manipulatives** to demonstrate how to divide 427 into 4 equal groups. Ask: ***Are there any left?*** *(yes, 3)* Point out that this is the **remainder.** Then work the problem through using paper and pencil. The quotient is 106 R3.

- Next, write *546 ÷ 12*. Show how to place the first digit of the **quotient** above the 4 in the **dividend,** and follow the steps to find the quotient, 45 R6.

- Next, write *54.6 ÷ 12*. Explain that dividing decimals by whole numbers is similar to dividing whole numbers. The only difference is where to place the decimal in the quotient. *(directly above the decimal in the dividend)* Point out that, instead of leaving a remainder, you add zeros to the dividend and continue working out the problem until the remainder is 0. The quotient becomes 4.55.

- Distribute Teacher Tool 1: Coins and Teacher Tool 3: Bills. Ask students to cut out the bills and coins. Distribute Learning Resource 11: Divide My Money.

- Ask students to solve the money division problems, first modeling the divisions with play money and then recording their quotients. Monitor their work to ensure the accuracy of their division. When they are finished, have a class discussion about how groups found their quotients. *(Answers: $1.05, $0.32, $1.30, $0.09, $1.14, $0.24)*

Challenge Have students check their division by using multiplication, the inverse operation of division.

Multilevel Strategies

1 Preproduction
Have students point to money amounts you name.

Writing Invite students to write a division equation with money.

2 3 Early Production and Speech Emergence
Ask students to identify the money as it is being sorted.

Writing Encourage students to write a division equation with money and label the parts.

4 5 Intermediate and Advanced Fluency
Ask students to explain how to divide decimals by whole numbers.

Writing Challenge students to write a sentence about how they divided the decimal money amounts.

Name _____

Divide My Money

Fill in the table with your quotients.

MONEY DIVIDED	QUOTIENT
$5.25 ÷ 5	
$0.64 ÷ 2	
$5.20 ÷ 4	
$0.27 ÷ 3	
$3.42 ÷ 3	
$1.20 ÷ 5	

UNIT 3

Problem Solving

Problem Solving

Reading for Math

Read → Plan → Solve → Look Back

Remind students of the basic steps of problem solving.

SKILL: Interpret the Remainder

Model the skill using a word problem such as the following:

Read The fifth-grade classes went to the amusement park. All 73 students want to ride the Tilt-a-Whirl. Each saucer holds 6 students. There are 5 saucers. How many rides will it take until everyone has had a chance?

Plan I can multiply to find how many ride each time. Then I'll divide 73 by that number.

Solve **Think:** $5 \times 6 = 30$. 30 students ride each time.
$73 \div 30 = 2$ R13
13 students still haven't gone.
2 rides is too few.
$30 \times 3 = 90$
3 rides is more than enough.
All of the fifth graders can ride in 3 rides.

Look Back Does my answer make sense?
Yes. $73 < 90$

Distribute **Math Center Card 3A** to students.

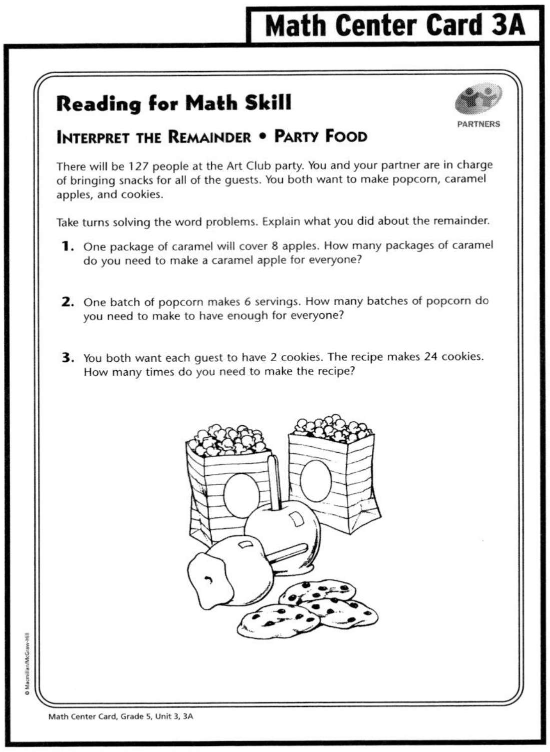
Math Center Card 3A

Reading for Math Skill

PARTNERS

INTERPRET THE REMAINDER • PARTY FOOD

There will be 127 people at the Art Club party. You and your partner are in charge of bringing snacks for all of the guests. You both want to make popcorn, caramel apples, and cookies.

Take turns solving the word problems. Explain what you did about the remainder.

1. One package of caramel will cover 8 apples. How many packages of caramel do you need to make a caramel apple for everyone?
2. One batch of popcorn makes 6 servings. How many batches of popcorn do you need to make to have enough for everyone?
3. You both want each guest to have 2 cookies. The recipe makes 24 cookies. How many times do you need to make the recipe?

Math Center Card, Grade 5, Unit 3, 3A

STRATEGY: Work Backward

Model the strategy using a word problem such as the following:

Read Mike bought 6 books. Each book cost \$6.00. He bought 4 pens. Each pen cost \$2.50. How much money did he start with if he has \$12.00 left?

Plan I can work backward to find the answer.

Solve **Think:** I know Mike has \$12.00 now.
I can multiply and add to find out how much he spent.
$\$6.00 \times 6 = \$36.00$
$4 \times \$2.50 = \$10.00$
$\$36.00 + \$10.00 = \$46.00$. Mike spent \$46.00.
I can add to find how much money he started with.
$\$46.00 + \$12.00 = \$58.00$. Mike started with \$58.00.

Look Back How can I check my answer? I can subtract the cost of the books and the pens from \$58.00.
$\$58.00 - \$46.00 = \$12.00$

Distribute **Math Center Card 3B** to students.

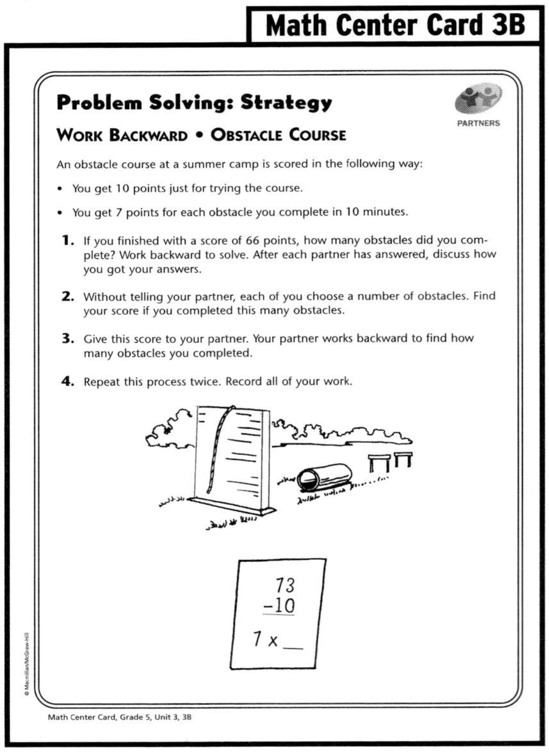
Math Center Card 3B

Problem Solving: Strategy

PARTNERS

WORK BACKWARD • OBSTACLE COURSE

An obstacle course at a summer camp is scored in the following way:

- You get 10 points just for trying the course.
- You get 7 points for each obstacle you complete in 10 minutes.

1. If you finished with a score of 66 points, how many obstacles did you complete? Work backward to solve. After each partner has answered, discuss how you got your answers.
2. Without telling your partner, each of you choose a number of obstacles. Find your score if you completed this many obstacles.
3. Give this score to your partner. Your partner works backward to find how many obstacles you completed.
4. Repeat this process twice. Record all of your work.

73
−10
7 x __

Math Center Card, Grade 5, Unit 3, 3B

Assessment Checklist

	STUDENT NAMES											
SCHOOL:												
TEACHER: **SCHOOL YEAR:**												
Mark: + = **Mastery** √ = **Satisfactory** – = **Needs Improvement**												
LEVEL OF LANGUAGE PROFICIENCY (1–5)												
MATH OBJECTIVES												
• Divide whole numbers by 1-digit and 2-digit numbers.												
• Multiply whole numbers.												
• Divide by 10, 100, and 1,000.												
• Estimate quotients of whole numbers.												
• Divide whole numbers and decimals.												
ESL/TESOL LISTENING/SPEAKING												
Observe and model how others speak in a particular situation.												
Practice new language.												
Retell information.												
Select, connect, and explain information.												
Use context to construct meaning.												
ESL/TESOL READING												
Read about subject matter information.												
Apply basic reading comprehension skills.												
Follow written directions, implicit and explicit.												
ESL WRITING												
Write to demonstrate comprehension.												
Write using spelling patterns and targeted English vocabulary.												

 **by Dinah Zike**

① Preproduction
- Did students write the unit vocabulary?
- Did they copy the definitions?

② ③ Early Production and Speech Emergence
- Did students label the tabs correctly?
- Did they write the unit vocabulary?
- Did they copy the definitions?

④ ⑤ Intermediate and Advanced Fluency
- Did students write definitions for the unit vocabulary?
- Did they use correct spelling and grammar?

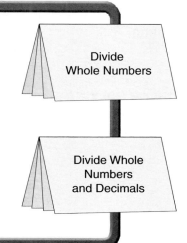

Divide Whole Numbers

Divide Whole Numbers and Decimals

Planner

Data, Graphs, and Statistics

LOG ON Visit **www.mmhmath.com**

Unit Activities	• **Activity 1** Readiness Keep on Truckin' p. 62 • **Activity 2** Counting Cards, p. 62	• **Activity 3** Buried Treasures p. 63 • **Activity 4** Polling Data, p. 63

Lessons	Key Objectives	Vocabulary	Materials	Resources
READ TOGETHER The Pet Graph *by Sandra Liatsos,* pp. 60–61	**Math:** Explore collecting, organizing, and displaying data. **ESL/TESOL:** Goal 2, Standard 2.	cats, dogs, gerbils, guinea pigs, graph, hang, laugh, pet show, row, snakes		
UNIT WARM-UP **Understanding Data, Charts, and Graphs** p. 64	**Math:** Read and interpret data. Organize and display data. **ESL/TESOL:** Goal 2, Standard 2.	data, pictograph, survey, tally chart, tally mark	graphs from magazines or newspapers, paper	Graphic Organizer 1
LESSON 1 **Displaying and Interpreting Data** pp. 66–67	**Math:** Read and interpret data. Find range, mean, median, and mode. **ESL/TESOL:** Goal 2, Standards 1, 2.	frequency, frequency table, line plot, pictograph, mean, median, mode, range	markers or crayons	Learning Resource 12
LESSON 2 **Bar Graphs and Line Graphs** pp. 68–69	**Math:** Organize, display, read, and interpret data in line graphs and bar graphs. **ESL/TESOL:** Goal 2, Standard 2.	axis, bar graph, coordinates, double bar graph, interval, line graph, ordered pair	chart paper, marker or crayons, rulers	Learning Resource 13, Teacher Tool 6
LESSON 3 **Using a Histogram** pp. 70–71	**Math:** Organize, display data in histograms. Read and make histograms. **ESL/TESOL:** Goal 2, Standards 2, 3.	histogram, leaf, stem, stem-and-leaf plot	markers or crayons, rulers	Learning Resource 14
LESSON 4 **Sampling** pp. 72–73	**Math:** Select a random sample. **ESL/TESOL:** Goal 2, Standards 1, 2.	biased sample, population, random sample, representative sample, sample	marker or crayons, rulers	Learning Resource 15
PROBLEM SOLVING p. 74 • Skill: Methods of Persuasion • Strategy: Make a Graph	Use skills and strategies to solve problems.			**Math Center Cards 4A, 4B**

Math at Home

See **Math at Home Family Guide** for additional math vocabulary, activities, and games in English, Spanish, and Haitian Creole.

English Vocabulary

Dear Family: *Please help your child practice the key vocabulary words for this unit.*

bar graph a graph that compares data by using vertical or horizontal bars

data collected information

frequency the number of times a response occurs or something happens

line graph a graph that uses one or more line segments to show changes in data

mean the quantity that is found by adding the numbers in a set of numbers and dividing their sum by the number of addends

median the middle number in a set of numbers arranged

in order from least to greatest. If the set contains an even number of numbers, the median is the mean of the two middle numbers

mode the number that occurs most often in a set of numbers

range the difference between the greatest and the smallest number in a set of numbers

sample a part of a population used to get information about that population

survey a method of gathering data that involves asking people questions or observing events

Vocabulario en español

Estimados familiares: *Por favor ayuden a su hijo/a a practicar las palabras del vocabulario de esta unidad.*

gráfica de barras gráfica que compara datos mediante barras verticales u horizontales

datos información recopilada

frecuencia número de veces que se produce un resultado o un suceso

gráfica lineal gráfica que usa uno o más segmentos de recta para mostrar cambios en los datos

media cantidad que resulta de sumar los números en un conjunto y dividir la suma entre la cantidad de sumandos

mediana valor central en un conjunto de números ordenados de menor a mayor. Si el conjunto tiene un

número par de números, la mediana será la media de los dos números centrales

moda número que aparece más veces en un grupo de números

rango diferencia entre el mayor y el menor de los números de un conjunto

muestra parte de una población que se usa para obtener información sobre esa población

encuesta método para reunir datos en el que se hacen preguntas a las personas o se observan sucesos

Vokabilè an kreyòl

Chè paran: *Tanpri ede pitit la pratike mo vokabilè nan seksyon sa a.*

tablo ak ba yon desen ki konpare done lè-w itilize ba vètikal osnon orizontal

done enfòmasyon ou kolekte

repetisyon kantite fwa yon repons parèt osnon yon bagay rive

tablo ak liy desen kote ou sèvi ak segman ou byen moso liy pou montre chanjman nan done yo

mwayèn sa ou jwen'n lè ou adisyone plizyè nimewo epi ou divize sòm nan pa kantite nimewo ki te genyen

mitan chif milye nan yon kantite ki ranje annòd de pi piti jiska pi gwo. Si gwoup la genyen yon total nimewo pè osnon plizye, mitan an se mwayèn de chif o milye yo

mòd nimewo ki parèt pi souvan nan yon gwoup nimewo

etandi total ant pi gwo ak pi piti ya nan yon gwoup nimewo

echantiyon pati yon popilasyon ou itilize pou jwenn enfòmasyon sou popilasyon sa a

ankèt metòd pou jwenn enfòmasyon lèw poze moun kesyon osnon lè wap obsève evenman

© Macmillan/McGraw-Hill

The Pet Graph
by Sandra Liatsos

 25 minutes

Math Objective
- Explore collecting, organizing, and displaying data.

ESL/TESOL Descriptors
- Represent and interpret information visually.
- Listen to, speak, read, and write about subject matter information.

Reading Skill
- Classify and categorize.

Vocabulary
- cats, dogs, gerbils, graph, guinea pigs, hang, laugh, pet show, pictograph, row, snakes

Before Reading

Build Background/Oral Language
Look at the illustration together and invite students to read the words on the pet graph as a group. Point to each row and ask: **What animal is in this row? How many (dogs) are there?** Ask students to write the number next to each row. Say: **This is a pet graph of animals in a pet show.**

During Reading

- Read the poem, pointing to the animals that are illustrated as you read each name. As you read the words *graph* and *row,* indicate the whole illustration and the individual rows.
- Have students track the text as you read the poem again. Then read it again, asking volunteers to say the words for pets as you point to them.
- Reread the poem once again, inviting students to join in.

Phonological/Phonemic Awareness
Draw attention to the digraphs: /ph/ in *graph,* and /gh/ in *laugh.* Point out that the letters *ph and gh* make the same sound as *f.* Make the sound together.

After Reading

Ask students to circle all the pet words in the poem that are listed in the pet graph or pictograph next to the pictures and say them together.

Art Have students draw on large index cards a picture of their pet or a pet they would like to have. Have them label their drawings with a word, phrase, or sentence. Group their drawings in a graph on chart paper as in the poem.

Assessment

Observe students' participation in the choral reading of the poem. See Assessment Checklist on page 75.

Multilevel Strategies

1 Preproduction
Say: **Point to the row of dogs.** Students should point to the row in the graph next to the pictures.

Writing Ask students to write the number of pets in each row.

2 3 Early Production and Speech Emergence
Ask: **What does this row show?** (five cats)

Writing Have students write the animal words in the graph and the number of each.

4 5 Intermediate and Advanced Fluency
Say: **Compare these rows in the graph.** (This row has six dogs. This row has three birds.)

Writing Ask students to write a list of ten animals from the poem.

The Pet Graph

by Sandra Liatsos

In this poem students count their pets and make a class Pet Graph.
Then they have to decide which pets are the most popular.

Our pets are dogs, and mice, and birds,
and rabbits, fish and cats,
and other pets, like guinea pigs,
and gerbils, snakes, and rats.
We'll put their pictures on a graph;
the dogs will have their row.
The snakes and cats will each have theirs,
each other kind also.

We'll hang the pet graph on the wall.
Each row of pets will show
how many of each kind our class
will bring to the pet show.
We hope to see a parrot or
a monkey on the graph.
And if we see them in the show
we know they'll make us laugh.

Pets our class will bring to the Pet Show

Dogs

Snakes

Cats

Gerbils

Guinea Pigs

© Macmillan/McGraw-Hill

Activities

Readiness

ACTIVITY 1

PARTNERS

Keep on Truckin'

Match a graphic organizer to each problem below. Explain your reasoning. Compare with your partner. Then solve.

A

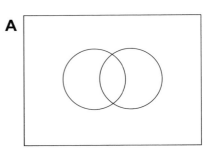

1. Out of 178 trucks, 85 were dented. 104 had loose tailpipes. 31 had both problems. How many had neither problem?

2. Out of 158 trucks, all had new hubcaps or a sunroof or both. 92 had both. 39 had the new hubcaps, but not the sunroof. How many had the sunroof but not the hubcaps?

B

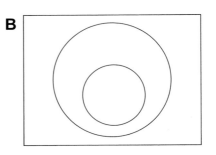

3. Out of 158 trucks, 92 were painted red. How many trucks were not painted red?

   See answers on page 292.   **Collecting, Organizing, and Displaying Data**

INDIVIDUAL

ACTIVITY 2

Counting Cards

Solve.

1. Ari, Bruce, and Carol counted their baseball cards. Bruce had 229 cards. The range of the cards was 120 and the median number of cards was 313. If Ari had fewer cards than Carol, how many cards did Carol have? How many cards did Ari have?

2. Don, Ellen, Luis, Gary, and Ana are just starting their sport card collections. They each have between 10 and 20 cards. The range is 10. The median and mode are 15. What are some possible numbers of cards each of them has?

3. Create a set of numbers. Find the range, mode, and median. Write a problem for your friends to solve.

See answers on page 292.   **Range, Median, Mode, and Mean**

Game Zone

ACTIVITY 3

SMALL GROUP

Buried Treasures

YOU NEED

graph paper, ruler

- **Each Player:** Draw a 10-by-10 graph on a piece of graph paper. Number the graph. Without showing your partners, find and mark 3 points on the graph map to show where 3 treasure chests are buried.

- **To Play:** Take turns guessing ordered pairs that locate the other player's treasure chests. To keep track of the ordered pairs you name, mark the points off on your own graph map.

- Continue until each player names 15 ordered pairs.
One point is scored for each treasure chest found. The player with the higher score wins. To break a tie, add treasures to each map and repeat.

Read Graphs

✂

ACTIVITY 4

INDIVIDUAL

Polling Data

- This stem-and-leaf plot shows the ages of people watching a new movie. The producers want to know how many teenagers, people in their 20s, 30s, 40s, and so on, were present.

- Show the same data as a line plot, pictograph, and a bar graph.

- Which graph best shows what the producers need to know? Explain.

Stems	Leaves
1	7
2	5 7
3	0 2 4 6 7 8
4	1 3 5 7 8 9
5	0 5 8

NOW SHOWING

1 The Argonauts
2 One Perfect Ending
3 My Distant Trail
4 Golden Oldie

Pictographs, Bar Graphs, and Line Graphs

© Macmillan/McGraw-Hill

Understanding Data, Charts, and Graphs

 20 minutes

▶ **Key Strategy**
Use charts and graphs

▶ **Format**
Whole class and pairs

▶ **Math Vocabulary**
data, pictograph, survey, tally chart, tally mark

▶ **Daily Vocabulary**
hamburger, lunch, pizza

▶ **Resource**
Graphic Organizer 1

▶ **Materials**
graphs from magazines or newspapers, paper

Math Objectives	ESL/TESOL Descriptors
▪ Read and interpret data. ▪ Organize and display data.	▪ Represent and interpret information visually. ▪ Compare and contrast information.

Activate Prior Knowledge Show students different kinds of charts and graphs (pie charts, line graphs, **pictographs**, etc.) from newspapers or magazines. Ask students to raise their hands if they have ever seen a chart or graph before.

Hands-on Lesson Discuss that a graph or chart is a picture showing **data,** which is information. Data can be shown in different ways. Say: *Today we are going to take a survey. We will ask a question. Then we will make a chart to show the data.* Write the word on the board.

- Write the numbers 5 to 50 on the board. Count together by fives, to fifty. The first student says *5,* the next *10,* etc. Model making **tally marks** as you count, emphasizing 5, 10, 15, etc. Say: *We are making tally marks. They are in groups of 5. We will use a tally chart for the data from our survey.*

- Say: *First we need a question for our survey.* Write: *Which do you like better, pizza or hamburgers?*

- Make a two-column chart on the board headed PIZZA in one column and HAMBURGER in the other. Ask volunteers to place a tally mark in one of the columns to indicate their preference. Remind students to draw a horizontal line for the fifth tally. Compare how many students picked each food.

- Pair fluent and nonfluent speakers. Distribute Graphic Organizer 1: Four-Column Chart. Have pairs come up with two survey questions, such as: *Which color do you like better? (Give two choices.)* Then have pairs walk around to survey the class.

- Encourage students to show the data on their tally charts in a different way, making pictographs (see glossary p. 267).

Multilevel Strategies

❶ Preproduction
Say: *Point to tally marks for the number 5.* Ask students to respond with *Yes* or *No* as you expand the choices.

❷❸ Early Production and Speech Emergence
Ask students to name each food and the number of tally marks they wrote for it using a word bank.

❹❺ Intermediate and Advanced Fluency
Ask students to explain what the tally marks on their chart tell. (For example, *Ten students like hamburgers.*) Have students compare and contrast.

 Visit **www.mmhmath.com** to find printable **Vocabulary Cards** that help build academic language.

Procedure: Help students make these Foldables to write vocabulary words and definitions throughout the unit. Encourage students to use the Foldables as a study guide.

 **by Dinah Zike**

Bound Tab Book

1. Provide each student with six sheets of notebook paper. Fold each page in half like hamburgers. Place each hamburger with the fold up.

2. Help your students cut along the left margin of the top sheet, stopping at the top fold. Cut all six papers, stack them together, and staple along the left margin. Now your students can label the tabs as illustrated.

3. As students work through the unit, have them take notes and record main ideas under the appropriate lesson tabs of their Foldables book.

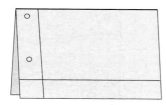 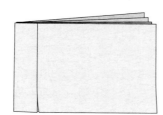

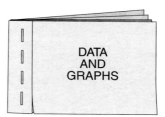

DATA
AND
GRAPHS

 **by Dinah Zike**

Bound Tab Book

1. Provide each student with six sheets of notebook paper. Fold each page in half like hamburgers. Place each hamburger with the fold up.

2. Help your students cut along the left margin of the top sheet, stopping at the top fold. Cut all six papers, stack them together and staple along the left margin. Now your students can label the tabs as illustrated.

3. As students work through the unit, have them take notes and record main ideas under the appropriate lesson tabs of their Foldables book.

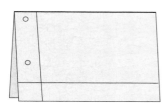 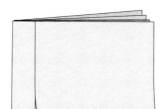

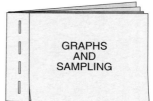

GRAPHS
AND
SAMPLING

Lesson 1

 35 minutes

▶ **Key Strategy**
Use charts and graphs

▶ **Format**
Whole class and small groups

▶ **Math Vocabulary**
frequency, frequency table, line plot, mean, median, mode, pictograph, range

▶ **Daily Vocabulary**
average, key, pets

▶ **Resource**
Learning Resource 12

Materials
• markers or crayons

Assessment

Check students' mastery of graphing as they do the activity. See Assessment Checklist on page 75. Remind students to work on their Foldables.

Home Connection

Have students keep a journal of the time they finished their homework at home for the week. Have them measure range, mean, median, and mode. Then invite them to report their experiences to the class.

Displaying and Interpreting Data

Math Objectives	**ESL/TESOL Descriptors**
▪ Read and interpret data. ▪ Find range, mean, median, and mode.	▪ Follow oral and written directions, implicit and explicit. ▪ Represent and interpret information visually.

Activate Prior Knowledge Show a tally chart made by a student. Ask: *What data did our (tally chart/pictograph) show?* Then hold up the **frequency chart** and **line plot** in Learning Resource 12. Explain that these charts and graphs also give information.

Hands-on Lesson Distribute Learning Resource 12: Favorite Pet. Together, look at the frequency chart. Explain how to read it. The first column shows the number of pets and the second shows how many students have each pet. Practice reading the chart and answering the questions together.

● Then, ask students to look at the line plot at the bottom. Explain that this shows the same information as the chart above. Answer the questions about the line plot.

● Say: *We are going to take a pet survey.* Write: *How many pets do you have?* Divide students into groups. Each group surveys their own and another group about the number of pets, and writes each student's name and number of pets. Then students compile their data in a frequency table and a line plot.

● Together, study the data from the frequency table students have made. Ask: *What is the highest/lowest number in the frequency column?* Together, find the **range,** the difference between the two numbers. Ask: *Which number appears the most?* Write this number, the **mode.** Have students list the numbers from least to greatest. Ask: *Which number is in the middle?* Write the number, the **median.** Have students add the numbers and divide by the number of addends to find the **mean,** or average.

Challenge Invite students to make up survey questions and for another class. Have them calculate and record the mean, median, mode, and range.

Multilevel Strategies

❶ Preproduction
Encourage students to point to specific information on the chart. *Point to the number of students with two pets.*

Writing Invite students to write the numbers for answers about the chart.

❷ ❸ Early Production and Speech Emergence
Elicit answers to questions about information on the chart, such as *How many students have one pet?*

Writing Encourage them to write the answers to the questions above.

❹ ❺ Intermediate and Advanced Fluency
Ask students to explain what one of the numbers on the chart shows.

Writing Have students write sentences summarizing data.

Name _____

Favorite Pet!

Frequency Chart

This chart shows the data from a survey on pets. Five students have no pets. Seven students have one pet.

How many students have two pets? _____

How many students have three pets? _____

NUMBER OF STUDENTS WITH PETS		
Number of pets	Tally	Frequency
0	卅	5
1	卅 //	7
2	卅 ///	8
3	卅 //	7
4	///	3

Line Plot

This line plot shows the same data as the frequency chart. There is one x for every student.

How many students have two pets? _____

How many students have four pets? _____

```
                          x
                  x       x       x
                  x       x       x
          x       x       x       x
Number of x       x       x       x
students  x       x       x       x       x
          x       x       x       x       x
          x       x       x       x       x
          _____
          0       1       2       3       4
                  Number of pets
```

 35 minutes

▶ **Key Strategy**
Use charts and graphs

▶ **Format**
Whole class and small groups

▶ **Math Vocabulary**
axis, bar graph, coordinates, double bar graph, interval, line graph, ordered pair, plot, scale

▶ **Daily Vocabulary**
absent, attendance, days of the week, present, school day

▶ **Resources**
Learning Resource 13
Teacher Tool 6

Materials
• chart paper
• marker or crayons
• rulers

Assessment

Check students' mastery of graphing as they do the activity. See Assessment Checklist on page 75.

Home Connection

Have students collect data at home on how many glasses of water or juice they drink in a day. Have students make a bar or line graph with family members. Ask them to share their graphs with the class.

Bar Graphs and Line Graphs

Math Objectives	ESL/TESOL Descriptors
■ Read and interpret data in line graphs and bar graphs.	■ Represent and interpret information visually.
■ Organize and display data in line graphs and bar graphs.	■ Gather information orally and in writing.

Activate Prior Knowledge Ask students to look at and show their charts and plots from the previous lesson. Ask: *What do these charts show?* (data about students' pets) *How do they show the data?* (Tally marks and numbers for each student. The line plot shows an X for each student). Display Learning Resource 13: Graphs! Explain that now students will make a **bar graph.** Show visual.

Hands-on Lesson Distribute Learning Resource 13. Together, read the **line graph** and the bar graph. Show examples of **ordered pairs** *(3, Monday)* and point out how each of the two **coordinates** in the pair are placed on the graph. Ask: *Which of the coordinates goes on the x-axis? on the y-axis? Remember that the x-axis is horizontal and the y-axis is vertical.*

• Say: *Now we are going to graph class attendance for another week.* Have students read the bottom of Learning Resource 13 for the data. Ask them to circle the necessary information for coordinates and ordered pairs. Then invite them to write the five ordered pairs.

• Distribute Teacher Tool 6: Grid Paper and have students **plot** or place the data. Show two finished graphs and ask: *How is a bar graph similar to /different from a line graph?*

• You may wish to show an example of a **double bar graph** (see glossary p. 260) showing how two groups of data can be displayed together.

Challenge Provide students with data for another class for the same week. Have students create a double bar graph to compare the attendance for both classes.

Multilevel Strategies

❶ Preproduction
Say: *Find the bar graph. Find the line graph.* Students should point to each graph to answer.

Writing Ask students to label their graphs.

❷ ❸ Early Production and Speech Emergence
Ask students to name the axes and name the two kinds of graphs.

Writing Encourage students to label the name and the parts of a graph.

❹ ❺ Intermediate and Advanced Fluency
Have students explain how they made their graphs.

Writing Ask students to write a sentence about the graphs.

Name _____

Graphs!

Line Graph

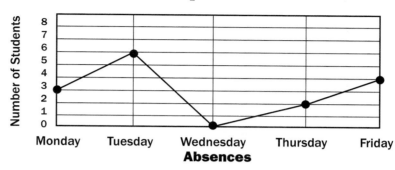

Bar Graph

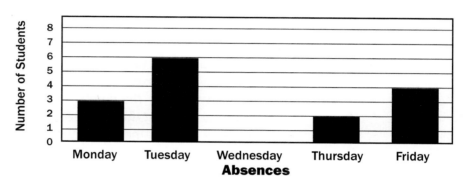

What day had the most absences? _____

What day had no absences? _____

What is the ordered pair for the day
with the most absences? _____

1. Look at the graphs and answer the questions.

2. Make a line graph and a bar graph. Use the sentences below.

   On Monday, seven students were absent. On Tuesday, three were
   absent. On Wednesday, four did not attend school. On Thursday,
   everybody was present. On Friday, two students were absent.

3. Write the ordered pairs you will need to make your graphs.

   _____ _____ _____ _____ _____

4. Now make your graphs on another piece of paper.

35 minutes

▶ **Key Strategy**
Use charts and graphs

▶ **Format**
Whole class and small groups

▶ **Math Vocabulary**
histogram, leaf, stem, stem-and-leaf plot

▶ **Daily Vocabulary**
blocks, bus, distance, how many, range, school, walk

▶ **Resource**
Learning Resource 14

Materials
• markers or crayons
• rulers

Assessment

Check students' mastery of graphing as they do the activity. See Assessment Checklist on page 75. Remind students to work on their Foldables.

Home Connection

Have students make a histogram of the number of minutes a day each family member gets up in the morning, using ranges of minutes such as 0–10, 10–20, etc. Then invite them to repeat their experiences to the class.

Using a Histogram

Math Objectives	**ESL/TESOL Descriptors**
■ Read and make histograms.	■ Represent and interpret information presented visually.
■ Organize and display data in histograms.	■ Actively connect new information to information previously learned.

Activate Prior Knowledge Show examples of line graphs and bar graphs that students have made, and ask them to name each kind. Talk about how these graphs show information with exact numbers.

Hands-on Lesson Explain that a **histogram** is a special kind of bar graph that displays a range of information over equal intervals.

• Distribute Learning Resource 14: Tally Chart and Graphs. Ask students to look at the tally chart and then the histogram. Point out that histograms, unlike bar graphs, do not have spaces between the bars. Ask students what the horizontal and the vertical axes show *(horizontal — the range of blocks students go to school; vertical — the number of students)* Point out that in one place there is no bar. After studying the histograms together, read the questions aloud with students and ask them to say and write the answers.

• Draw a three-column chart. Divide students into groups, have them copy the chart, and ask them to conduct a survey: *How many blocks do you travel to school?* The first column is labeled **DISTANCE**, the middle **STUDENTS**, and the third **NUMBERS.** Each group surveys its members and another groups'. Answers can include blocks traveled by foot, car, or bus. Have students first tally numbers as on the Learning Resource, and then display the information in histograms.

• After making histograms, gather the graphs and charts made by students and assemble examples for the bulletin board called **CHARTS AND GRAPHS.** You may want to add an example of a **stem-and-leaf plot** to show another graph that organizes data by place values.

Challenge Have students make a histogram of the heights of students in the class.

Multilevel Strategies

1 Preproduction
Ask students to point to information on the histogram.

Writing Invite students to write the number of students that went 4–6 blocks.

2 3 Early Production and Speech Emergence
Ask: *How many students went 10-12 blocks?*

Writing Have students write a phrase comparing a histograph to a bar graph.

4 5 Intermediate and Advanced Fluency
Ask students to explain what each bar on the histogram shows.

Writing Encourage them to summarize all the data in two or three sentences.

Name _____

Tally Chart and Graphs

DISTANCE IN BLOCKS	STUDENTS	NUMBERS
1–3	//	2
4–6	~~////~~/	5
7–9	/	1
10–12	~~////~~/	5
13–15		0
16–18	//	2
19–21	///	3

Histogram

Use the information from the chart and graph to answer the questions.

How many students go from 1–3 blocks to school? _____

Do more students go 2 blocks, or 16 blocks? _____

Why isn't there a bar at 13–15? _____

35 minutes

▶ **Key Strategy**
Use charts and graphs

▶ **Format**
Whole class and small groups

▶ **Math Vocabulary**
biased sample, population, random sample, representative sample, sample

▶ **Daily Vocabulary**
opinion, people, large group, small group

▶ **Resource**
Learning Resource 15

Materials
- marker or crayons
- rulers

Assessment

Check students' mastery of sampling as they do the activity. See Assessment Checklist on page 75. Remind students to work on their Foldables.

Home Connection

Have students make a collage of tables, charts, or graphs found in magazine or supermarket flyers. Have them label the types of graphs. Then invite them to report their experiences to the class.

Sampling

Math Objective	ESL/TESOL Descriptors
■ Select a random sample.	■ Demonstrate knowledge through application in a variety of contexts.
	■ Follow oral and written directions, implicit and explicit.

Activate Prior Knowledge Draw a large group of stick figures on the board. Say: *This is a group of students. What is it called when I ask everyone in a group the same question?* (a survey). Remind students of the surveys they took when they made tally charts. Then say: *Sometimes we need to survey a very large group.*

Hands-on Lesson Circle the whole group of people on the board. Say: *This is the population.* Circle just a few. Say: *This is a sample of the population.* Explain that we can use a **sample** to get information about the whole population.

- Choose five girls. Ask: *Is pink your favorite color?* Elicit that this is a **biased sample** because you only asked girls. Say: *I don't want a biased sample. Who should I ask?* (the same number of boys and girls) Ask five boys the same question. Say: *Now we have a representative sample of this fifth-grade class.*

- Have students write their names on index cards and put them in a bag. Mix the bag and let a few volunteers draw one card each. Ask: *What are all the cards in the bag?* (the population) *What did we pick?* (a sample) Explain that it is a **random sample** because all the cards had the same chance of getting picked.

- Distribute Learning Resource 15: Samples. Read the sentences and questions together. Ask students to circle the answers and discuss them. Divide the class into groups and have them complete survey questions, about populations and samples.

Challenge Have students survey their school, using the questions they created.

Multilevel Strategies

❶ Preproduction
Using the picture on the board, say: *Point to the population. Point to the sample.*

Writing Ask students to draw a bunch of dots and circle the population and a sample of it.

❷❸ Early Production and Speech Emergence
Point to the whole group and then to the small group of figures on the board and ask what they are.

Writing Have students label a drawing with phrases about population and sample.

❹❺ Intermediate and Advanced Fluency
Ask students to compare a biased sample to a random sample.

Writing Encourage students to write a sentence describing a representative sample.

Name _____

Samples

Read about the survey and answer the questions.

Some students are taking surveys to find out information about all the children in their school. Each group is studying 25 students. Circle the answers.

1. What is the sample for each survey?
   - 25 students
   - 50 students

2. One group surveys 25 fifth-grade girls. What kind of sample is this?
   - biased
   - random

3. One group surveys every fifth person in the school. What kind of sample is this?
   - biased
   - random

4. What is the population?
   - the whole school
   - 25 girls

Create a survey

5. What is the population you want to know about?

6. How big will your sample be?

7. What will be a representative sample?

8. What would be a biased sample of this population?

Problem Solving
Reading for Math

SKILL: Methods of Persuasion

Model the skill using a word problem such as:

 Read

Delia and Ruth collected data about the recycling. In one week, the third grade collected 725 cans, the fourth grade collected 691 cans, and the fifth grade collected 670 cans. Delia made a graph with intervals of 100. Ruth's graph has intervals of 20. Which graph shows the data better? Explain.

 Plan

I can make both graphs. I can compare the bars.

 Solve

Delia's Graph Ruth's Graph

Ruth's graph shows the data better because the difference in lengths of the bars is more clear.

 Look Back

Does my answer make sense? Yes.

Distribute **Math Center Card 4A** to students.

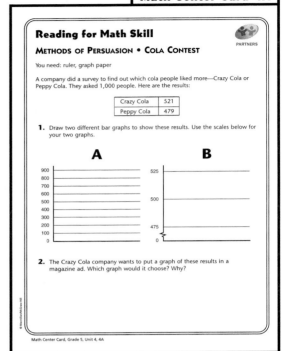
STRATEGY: Make a Graph

Model the strategy using a word problem such as:

 Read

Haille measured his bean plant every Friday. It was 1 inch tall the first week. It was 3 inches tall on the second Friday. It had grown another 3 inches by the 3rd Friday. This Friday it was 7 inches tall. What graph could he use to show how many inches his bean plant grew each week? Between which weeks did the plant grow most?

 Plan

I can use the information in the problem to make a line graph to show the growth of the plant.

 Solve

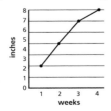 Haille's plant grew the most between week 2 and week 3.

 Look Back

Does my answer make sense? Yes.

Distribute **Math Center Card 4B** to students.

Assessment Checklist

	STUDENT NAMES									
SCHOOL:										
TEACHER: **SCHOOL YEAR:**										

Mark: + = Mastery
       √ = Satisfactory
       – = Needs Improvement										

LEVEL OF LANGUAGE PROFICIENCY (1–5)										
MATH OBJECTIVES										
• Explore collecting, organizing, and displaying data.										
• Find range, mean, median, and mode.										
• Read and interpret data in line graphs and bar graphs.										
• Organize and display data in histograms , line graphs, and bar graphs.										
• Select a random sample.										
ESL/TESOL LISTENING/SPEAKING										
Actively connect new information to information previously learned.										
Compare and contrast information.										
Follow oral and written directions, implicit and explicit.										
Gather information orally and in writing.										
Listen to, speak, read, and write about subject matter information.										
ESL/TESOL READING										
Read about subject matter information.										
Apply basic reading comprehension skills.										
Follow written directions, implicit and explicit.										
ESL/WRITING										
Write to demonstrate comprehension.										
Write using spelling patterns and targeted English vocabulary.										

 **by Dinah Zike**

❶ Preproduction
- Did students write the unit vocabulary?
- Did they illustrate the concepts?

❷ ❸ Early Production and Speech Emergence
- Did students label the tabs correctly?
- Did they write the vocabulary words?

❹ ❺ Intermediate and Advanced Fluency
- Did students write definitions for the unit vocabulary?
- Did they use correct spelling and grammar?

DATA AND GRAPHS

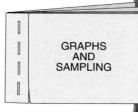

GRAPHS AND SAMPLING

Planner
Number Theory and Fractions

LOG ON Visit **www.mmhmath.com**

Unit Activities
• **Activity 1** (Readiness) Prime Sums, p. 80   • **Activity 3** Fraction Dominoes, p. 81   • **Activity 2** A Class Act, p. 80   • **Activity 4** Fraction Rummy, p. 81

Lessons	Key Objectives	Vocabulary	Materials	Resources
READ TOGETHER "The Birthday Party Surprise!" pp. 78–79	**Math:** Find equivalent fractions and simplify fractions. **ESL/TESOL:** Goal 2, Standard 2.	blow out, breath, colorful, my goodness, Prague, represent, surprise, throw him		
UNIT WARM-UP Understanding Factors p. 82	**Math:** Identify prime and composite numbers. Find common and greatest common factors. **ESL/TESOL:** Goal 1, Standard 3.	composite number, divisible, factors, prime number		Teacher Tool 7 **Overhead Manipulatives**
LESSON 1 Greatest Common Factor pp. 84–85	**Math:** Identify prime and composite numbers. Find common and greatest common factor. **ESL/TESOL:** Goal 2, Standard 1	common factor, factor tree, greatest common factor (GCF), prime factorization	cardboard, crayons or markers	Learning Resource 16 Teacher Tool 11
LESSON 2 Fractions pp. 86–87	**Math:** Find common and greatest common factors. Find equivalent fractions and simplify fractions. **ESL/TESOL:** Goal 1, Standard 3.	denominator, equivalent fractions, fraction, numerator, simplest form	construction paper, crayons or markers, ruler	Learning Resource 17
LESSON 3 Common Multiples pp. 88–89	**Math:** Find common multiples, least common multiple, and least common denominator. **ESL/TESOL:** Goal 2, Standard 1.	least common denominator (LCD), least common multiple (LCM), multiple	crayons or markers, number cubes	Learning Resource 18 Teacher Tool 4
LESSON 4 Fractions and Decimals pp. 90–91	**Math:** Change a fraction to a decimal and a decimal to a fraction. **ESL/TESOL:** Goal 2, Standards 1, 3.	decimal, denominator, divisible, fraction, numerator	empty food and drink containers	Learning Resource 19
LESSON 5 Mixed Numbers pp. 92–93	**Math:** Compare and order fractions, mixed numbers and decimals. **ESL/TESOL:** Goal 2, Standard 1	improper fraction, mixed number	crayons or markers	Learning Resource 20
PROBLEM SOLVING p. 94 • Skill: Extra and Missing Information • Strategy: Make a Table	Use skills and strategies to solve problems.			**Math Center Cards 5A, 5B**

See **Math at Home Family Guide** for additional math vocabulary, activities, and games in English, Spanish, and Haitian Creole.

English Vocabulary

Dear Family: *Please help your child practice the key vocabulary words for this unit.*

composite number a whole number greater than 1 that is divisible by more numbers than just itself and the number 1

divisible a whole number is divisible by another whole number if the remainder is 0 when the first is divided by the second

equivalent fractions fractions that name the same number

improper fraction a fraction that has a numerator greater than or equal to its denominator

least common denominator (LCD) the least common multiple of the denominators of two or more fractions

least common multiple (LCM) the least common whole number greater than 0 that is a multiple of each of two or more numbers

mixed number a number that combines a whole number and a fraction

prime number any whole number with only two factors, 1 and itself

simplest form a fraction is in simplest form when 1 is the only common factor of the numerator and denominator

Vocabulario en español

Estimados familiares: *Por favor ayuden a su hijo/a a practicar las palabras del vocabulario de esta unidad.*

número compuesto número entero mayor que 1 que es divisible entre otros números además de 1 y él mismo

divisible un número entero es divisible entre otro número entero cuando el primero se divide entre el segundo y el residuo es 0

fracciones equivalentes fracciones que representan la misma cantidad

fracción impropia fracción en la que el numerador es mayor o igual que el denominador

mínimo común denominador es el mínimo común múltiplo de los denominadores de dos o más fracciones

mínimo común múltiplo el mínimo común múltiplo de dos o más números enteros es el menor número entero mayor que 0 que es múltiplo de cada uno de los números

número mixto número que combina un número entero y una fracción

número primo cualquier número entero que sólo tiene dos factores, el 1 y él mismo

mínima expresión una fracción está en su mínima expresión cuando el único factor común del numerador y el denominador es 1

Vokabilè an kreyòl

Chè paran: *Tanpri ede pitit la pratike mo vokabilè nan seksyon sa a.*

nimewo miltip yon nimewo antye pi gwo pase 1 ki ka divize pa plizyè nimewo anplis limenm ak nimewo 1 an

divizib Yon nimewo antye divizib pa yon lòt nimewo antye si rès la se zewo (0) lè pwemye a divize pa dezyèm lan

fraksyon egal fraksyon ki eksprime menm nimewo

fo fraksyon yon fraksyon nimeratè a pi gwo osnon menm ak denominatè li

pi piti denominatè komen pi piti miltip komen denominatè de osnon plizyè fraksyon yo

pi piti miltip komen pi piti nimewo antye pi gran pase 0 ki se miltip de osnon plis nimewo

nimewo konpoze yon antye ak yon fraksyon

nimewo senp nenpòt nimewo ki gen sèlman de faktè 1 ak tèt li

fòm ki pi senp Yon fraksyon nan fòm ki pi senp lè 1 se sèl faktè komen nimerate a ak denominatè a

© Macmillan/McGraw-Hill

Read Together

THE BiRTHDAY PARTY SURPRiSE!

 25 minutes

Math Objective
- Find equivalent fractions and simplify fractions.

ESL/TESOL Descriptors
- Retell information.
- Represent information visually.

Reading Skill
- Sequence of Events

Vocabulary
blow out, breath, ceiling, colorful, my goodness, Prague, remaining, represent, surprise, throw him

Before Reading

Build Background/Oral Language
Discuss birthdays with students. Ask them if they know how birthdays are celebrated in the U.S. Poll the class for their favorite kind of cake. Tell students you will read a story about a birthday party. Ask them to listen for the order in which the events occur.

Cultural Link Ask students how birthdays are celebrated in their native countries or if they celebrate something similar to birthdays. Invite students to sing "Happy Birthday" in their native language.

During Reading
Read the story. Ask students to listen as you read again and then tell you what happened. Elicit the order of the events in the story. List them on the board using words such as, *first, second,* etc.

Phonological/Phonemic Awareness
Write *breath, breathe, blow, blew.* Pantomime and say the words. Say: ***Charlie blew out the candles yesterday.*** Explain that this is past tense. Have students pantomime and say the four words. Underline the *br-* and *bl-* consonant clusters. Have students repeat after you. Brainstorm other words.

After Reading
Say: ***Charlie blew out only $\frac{1}{4}$ of the candles.*** Draw a circle and divide it into quarters. Shade in one quarter. Ask: ***What fraction of candles were left?***

Say: ***Charlie wants everyone to get a piece of cake and he wants two pieces.*** Write *Students* and *Charlie.* Draw eight tally marks under *Students.* Ask students how many tally marks you need to put under *Charlie.* (2)

Ask: ***How many pieces of cake does Charlie need to cut?*** *(10)* ***What fraction of the cake will Charlie eat if he wants two pieces?*** $(\frac{2}{10} = \frac{1}{5})$

Art Give each student a large oak-tag circle. Have students decorate the cakes and cut them into enough equal pieces to share with the class. Then have students exchange pieces so they each get a piece of one another's cake.

Assessment
Observe students as they cut their cakes into pieces. See Assessment Checklist on page 95.

Multilevel Strategies

1 Preproduction
Say: ***Point to one quarter.*** *(one tenth)*

Writing Invite students to draw a circle and divide it into quarters and tenths.

2 3 Early Production and Speech Emergence
Ask: ***What fraction do you get if you divide something in four? in ten?***

Writing Have students write the fractions $\frac{1}{4}$, $\frac{3}{4}$, and $\frac{1}{10}$ and draw illustrations.

4 5 Intermediate and Advanced Fluency
Ask: ***How much is a quarter of something? What fraction of the cake will Charlie eat?***

Writing Encourage students to write what fraction of the candles Charlie blew out.

THE BIRTHDAY PARTY SURPRISE!

Charlie was teaching English in Prague one summer when his students decided to throw him a surprise birthday party. When Charlie walked into the classroom, the students all yelled, "Surprise!" and took his picture.

"Oh, my goodness, what's all this?" said Charlie. There was a sign on the board that said "Happy Birthday Charlie!" in colorful letters and a balloon floating under the ceiling. He was very happy to see the big chocolate cake in the middle of the table.

Now the students weren't sure how old Charlie was so they put about 28 candles in the cake. When his students told him to blow out the candles, he only blew out $\frac{1}{4}$ of the candles. He had to take another deep breath to blow out the rest. Can you represent in a fraction the remaining part of the candles he needed to blow out?

Charlie was very hungry because he hadn't had any lunch that day. He wanted to share the cake equally but since it was, after all, *his* birthday, he wanted to make sure he got two pieces. If there are 8 people in the class plus Charlie, what part of the cake will he eat?

You can use a fraction to represent the parts of a whole.

Activities

Readiness
ACTIVITY 1

PARTNERS

Prime Sums

A mathematician named Goldbach wrote the following:

Every even number can be written as the sum of two prime numbers. Work with a partner.

Examples: $8 = 5 + 3$ $32 = 19 + 13$

$18 = 13 + 5$ $40 = 23 + 17$

Test Goldbach's theory. Write each number as the sum of two prime numbers. Work with a partner.

1. 16   **2.** 14   **3.** 28   **4.** 30   **5.** 36

6. 42   **7.** 56   **8.** 62   **9.** 78   **10.** 100

11. Is there only one way to write each sum? Discuss your answers with your partner.

 See answers on p. 292.

Prime Numbers

ACTIVITY 2

INDIVIDUAL

A Class Act

• This Venn Diagram shows the factors and the GCF of 48 and 50.

Draw Venn Diagrams to show the factors and the GCF of:

1. 20 and 24   **2.** 30 and 40   **3.** 16 and 28   **4.** 30, 36, and 42

• Use the Venn Diagram to show the solution to this problem:

There are 360 students in the fifth grade. There are 336 students in the sixth grade. Both grades have classes with the same number of students in each room. What is the greatest number of students each room can have? How many classes will there be in each grade?

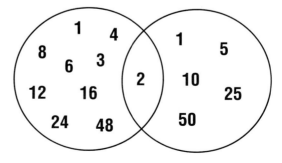

See answers on p. 292.

Common Factors and Greatest Common Factor

ACTIVITY 3

© Macmillan/McGraw-Hill

Fraction Dominoes

- Each player takes 14 cards. Draw a line across the middle of each card.

- On one-half of a card, write a fraction that can be simplified. On one-half of another card, have your partner write its simplified form.

- Now write on one-half of another card a fraction in its simplest form. Have your partner write its equivalent fraction on another card.

- Take turns writing fractions until all cards have two fractions.

- Mix up the cards. Each partner takes 14 cards.

- Play the game like dominoes by matching equivalent fractions. Record each match.

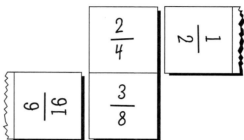

Equivalent Fractions

ACTIVITY 4

SMALL GROUP

Fraction Rummy

- Write a fraction in simplest form on 16 cards. Write two equivalent fractions on the remaining 32 cards. Mix the cards.

- Deal six cards to each player. Put the rest of the cards facedown. Players arrange the cards in their hands in matching sets. The first player draws a card from the pile and chooses to keep it, discarding one of the other cards in his hand, or discard it. A discard is placed faceup next to the center pile. The next player can either pick up the discarded card or choose a card from the pile.

- The player wins who first collects two sets of matching cards. The winning player calls, *Fraction Rummy,* and shows the matching sets.

Simplify Fractions

UNIT 5

Understanding Factors

 20 minutes

▶ **Key Strategy**
Use graphs and charts

▶ **Format**
Whole class and small groups

▶ **Math Vocabulary**
composite number, divisible, factors, prime number

▶ **Daily Vocabulary**
even, odd

▶ **Resources**
Teacher Tool 7
Overhead Manipulatives:
Counters

 LOG ON Visit **www.mmhmath.com** to find printable **Vocabulary Cards** that help build academic language.

Math Objectives	ESL/TESOL Descriptors
▪ Identify prime and composite numbers. ▪ Find common factors and greatest common factors.	▪ Seek support and feedback from others. ▪ Interpret and respond appropriately to nonverbal cues.

Activate Prior Knowledge You may want to use Counters from **Overhead Manipulatives** to model prime and composite numbers. Use counters to model factors of 12: 1 by 12, 2 by 6, 3 by 4.

Hands-on Lesson Say and write another multiplication fact, such as $7 \times 8 = 56$, on the board for volunteers to complete: $8 \times 7 = 56$; $56 \div 7 = 8$; $56 \div 8 = 7$. Continue with other fact families. Remind students that numbers that are multiplied are called **factors**. A number is **divisible** by its factors.

- Write the numbers 6 and 7 on the board. Ask students what the factors of each number are. For 6: 6×1; 2×3. For 7: 7×1. Circle 7. Explain that 7 is a **prime number.** This means the number has only two factors, 1 and itself.

- Explain that 6 is a **composite number** because it has more than two factors.

- Distribute Teacher Tool 7: 10×10 Grid. Have students fill in numbers 1–100 on the grid.

- Divide students into groups and have them work on different sections of the grid. Ask them to find the factors of each composite number.

- Have students circle prime numbers. *(2, 3, 7, 11, 13, 17, 19, 23, 29, 31, 37, 41, 43, 47, 53, 59, 61, 67, 71, 73, 79, 83, 89, 97)*

- Ask: *Except for 2, what do you notice about all these prime numbers?* Elicit that they are all odd numbers. All end in 1, 3, 7, or 9. None ends in 5.

- Review even and odd numbers. Ask: *What makes a number even?* Elicit that it is divisible by 2. Ask: *What makes a number odd?* Elicit that when it is divided by 2, there is a remainder of 1.

Multilevel Strategies

1 Preproduction
Have students point to the prime numbers on the grid.

2 3 Early Production and Speech Emergence
Have students say which numbers on the grid are prime.

4 5 Intermediate and Advanced Fluency
Ask students to explain prime numbers.

Procedure: Help students make these Foldables to write vocabulary words and definitions throughout the unit. Encourage students to use the Foldables as a study guide.

 **by Dinah Zike**

Eight-Tab Book

1. Provide each student with a sheet of paper. Fold the paper like a hot dog. Fold the hot dog into fourths. Fold in half again to form eighths.

2. Help your students to unfold the paper and cut up along the seven fold lines on one side only.

3. Students can label the tabs with key terms. As students work through the unit, they can define, describe, and/or give examples of the terms under the tabs.

| Divisibility |
| Prime |
| Composite |
| Common Factors |
| GCF |
| Fractions |
| Equivalent Fractions |
| Simplest Form |

Labels may include:

A common factor of two or more numbers is a whole number that is a factor of all of the numbers.

Two fractions are equivalent if they name the same number.

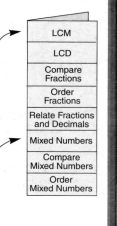 **by Dinah Zike**

Eight-Tab Book

1. Provide each student with a sheet of paper. Fold the paper like a hot dog. Fold the hot dog into fourths. Fold in half again to form eighths.

2. Help your students to unfold the paper and cut up along the seven fold lines on one side only.

3. Students can label the tabs with key terms. As students work through the unit, they can define, describe, and/or give examples of the terms under the tabs.

Labels may include:

The lowest common multiple of 5 and 6 is 30.

A mixed number combines a whole number and a fraction. Example: $3\frac{1}{4}$

| LCM |
| LCD |
| Compare Fractions |
| Order Fractions |
| Relate Fractions and Decimals |
| Mixed Numbers |
| Compare Mixed Numbers |
| Order Mixed Numbers |

35 minutes

▶ **Key Strategy**
Use manipulatives

▶ **Format**
Whole class and pairs

▶ **Math Vocabulary**
common factor, factor tree, greatest common factor (GCF), prime factorization

▶ **Daily Vocabulary**
exactly, larger, smaller, spinner, take turns

▶ **Resources**
Learning Resource 16
Teacher Tool 11

Materials
• cardboard
• crayons or markers

Assessment

Check students' mastery of greatest common factor (GCF) as they do the activity. See Assessment Checklist on page 95. Remind students to work on their Foldables.

Home Connection

Have students record when and where they see fractions during the day. Have them share the results with family members and the class.

Greatest Common Factor

Math Objectives	**ESL/TESOL Descriptors**
■ Identify prime and composite numbers.	■ Participate in full-class, group, and pair discussions.
■ Find common factors and greatest common factor.	■ Observe and model how others speak in a particular situation.

Activate Prior Knowledge Review the words even, odd, quarter, and factor. Have students take out their grid from the Warm-Up. Review prime and composite numbers with them. Ask volunteers to give examples of each and tell their factors.

Hands-on Lesson Write the numbers 8 and 12 on the board. Ask: *What are the factors for each number?* (8: 1, 2, 4, 8; 12: 1, 2, 3, 4, 6, 12) Write the factors under each number. Ask: *What factors do both 8 and 12 have?* (1, 2, 4) Circle the numbers. Explain that these are the **common factors** of 8 and 12. Ask: *What is the greatest common factor (GCF) of 8 and 12?* (4)

• Tell students that they are going to use a spinner to find the greatest common factor (GCF).

• Distribute Teacher Tool 11: Spinner Blanks. Write *3, 4, 5, 6, 7* on the board and have students write them on the spinner. Then as they spin, they identify each number as a prime or composite number. Have volunteers write the factors under each number on the board. Have them circle each prime number.

• Have students write the following numbers on another blank spinner: 4, 5, 8, 10, 12, 15, 16, 20, 24, 30.

• Tell pairs to spin twice to get two numbers and write them on Learning Resource 16: Greatest Common Factor. Then have them write the factors for each number and find the GCF. Have them repeat with other pairs of numbers and record them.

Challenge Have students write how to find the greatest common factor in their math journals.

Multilevel Strategies

❶ Preproduction
Say: *Show me the greatest common factor.* (Students should point.)

Writing Invite them to write a number that is the GCF of two given numbers.

❷ ❸ Early Production and Speech Emergence
Have students say the GCF of model numbers on the board.

Writing Encourage them to write a sentence using GCF.

❹ ❺ Intermediate and Advanced Fluency
Have students explain how to find the GCF.

Writing Challenge them to write about how to find the GCF.

Name _____

Greatest Common Factor

Spin twice to get 2 numbers. Write them in the blanks and write factors for each number. Find the greatest common factor (GCF).

1. 1st Number_____ 2nd Number _____

Factors _____

GCF _____

2. 1st Number_____ 2nd Number _____

Factors _____

GCF _____

3. 1st Number_____ 2nd Number _____

Factors _____

GCF _____

4. 1st Number_____ 2nd Number _____

Factors _____

GCF _____

5. 1st Number_____ 2nd Number _____

Factors _____

GCF _____

 35 minutes

▶ **Key Strategy**
Use charts and graphs

▶ **Format**
Whole class and small groups

▶ **Math Vocabulary**
denominator, equivalent fractions, fraction, numerator, simplest form

▶ **Daily Vocabulary**
model, pie chart

▶ **Resource**
Learning Resource 17

Materials
• construction paper
• crayons or markers
• ruler

Assessment

Check students' mastery of fractions as they do the activity. See Assessment Checklist on page 95.
Remind students to work on their Foldables.

Home Connection

Have students explain to family members what they learned in class and invite them to share their experience with the class.

Fractions

Math Objectives
■ Find common factors and greatest common factors.
■ Find equivalent fractions and simplify fractions.

ESL/TESOL Descriptors
■ Self-monitor and self-evaluate language development.
■ Use context to construct meaning.

Activate Prior Knowledge Write the number of students in the class on the board to use as the **denominator.** Then survey the class to find out how many are wearing sneakers, glasses, T-shirts, and so on. Write these numbers as **numerators.** Invite volunteers to say each **fraction** and explain what it means.

Hands-on Lesson Write some fractions on the board, such as $\frac{4}{12}$; $\frac{9}{45}$; $\frac{3}{22}$; $\frac{15}{60}$; $\frac{27}{99}$; $\frac{81}{93}$. With students, find the greatest common factor to reduce the fraction to its **simplest form.**

• Write two fractions on the board, such as $\frac{1}{4}$ and $\frac{6}{8}$, and illustrate them as shaded sections on a circle graph. Have students identify the numerator and denominator in the examples. Explain that the denominator represents the number of pieces into which a whole unit is divided. The numerator represents the part of that whole.

• Divide students into groups of three. Distribute materials and Learning Resource 17: Number Line and Circle Graph. Ask each group to decide on a model to represent a fraction of their choice.

• Have them draw on the number line, the circle graph, or use fraction strips to represent the fraction. When they are finished, write **equivalent fractions** on the board to explain that they represent the same relationship (*example:* $\frac{1}{2} = \frac{2}{4}$).

• Have groups find an equivalent fraction for the fraction they represented. Have groups present their fractions to the class.

Cultural Link Invite students to bring in recipes from their native countries the next day.

Multilevel Strategies

① Preproduction
Say: *Show me two equivalent fractions.*

Writing Encourage students to show fractions on a circle graph.

② ③ Early Production and Speech Emergence
Have students name their fractions and equivalents.

Writing Have them write the fraction in simplest form.

④ ⑤ Intermediate and Advanced Fluency
Ask students to explain how they made their equivalent fractions.

Writing Invite students to write a sentence describing numerator and denominator.

Name _____

Number Line and Circle Graph

Show your equivalent fractions on the number line and on the circle graph.

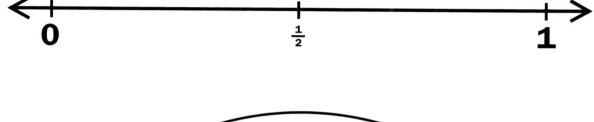

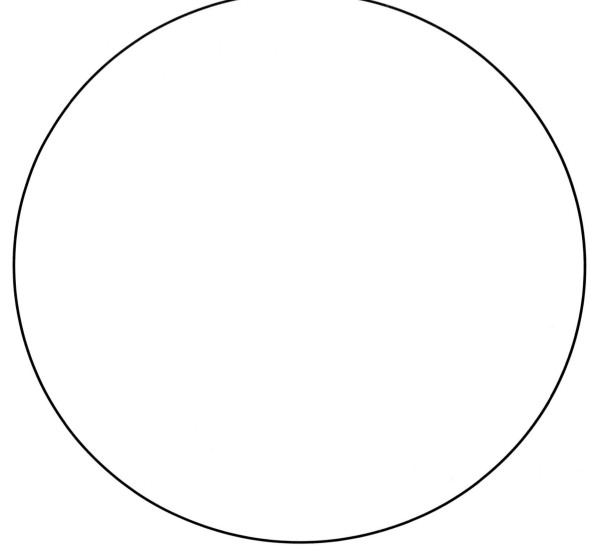

Lesson 3

⏱ **35 minutes**

▶ **Key Strategy**
Use manipulatives

▶ **Format**
Whole class and small groups

▶ **Math Vocabulary**
least common denominator (LCD), least common multiple (LCM), multiple

▶ **Daily Vocabulary**
recorder

▶ **Resources**
Learning Resource 18
Teacher Tool 4

Materials
- crayons or markers
- number cubes

Assessment

Check students' mastery of fractions as they complete the lesson. See Assessment Checklist on page 95. Remind students to work on their Foldables.

Home Connection

Have students ask a family member or a friend to pick two numbers and find the LCM. Ask students to share their results with the class.

Common Multiples

Math Objective	ESL/TESOL Descriptors
■ Find common multiples, least common multiple, and least common denominator.	■ Participate in full-class, group, and pair discussions. ■ Negotiate and manage interaction to accomplish tasks.

Activate Prior Knowledge Pass out number cubes to pairs. Have students toss the cube four times to make the numerators and denominators of two fractions. Have them say if the fractions are in simplest form and then write an equivalent fraction for each.

Hands-on Lesson Write the numbers 2 and 3 on the board. Tell students they are going to find common **multiples** for these numbers. Write the multiples on the board and elicit the **least common multiple (LCM).** *(6)*

- Now write $\frac{1}{2}$ and $\frac{1}{3}$ on the board. Say: ***You can use the least common multiple of the demoninators to write equivalent fractions for $\frac{1}{2}$ and $\frac{1}{3}$. The least common multiple of 2 and 3 is 6, so the*** **least common denominator (LCD)** ***of $\frac{1}{2}$ and $\frac{1}{3}$ is 6:*** $\frac{1}{2} = \frac{3}{6}, \frac{1}{3} = \frac{2}{6}$.

- Divide students into small groups of fluent and nonfluent speakers. Distribute number cubes (or Teacher Tool 4: Number Cube Patterns). Divide students into groups of three. Distribute number cubes. Have groups choose a recorder. One group member tosses a cube twice, recording the numbers and creating a fraction. The lower number will be the numerator, the higher number the denominator. Repeat to create the second fraction.

- Ask groups to find the LCM and LCD of each pair of fractions. Then have them order the mixed numbers from least to greatest.

Challenge Have students create a game that compares and orders mixed numbers. Then have them show a classmate how to play.

Multilevel Strategies

1 **Preproduction**
Have students point to the least common multiple.

Writing Invite students to write the least common denominator as a numeral and word.

2 **3** **Early Production and Speech Emergence**
Have students read the numbers the recorder writes.

Writing Have them write the phrase *least common denominator.*

4 **5** **Intermediate and Advanced Fluency**
Have students explain how to find the least common denominator.

Writing Encourage them to write a sentence telling the least common multiple.

Name _____

Least Common Denominators

Roll the number cube to make fractions.

Find the least common multiple of the denominators.

Find the least common denominator.

NUMBERS	FIRST FRACTION	NUMBERS	SECOND FRACTION	LCM	LCD
—— ——	——	—— ——	——		
—— ——	——	—— ——	——		
—— ——	——	—— ——	——		
—— ——	——	—— ——	——		
—— ——	——	—— ——	——		
—— ——	——	—— ——	——		
—— ——	——	—— ——	——		
—— ——	——	—— ——	——		

Lesson 4

35 minutes

▶ **Key Strategy**
Use visuals

▶ **Format**
Whole class and small groups

▶ **Math Vocabulary**
decimal, denominator, divisible, fraction, numerator

▶ **Daily Vocabulary**
bar, box, can, cereal, cheese, ounce, package, pound, weight

▶ **Resource**
Learning Resource 19

Materials
• empty food and drink containers

Assessment

Check students' mastery of fractions and decimals as they do the activity. See Assessment Checklist on page 95. Remind students to work on their Foldables.

Home Connection

Have students work with family members at home to find items with weights in fractions or decimal amounts to compare. Encourage them to share their experience with the class.

Fractions and Decimals

Math Objectives	**ESL/TESOL Descriptors**
■ Compare and order fractions, mixed numbers, and decimals.	■ Negotiate and manage interaction to accomplish tasks.
■ Change a fraction to a decimal and a decimal to a fraction.	■ Use context to construct meaning.

Activate Prior Knowledge Hold up a dollar and a quarter. *Ask: How many quarters are in a dollar? There are 4, so a quarter is $\frac{1}{4}$ of a dollar.* Write $\frac{1}{4}$ as .25. Review other U.S. currency in fractions and **decimals,** for example: a dime is $\frac{1}{10}$ or .10 of a dollar, and so on.

Hands-on Lesson With students, convert the decimal .25 to the fraction $\frac{1}{4}$. The decimal .25 becomes $\frac{25}{100}$. When you divide the numerator and denominator by the GCF, 25, you get $\frac{1}{4}$. Then to convert $\frac{1}{4}$ to a decimal, you multiply both numbers by 25. ($\frac{25}{100}$ becomes .25)

• Discuss with students why it is important to know both fractions and decimals. Demonstrate with some empty food/drink containers that show weight in decimals and/or fractions. Write $2\frac{1}{4}$ oz and 2.25 oz on the board. Ask: *Are these amounts the same or different?*

• Divide class into small groups of fluent and nonfluent speakers. Distribute Learning Resource 19: Change Fractions and Decimals. Ask them to convert the decimal to fractions and fractions to decimals, then order the fractions and the decimals from least to greatest.

• When they have finished, have the groups exchange papers and compare their numbers.

Challenge Have students create illustrated word problems that compare decimal and fractional amounts. Have them exchange problems with classmates to solve, then write them in their journals.

Multilevel Strategies

1 Preproduction
Ask students to point and/or say equivalent decimal and fractional amounts.

Writing Ask students to write fractions ordered from least to greatest.

2 3 Early Production and Speech Emergence
Have students read equivalent decimal and fractional amounts.

Writing Invite them to write 6 decimals and fractions.

4 5 Intermediate and Advanced Fluency
Ask students to tell an equivalent decimal and fraction (one half equals .5).

Writing Encourage students to write a sentence comparing fractional and decimal amounts.

Name _____

Change Fractions and Decimals

Look at the products. Then convert the fractions to decimals or the decimals to fractions on the lines provided. Show your work.

 _____

 _____

 _____

 _____

 _____

Write the fractions from the least to the greatest.

1. _____ 2. _____ 3. _____ 4. _____ 5. _____

Write the decimals from the least to the greatest.

1. _____ 2. _____ 3. _____ 4. _____ 5. _____

◔ **35 minutes**

▶ **Key Strategy**
Use graphs and charts

▶ **Format**
Whole class and small groups

▶ **Math Vocabulary**
improper fraction, mixed number

▶ **Daily Vocabulary**
list, organized, party

▶ **Resource**
Learning Resource 20

Materials
• crayons or markers

Assessment

Check students' mastery of fractions as they do the activity. See Assessment Checklist on page 95.
Remind students to work on their Foldables.

Home Connection

Have students work with family members to create word problems using mixed numbers to share with the class.

Mixed Numbers

Math Objectives	**ESL/TESOL Descriptors**
■ Compare and order fractions, mixed numbers, and decimals.	■ Negotiate and manage interaction to accomplish tasks.
■ Use skills and strategies to solve problems.	■ Follow oral and written descriptions.

Activate Prior Knowledge Brainstorm a list of celebrations with students: birthdays, weddings, holidays and so on. Then ask students what kind of party they would like for their celebrations: where they would celebrate them, how many people would attend, food, drinks, cups, plates, utensils, decorations needed, and so on. Explain to students that they will be planning a party. They will need to use **mixed numbers** in their plans.

Hands-on Lesson Write a mixed number on the board such as $5\frac{3}{8}$. Elicit that to convert a mixed number into an **improper fraction,** the 5, the whole number, has to be converted into eighths. Multiply 5×8 to change the 5 into eighths, then add: $40 + 3 = \frac{43}{8}$. Cite that $\frac{43}{8}$ is an improper fraction. Have students suggest other mixed numbers to convert to improper fractions.

• Divide class into pairs of fluent and nonfluent speakers. Distribute Learning Resource 20. Have each pair write a short word problem about the party. For example, you need food for 20 people. Each will eat $\frac{1}{4}$ of a pizza. How many pizzas should you order. Each pizza costs $7.48. How much will pizzas cost in all? Students must use fractions and mixed numbers in the problem. They may wish to calculate the amount of food, drinks, and/or the cost of the entire party.

• All pairs have 15–20 minutes to write their word problems. When finished, have pairs exchange their work with other pairs. Give pairs 10 minutes to work out the problem. Encourage students to make an organized list to facilitate the task.

• Elicit an explanation of how they worked through their problem. Ask: *Was it easy or hard to solve? Why?*

Multilevel Strategies

❶ Preproduction
Have students point to fractions and mixed numbers in a word problem when partners read it.

Writing Ask students to write a mixed number and an improper fraction.

❷❸ Early Production and Speech Emergence
Have students read fractions and mixed numbers in a word problem.

Writing Have them write a list of items for their celebration.

❹❺ Intermediate and Advanced Fluency
Ask students to read aloud one problem they have worked on.

Writing Have students write a sentence about their celebration.

Name _____

Party Planner

Fill in the Planner below with the kind of party you want to have. List the items you need, and what you think they will cost. Use the information to write one word problem. Make sure to use fractions, mixed numbers, or decimals in your word problem.

Kind of Party: _____ **Date of Party:** _____

How many people: _____

ITEM	QUANTITIES LISTED IN MIXED NUMBERS AND IMPROPER FRACTIONS	COST
Food		
Drink		
Cups		
Plates		

The problem is: _____

_____

_____

Problem Solving
Reading for Math

Read → Plan → Solve → Look Back

Remind students of
the basic steps
of problem solving.

SKILL: Extra and Missing Information
Model the skill using a word problem such as the
following:

 Read

Jamie wants to buy 6 model cars for $3.50 each.
He wants a carrier for them that costs $5.25. How
much change will he get?

 Plan

I can multiply to find how much the cars cost.
I can add to find how much the cars and carrier
cost.

 Solve

$6 \times \$3.50 = \$21.00$ is the cost of the cars.
$\$21.00 + \$5.25 = \$26.25$ is the cost of the cars
and the carrier.
Think: I don't know how much money Jamie has to
start with. I can't answer the question because I
don't have enough information.

 Look Back

What information did I need to answer the
question? I needed to know how much money
Jamie had to start with.

Distribute **Math Center Card 5A** to students.

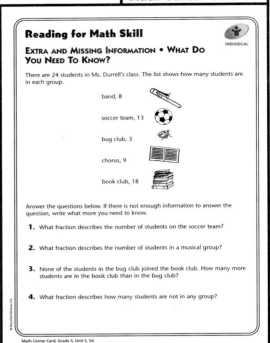

Math Center Card 5A

Reading for Math Skill
EXTRA AND MISSING INFORMATION • WHAT DO YOU NEED TO KNOW?

INDIVIDUAL

There are 24 students in Ms. Durrell's class. The list shows how many students are in each group.

band, 8

soccer team, 13

bug club, 3

chorus, 9

book club, 18

Answer the questions below. If there is not enough information to answer the question, write what more you need to know.

1. What fraction describes the number of students on the soccer team?

2. What fraction describes the number of students in a musical group?

3. None of the students in the bug club joined the book club. How many more students are in the book club than in the bug club?

4. What fraction describes how many students are not in any group?

Math Center Card, Grade 5, Unit 5, 5A

STRATEGY: Make a Table
Model the strategy using a word problem such as
the following:

 Read

Each of the team members ate $\frac{1}{4}$ of a pizza. How
many pizzas did they need for all 8 players to eat?

 Plan

I can make a table to find the answer.

 Solve

players	1	2	3	4	5	6	7	8
pizza	$\frac{1}{4}$	$\frac{2}{4}$	$\frac{3}{4}$	$\frac{4}{4}$	$\frac{5}{4}$	$\frac{6}{4}$	$\frac{7}{4}$	$\frac{8}{4}$

I can write the fraction in its simplest form. $\frac{8}{4} = 2$.
They need 2 pizzas.

 Look Back

How can I be sure my answer is correct? I can
think it through. If each player eats as $\frac{1}{4}$ of a pizza,
then 4 players eat 1 pizza. 8 players eat 2 pizzas.

Distribute **Math Center Card 5B** to students.

Math Center Card 5B

Problem Solving: Strategy
MAKE A TABLE • FRACTIONAL NUMBER CUBES

PARTNERS

You need: 2 number cubes

Each player follows these directions:

1. Toss the two number cubes 24 times. For each toss, write down the sum of the numbers on each cube.

2, 5, 4, 3, 9, 7, 6, 7, 7

2. Now put your data in a table. Show numbers 2–12 on the left. Write how many times you got each number on the right.

Number Tossed	Number of Times
2	1
3	1
4	2
5	3
6	2
7	4
8	6
9	3
10	1
11	1
12	0

3. Make fractions by writing the number of times you got each number (2–12) in a total of 24 tosses. The player with the greater fraction for each number scores one point.
• What fraction of your tosses had a sum of 2? 5? 7? 10? 12?
The player with more points wins.

Math Center Card, Grade 5, Unit 5, 5B

Assessment Checklist

	STUDENT NAMES									
SCHOOL:										
TEACHER: **SCHOOL YEAR:**										
Mark: + = Mastery √ = Satisfactory – = Needs Improvement										
LEVEL OF LANGUAGE PROFICIENCY (1–5)										
MATH OBJECTIVES										
• Find equivalent fractions and simplify fractions.										
• Identify prime and composite numbers.										
• Find common factors and greatest common factor.										
• Compare and order fractions, mixed numbers, and decimals.										
• Change a fraction to a decimal and a decimal to a fraction.										
ESL/TESOL LISTENING/SPEAKING										
Negotiate and manage interaction to accomplish tasks.										
Observe and model how others speak and behave in a particular situation or setting.										
Use context to construct meaning.										
Seek support and feedback from others.										
Self-monitor and self-evaluate language development.										
Use context to construct meaning.										
ESL/TESOL READING										
Read about subject matter information.										
Apply basic reading comprehension skills.										
Follow written directions, implicit and explicit.										
ESL WRITING										
Write to demonstrate comprehension.										
Write using spelling patterns and targeted English vocabulary.										

 **by Dinah Zike**

1 **Preproduction**
• Did students write the unit vocabulary?
• Did they copy the definitions?

2 **3** **Early Production and Speech Emergence**
• Did students label the tabs correctly?
• Did they write the vocabulary words?
• Did they copy the definitions?

4 **5** **Intermediate and Advanced Fluency**
• Did students write definitions for the unit vocabulary?
• Did they use correct spelling and grammar?

LCM
LCD
Compare Fractions
Order Fractions
Relate Fractions and Decimals
Mixed Numbers
Compare Mixed Numbers
Order Mixed Numbers

Divisibility
Prime
Composite
Common Factors
GCF
Fractions
Equivalent Fractions
Simplest Form

Planner

Add and Subtract Fractions

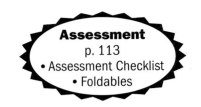

LOG
ON Visit **www.mmhmath.com**

Planner

Unit Activities		
• **Activity 1** Readiness Bag It, Please! p. 100		• **Activity 3** Mixed Number Bingo, p. 101
• **Activity 2** Mixed Number Drop, p. 100		• **Activity 4** Views from the Cube, p. 101

Lessons	Key Objectives	Vocabulary	Materials	Resources
READ TOGETHER "Mathemagician," by Sandra Liatsos, pp. 98–99	**Math:** Use skills and strategies to solve problems. **ESL/TESOL:** Goals 2, 1; Standards 2,3.	defeat, instant, marvelous, millionth, pirate, practice, spark, tough, treasure, winking		Graphic Organizer 5
UNIT WARM UP Understanding Adding Fractions p. 102	**Math:** Add fractions and mixed numbers. **ESL/TESOL:** Goal 1, Standards 3, 1.	denominator, fractions, half, mixed numbers, numerator, quarter, third,	measuring cups, recipes, water	**Overhead Manipulatives**
LESSON 1 Adding with Like Denominators pp. 104–105	**Math:** Add fractions and mixed numbers. Identify and use addition properties with fractions. **ESL/TESOL:** Goal 2, Standard 2.	Associative, Commutative, and Identity Properties of Addition, like denominators	crayons or markers, paper plates, scissors	Learning Resource 21 Teacher Tool 10
LESSON 2 Add Unlike Denominators pp. 106–107	**Math:** Add fractions. Add mixed numbers. **ESL/TESOL:** Goal 2, Standard 2.	least common denominator, least common multiple, like and unlike denominators	crayons or markers, pencils, scissors	Learning Resource 22 Teacher Tools 10 and 17
LESSON 3 Subtract Fractions and Mixed Numbers pp. 108–109	**Math:** Subtract fractions. Subtract mixed numbers. **ESL/TESOL:** Goal 2, Standard 2.	least common denominator (LCD), like denominators	markers, number cubes, pencils	Learning Resource 23 Teacher Tools 4 and 10
LESSON 4 Estimate with Fractions pp. 110–111	**Math:** Subtract fractions and mixed numbers. Estimate sums and differences of mixed numbers. **ESL/TESOL:** Goal 2, Standard 2.	estimate, round	markers or pencils	Learning Resource 24
PROBLEM SOLVING p. 112 • Skill: Choose an Operation • Strategy: Write an Equation	Use skills and strategies to solve problems.			

See **Math at Home Family Guide** for additional math vocabulary, activities, and games in English, Spanish, and Haitian Creole.

English Vocabulary

Dear Family: Please help your child practice the key vocabulary words for this unit.

Associative Property of Addition when three addends are added, the grouping of the addends does not change the sum

common denominator a common multiple of the denominators of two or more fractions

Commutative Property of Addition when adding, the order of the addends does not change the sum

Identity Property of Addition when a number is added to 0, the sum is that number

like denominators denominators that are the same number

Vocabulario en español

Estimados familiares: Por favor ayuden a su hijo/a a practicar las palabras del vocabulario de esta unidad.

Propiedad asociativa de la suma al sumar varios sumandos, la agrupación de los sumandos no altera el resultado

común denominador el común denominador de dos o más fracciones es un número que es múltiplo de los denominadores de las fracciones

Propiedad conmutativa de la suma al sumar, el orden de los sumandos no altera el resultado

Propiedad de identidad de la suma la suma de cualquier número y cero es igual al número mismo

denominadores iguales denominadores que son el mismo número

Vokabilè an kreyòl

Chè paran: Tanpri ede pitit la pratike mo vokabilè nan seksyon sa a.

Kalite asosiasyon nan adisyon lè ou gen twa chif pou adisyone, fason ou ranje yo pa chanje rezilta

denominatè komen denominatè komen de osnon plizyè fraksyon se nimewo ki miltip denominatè fraksyon yo

Pwopriyete kimilatif adisyon lè-w adisyone, lòd chif w-ap adisyone yo pa chanj sòm lan

Pwopriyete idantite adisyon lè-w ajoute zewo nan yon nimewo, sòm nan se nimewo an

denominatè ki sanble denominatè ki eksprime menm nimewo

Mathemagician
by Sandra Liatsos

 25 minutes

Math Objective
- Use skills and strategies to solve problems.

ESL/TESOL Descriptors
- Listen to, speak, read, and write about subject matter.
- Use context to construct meaning.

Reading Skill
- Distinguish between reality and fantasy.

Vocabulary
defeat, instant, marvelous, millionth, pirate, practice, spark, tough, treasure, winking, worry

Before Reading

Build Background/Oral Language
Write the words *mathematics* and *magician*. Elicit meanings for both. Point out cognates and model examples. Ask: *If I combine these two words, I can make the word* mathemagician. *What do you think that is?* Tell students you are going to read a poem about a mathemagician. Say: *Raise your hand each time I read a math word.*

During Reading

- Read the poem, acting out words where possible, such as *winking*. Note how many students are able to identify math words.

Phonological/Phonemic Awareness
Write *quickly multiply* on the board. Say the words and have students repeat. Explain that the words end the same way but the *-y* sound is different. Say: *The -y can have two sounds: a long e sound and a long i sound.* Make two columns on the board and brainstorm words (*by, try, my, cry; monkey, worry, party, happy*).

After Reading

Ask: *What math words were in the poem?* Draw Graphic Organizer 3: Main Idea Pyramid, and write *Mathemagician* in the middle. Elicit the four operations from the poem and write them in the outside ovals. Read the poem again and see if students are able to pick out the words *fraction* and *one/one millionth* as math words.

Drama Make index cards with the symbols $+$, $-$, $\times$, and $\div$. Make a magician's hat out of cardboard and put the cards in it. Have volunteers take turns being the magician and picking a card out of the hat. Model the following sentence and have them use an operation to make their own: *If I were a mathemagician, I could (multiply the leaves on trees).*

Assessment

Observe students' participation in class activities. See Assessment Checklist on page 113.

Multilevel Strategies

1 Preproduction
Have students point to an operation symbol on the index cards as you say its name.

Writing Have children write an equation for each operation.

2 3 Early Production and Speech Emergence
Have students say the name of each operation as you hold up the symbol.

Writing Encourage students to write an equation for each operation and read it out loud.

4 5 Intermediate and Advanced Fluency
Ask students to say an equation for each operation.

Writing Invite students to write an equation using each operation and solve it.

Mathemagician

by Sandra Liatsos

I think I'll practice being
a marvelous mathemagician
knowing instant answers
to any tough addition.
My mind like a computer
will quickly multiply
birds, monkeys, or bananas
quick as a winking eye.

No number will defeat me,
not even the smallest fraction.
one/one millionth of a bug
will spark my math to action.

Subtracting candies from a jar
will by my greatest pleasure.
And when we find old, pirate gold
I'll divide our treasure.
Without a minute's worry
over answers right or wrong.
With practice all of math will be
like singing a favorite song.

Activities

Activities

Readiness

ACTIVITY 1

INDIVIDUAL

Bag It, Please!

YOU NEED
fraction strip-4 halves, 4 quarters, and 4 eighths (or copies and cutouts of the strips shown here)
paper bag
scissors

- Put the fraction strips in the paper bag. Pick out three or four strips. Choose any two of these to make a subtraction exercise. What is the greatest difference you can make? the least?

- Now try adding two of the strips together (do not go beyond a sum of 1 to get a new fraction). Then, subtract, making sure to subtract the lesser fraction from the greater. Now what is the greatest difference you can end up with? What is the least? (You may want to spill out strips from the bag to help.)

- Pick out a different set of strips and try again.

$\frac{1}{8}$	$\frac{1}{8}$	$\frac{1}{8}$	$\frac{1}{8}$
$\frac{1}{4}$		$\frac{1}{4}$	
$\frac{1}{2}$			
$\frac{1}{2}$			

Add and Subtract Fractions

ACTIVITY 2

INDIVIDUAL

Mixed Number Drop

YOU NEED
fraction strips

Can you get from 10 to either $\frac{1}{2}$ or a fraction less than $\frac{1}{2}$ by writing a mixed number in each space with a minus sign? Make a copy of this slide and write the difference in each circle. The whole number of the mixed numbers you choose cannot be greater than 3. You may not repeat the same mixed number anywhere on the slide.

- How many solutions can you find?

- Make another slide that has one extra minus sign space and circle space. Try the game again.

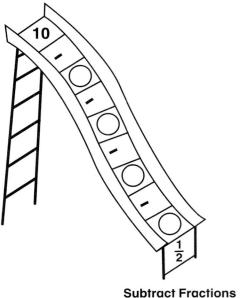

Subtract Fractions

Game Zone

ACTIVITY 3

SMALL GROUP

Mixed Number Bingo

- **Setup:** Each player makes a playing card with 9 squares such as the one in the picture. In each square write a whole number from 1 to 7. A number can be repeated as often as you like.

YOU NEED
number cubes
connecting cubes
index cards

- **Group Leader:** Take turns being the Group Leader. Roll one number cube to get the whole-number part of a mixed number. Roll two cubes to get the proper fraction part of the mixed number. (Use the larger number as the denominator and the smaller number as the numerator.)

- All players round the mixed number and mark the rounded number with a connecting cube if it appears on their playing cards.

- You win if you are first to fill in a row, column, or diagonal on your playing card.

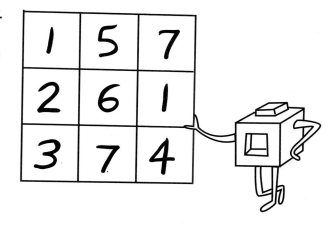

Mixed Numbers

ACTIVITY 4

SMALL GROUP

Views from the Cube

Below are three views of the same cube. Work together to answer these questions.

1. Find the sum of the six mixed numbers on the cube.

2. Find the difference between $6\frac{1}{4}$ and the number opposite it.

3. Find the difference between $2\frac{1}{4}$ and the number opposite it.

4. Find the difference between $1\frac{1}{8}$ and the number opposite it.

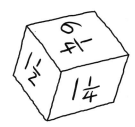 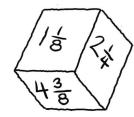 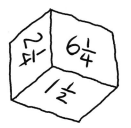

See answers on p. 292.

Subtract Mixed Numbers

© Macmillan/McGraw-Hill

Understanding Adding Fractions

⏱ 20 minutes

▶ **Key Strategy**
Use realia

▶ **Format**
Whole class and small groups

▶ **Math Vocabulary**
denominator, fractions, half, mixed numbers, numerator, quarter, third

▶ **Daily Vocabulary**
butter, flour, ice water, ingredients, recipe

▶ **Resource**
Overhead Manipulatives: Fraction Strips

▶ **Materials**
measuring cups, recipes, water

Math Objective	**ESL/TESOL Descriptors**
■ Add fractions and mixed numbers.	■ Listen to and imitate how others use English. ■ Use nonverbal communication in social interactions.

Activate Prior Knowledge Write $\frac{1}{4}$ and $\frac{1}{2}$ on the board. Draw circles divided into **quarters** and halves and ask volunteers to write the **fractions** inside them. Ask: *What is the top number in a fraction called?* (numerator) *the bottom number?* (denominator). Write $1\frac{1}{2}$ and ask: *What is this kind of number?* (a *mixed number*) Say the fractions and have students repeat them. Write out the words *one fourth*, *two **thirds**,* and *one **half*** on the board.

Hands-on Lesson Bring in examples of simple recipes to share with the class. Write this recipe on the board:

Pie Crust

$1\frac{1}{4}$ cup flour	$\frac{1}{2}$ cup butter	$\frac{1}{2}$ teaspoon salt	3 tablespoons ice water

- Read the recipe aloud with students and ask them to identify the fractions, numerators, denominators, whole numbers, and mixed numbers they see.

- Ask: *If you only have a $\frac{1}{4}$ measuring cup, how could you use it to measure 1 cup?* Elicit that four $\frac{1}{4}$ cups could be used to make one cup. Have a student demonstrate with measuring cups and water. Write the addition sentence on the board.

- You may want to use **Overhead Manipulatives:** Fraction Strips to reinforce fractions. Ask students to demonstrate the addition sentence on the overhead projector. $(\frac{1}{4}+\frac{1}{4}+\frac{1}{4}+\frac{1}{4}=1)$ Invite students to use the strips to model other problems.

Multilevel Strategies

1 Preproduction
Have students point to the fractions and mixed numbers as you name them.

2 3 Early Production and Speech Emergence
Point to fractions and mixed numbers and ask students to name them.

4 5 Intermediate and Advanced Fluency
Encourage students to read the recipe aloud.

 LOG ON Visit **www.mmhmath.com** to find printable **Vocabulary Cards** that help build academic language.

Procedure: Help students make these Foldables to write vocabulary words and definitions throughout the unit. Encourage students to use the Foldables as a study guide.

Foldables

by Dinah Zike

Folded Table

1. Provide each student with a large sheet of paper. Have students fold paper into thirds.

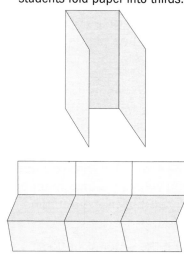

2. Next, students will open the paper and refold it into thirds along the other side. Have your students unfold the paper and draw lines along all of the folds.

Labels may include:

Add Fractions and Mixed Numbers	Like Denominators	Unlike Denominators
Fractions		
Mixed Numbers		

This will allow them to label rows and columns.

3. As students work through the lessons, have them take notes and record main ideas in the appropriate sections of their Foldables Table.

$$\frac{3}{8} + \frac{1}{4} \qquad \frac{1}{4} \text{ is the same as } \frac{2}{8}$$

$$\frac{3}{8} + \frac{2}{8} = \frac{5}{8}$$

To add mixed numbers with unlike denominators, just find the LCD of both fractions, rename them using the LCD, add the whole numbers, add the fractions, and finally simplify!

$$\begin{array}{r} 1\frac{3}{4} \\ + 2\frac{1}{4} \\ \hline 3\frac{4}{4} \end{array}$$

Simplify: $3\frac{4}{4} = 4$

To add fractions with common denominators, just add the numerators and place over the common denominator.

Foldables

by Dinah Zike

Folded Table

1. Provide each student with a large sheet of paper. Have students fold the paper into thirds.

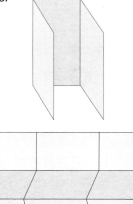

2. Next, students will open the paper and refold it into thirds along the other side.

Labels may include:

Subtract Fractions and Mixed Numbers	Like Denominators	Unlike Denominators
Fractions		
Mixed Numbers		

3. As students work through the lessons, have them take notes and record main ideas in the appropriate sections of their Foldables Table.

To subtract fractions with common denominators, just subtract the numerators and place over the common denominator.

$$\frac{1}{3} = \frac{4}{12}$$
$$-\frac{1}{4} = -\frac{3}{12}$$

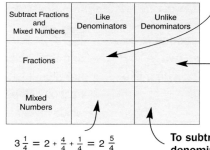

$$3\frac{1}{4} = 2 + \frac{4}{4} + \frac{1}{4} = 2\frac{5}{4}$$
$$-1\frac{3}{4} \qquad\qquad -1\frac{3}{4}$$
$$\hline$$
$$\qquad\qquad 1\frac{2}{4} = 1\frac{1}{2}$$

To subtract mixed numbers with unlike denominators, just find the LCD of both mixed numbers and rename them using the LCD. Subtract fractions and then the whole numbers. Simplify if needed!

 35 minutes

▶ **Key Strategy**
Use manipulatives

▶ **Format**
Whole class and small groups

▶ **Math Vocabulary**
Associative Property of Addition, Commutative Property of Addition, Identity Property of Addition, like denominators

▶ **Daily Vocabulary**
baking soda, brown sugar, chocolate chips, flour, pecans, salt, softened, vanilla extract

▶ **Resources**
Learning Resource 21
Teacher Tool 10

Materials
- crayons or markers
- paper plates
- scissors

Assessment

Check students' mastery of fractions as they complete the lesson. Remind students to work on their Foldables.

Home Connection

Have students find objects at home that can be shown as parts of a whole (2 sticks of butter in a 4-pack, 4 cans of soda in a 6-pack) and write them as fractions to share with the class.

Adding with Like Denominators

Math Objectives
- Add fractions and mixed numbers.
- Identify and use addition properties with fractions.

ESL/TESOL Descriptors
- Interpret information presented visually.
- Follow oral and written directions.

Activate Prior Knowledge Distribute paper plates to groups of students. Assign each group a number of parts into which to divide their plates, such as halves, thirds, fourths, sixths, and eighths. Have them shade and label the parts.

Hands-on Lesson Distribute Learning Resource 21: Recipe for Chocolate Chip Cookies. Read the recipe and ask students to identify the fractions, the numerators, denominators, whole numbers, and mixed numbers. Model and show many examples.

- Ask: *What would you do if you had to double the recipe?* Elicit that you would add each amount to itself. Ask students to help you write an addition sentence to double the amount of sugar: $\frac{3}{4} + \frac{3}{4} =$ ____. Point out that these fractions have *like denominators,* so only the numerators are added.

- Now ask students to write the sentence for doubling the amount of flour: $2\frac{1}{4} + 2\frac{1}{4} =$ ____. Ask: *How do you add these mixed numbers?* Elicit that you add the whole numbers and then add the fractions.

- Divide students into groups and distribute scissors and Teacher Tool 10: Fraction Strips. Have them show the above sentences with their strips.

- Review using Properties of Addition for whole numbers. Explain that these properties are also true for fractions and mixed numbers. Write new words **Associative** and **Commutative** on the board and have students repeat after you. Model how to use the **Commutative Property**—the order of addends does not change the sum: $2\frac{3}{4} + 3\frac{1}{4} = 6$, $3\frac{1}{4} + 2\frac{3}{4} = 6$. Model the **Identity Property**—when a number is added to zero, the sum is that number: $\frac{3}{4} + 0 = \frac{3}{4}$, $0 + \frac{3}{4} = \frac{3}{4}$. Model the **Associative Property**—the grouping of three addends does not change the sum: $(7\frac{1}{4} + 5\frac{1}{4}) + \frac{3}{4} = 7\frac{1}{4} + (5\frac{1}{4} + \frac{3}{4})$.

Multilevel Strategies

1 Preproduction
Say: *Show me two fraction strips with a like denominator.*

Writing Encourage students to write two fractions with like denominators.

2 3 Early Production and Speech Emergence
Ask students to read their fractions strips and tell you which ones have like denominators.

Writing Ask students to write a fraction sentence using like denominators.

4 5 Intermediate and Advanced Fluency
Have students explain how to add fractions and mixed numbers.

Writing Invite students to write addition sentences and read them to the class.

Name _____

Recipe for Chocolate Chip Cookies

Look for fractions and mixed numbers in this recipe.

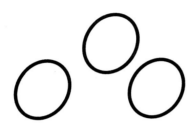

INGREDIENTS

$2\frac{1}{4}$ cups sifted flour

1 teaspoon baking soda

1 teaspoon salt

1 cup softened butter

$\frac{3}{4}$ cup packed brown sugar

1 teaspoon vanilla extract

2 large eggs

2 cups chocolate chips

1 cup pecans

 35 minutes

▶ **Key Strategy**
Use manipulatives

▶ **Format**
Whole class and small groups

▶ **Math Vocabulary**
least common denominator (LCD), least common multiple (LCM), like denominators, unlike denominators

▶ **Daily Vocabulary**
color, cut, shade

▶ **Resources**
Learning Resource 22
Teacher Tools 10 and 17

Materials
- crayons or markers
- pencils
- scissors

Check students' mastery of adding fractions as they complete the lesson. See Assessment Checklist on page 113. Remind students to work on their Foldables.

Have students and family members find different food containers with fractions to add. Have them write the products and fractions to share with the class.

Add Unlike Denominators

Math Objectives	**ESL/TESOL Descriptors**
■ Add fractions. ■ Add mixed numbers.	■ Listen to, speak, and write about subject matter information. ■ Demonstrate knowledge through application in a variety of contexts.

Activate Prior Knowledge Review terms commutative and associative from the previous lesson. Cut up fractions strips (Teacher Tool 10) and hand them out. Ask students to add their age to the fraction. Then have students form groups with others with **like denominators**. Ask group members to add their ages and fractions.

Hands-on Lesson Say: *We added fractions with like denominators. Now let's add fractions with* **unlike denominators.** *Unlike means different.*

- Review what students learned in Unit 5 about finding the **least common multiple (LCM)** and the **least common denominator (LCD).**

- Distribute Teacher Tool 10: Fraction Strips, to small groups. Write $\frac{1}{8} + \frac{1}{4}$ on the board. Help students use fraction strips to find an equivalent fraction for $\frac{1}{4}$ by placing a $\frac{1}{8}$ strip under the $\frac{1}{4}$. Elicit that there are $\frac{2}{8}$ in $\frac{1}{4}$, and $\frac{6}{8}$ in $\frac{3}{4}$. Then ask groups to add the fractions: $\frac{1}{8} + \frac{6}{8} = \frac{7}{8}$.

- Distribute Teacher Tool 17 (2-D Shapes) to pairs. Have students color two-thirds of the first circle or square. Ask: **What fraction did you show?** ($\frac{2}{3}$) Have them draw lines to divide the circle into six equal parts. Ask them to count the shaded part again and tell you the number. *(4)* They have just shown that $\frac{2}{3} = \frac{4}{6}$. Repeat the process with mixed numbers. Then repeat using fraction strips.

- Distribute scissors and Learning Resource 22: Unlike Denominators. Have students use fraction strips and circle graphs to solve problems they create.

Challenge Ask students to add larger mixed numbers and fractions with larger denominators and numerators.

Multilevel Strategies

1 Preproduction
Say: **What is the common denominator of ($\frac{2}{3}$ and $\frac{1}{6}$)?**

Writing Encourage students to convert two fractions using the LCD.

2 3 Early Production and Speech Emergence
Ask: **What fractions do you have? Which ones have like denominators?**

Writing Ask students to write a fraction sentence using like denominators.

4 5 Intermediate and Advanced Fluency
Have students name all the fractions on the strips.

Writing Invite students to write and label fractions with like and unlike denominators.

Name _____

Unlike Denominators

Create your own fraction sentence. Use fractions with unlike denominators. Show how to solve it. Then draw fraction strips and circles to show the problem.

My Fraction Sentence _____

How I Solved It:

My Fraction Sentence _____

Fraction Strips:

My Fraction Sentence _____

Circle Chart:

Lesson 3

 40 minutes

▶ **Key Strategy**
Use manipulatives

▶ **Format**
Whole class and pairs

▶ **Math Vocabulary**
least common denominator (LCD), like denominators

▶ **Daily Vocabulary**
pick, roll, steps

▶ **Resources**
Learning Resource 23
Teacher Tools 4 and 10

Materials
- markers
- number cubes
- pencils

Assessment

Check students' understanding of the steps in subtracting fractions as they complete the lesson. See Assessment Checklist on page 113. Remind students to work on their Foldables.

Home Connection

Have students and family members find different drink containers with fractions to subtract. Have them share the subtraction sentences with the class.

Subtract Fractions and Mixed Numbers

Math Objectives	ESL/TESOL Descriptors
■ Subtract fractions. ■ Subtract mixed numbers.	■ Gather information orally and in writing. ■ Participate in full-class and pair discussions.

Activate Prior Knowledge Write several fractions with **like denominators** and ask: *How do we add fractions with like denominators?* (*add the numerators*) Then ask: *How can we subtract fractions with like denominators?* Elicit that we subtract them the same way, by subtracting the numerators.

Hands-on Lesson Write fraction and mixed number subtraction problems with like denominators. Ask students to help you subtract.

- Now write problems with unlike denominators. Ask: *How can we subtract these numbers?* Elicit that, again, the process is the same as for addition—first they find the least common multiple between the two denominators and rename numerators and denominators by that number. This will change them to fractions with the **least common denominator (LCD)** so they can subtract. Show examples.

- Have students work in pairs. Distribute Teacher Tools 4 and 10 (Number Cube Patterns and Fraction Strips) and Learning Resource 23: Fractions and Mixed Number Subtraction. Go through the steps in the example. Each student will roll a number cube to get a whole number, and pick a fraction strip. Then they write the whole number, the fraction, and the mixed number they form.

- Students then decide which is the greater mixed number and write it first in the subtraction sentence. They find the LCD and convert the mixed numbers to improper fractions. Then they subtract the fractions and simplify the answer.

Challenge Have students do other subtractions using 3-digit whole numbers.

Multilevel Strategies

❶ Preproduction
Ask students to show you the whole number, the fraction, and the mixed number.

Writing Encourage students to write the subtraction sentence.

❷❸ Early Production and Speech Emergence
Ask: *Are you subtracting fractions with like denominators or unlike denominators?*

Writing Ask students to write a mixed fraction subtraction sentence using like denominators.

❹❺ Intermediate and Advanced Fluency
Say: *Tell me how you subtracted these two mixed numbers.*

Writing Have students write sentences telling the steps in subtracting fractions.

Name _____

Fractions and Mixed Number Subtraction

Roll numbers and pick fractions. Combine them to form mixed numbers. Then write and solve subtraction sentences.

	EXAMPLE	ROUND 1	ROUND 2
Student 1 Roll a number	1		
Student 1 Pick a fraction	$\frac{1}{2}$		
Mixed number	$1\frac{1}{2}$		
Student 2 Roll a number	3		
Student 2 Pick a fraction	$\frac{1}{4}$		
Mixed number	$3\frac{1}{4}$		
Subtraction sentence	$3\frac{1}{4} - 1\frac{1}{2}$		
LCD	4		
Subtract improper fractions	$\frac{13}{4} - \frac{6}{4} = \frac{7}{4}$		
Simplify answer	$1\frac{3}{4}$		

Lesson 4

 35 minutes

▶ **Key Strategy**
Use visuals

▶ **Format**
Whole class and small groups

▶ **Math Vocabulary**
estimate, round

▶ **Daily Vocabulary**
closer, dots, number line, segment

▶ **Resource**
Learning Resource 24

Materials
• markers or pencils

Assessment

Check students' mastery of rounding fractions as they complete the lesson. See Assessment Checklist on page 113.
Remind students to work on their Foldables.

Home Connection

Have students take copies of number lines home and share their work with family members.

Estimate with Fractions

Math Objectives	**ESL/TESOL Descriptors**
■ Subtract fractions and mixed numbers.	■ Gather information orally or in writing.
■ Estimate sums and differences of mixed numbers.	■ Follow oral and written directions.

Activate Prior Knowledge Write $31\frac{2}{15} - 12\frac{1}{5}$ on the board. Work through the problem. Then say: *That was a hard problem! Is there an easier way to find the answer?* Elicit that with mixed numbers we can come close to the answer by estimating, just as we can when we have problems with whole numbers.

Hands-on Lesson Discuss that when you estimate sums or differences with mixed numbers, you round to the nearest whole number. If the fraction is less than one half, you round down. If it is more than one half, you round up.

• Divide students into small groups. Distribute markers and Learning Resource 24.

• Write $4\frac{1}{8} - 2\frac{7}{8}$ on the board. Tell groups they will use the number lines to round the fractions to the nearest whole number, then find the answer.

• Explain that each segment on the first number line represents $\frac{1}{8}$. Ask groups to locate and mark the point $4\frac{1}{8}$ with a small dot on the number line. Ask: *Is $4\frac{1}{8}$ nearer to 4 or 5?* Elicit that it is nearer to 4. Have groups place a large dot on the 4. Repeat the process by marking $2\frac{7}{8}$, rounding to 3, and placing a dot on 3.

• Tell groups to look at the number line. Ask: *How could you estimate $4\frac{1}{8} - 2\frac{7}{8}$?* Elicit that they would subtract 3 from 4. Ask groups to show this on the number line by starting at 4 and drawing an arrow three units to the left to the 1.

• Repeat this activity with the following problems: $\frac{7}{8} + 3\frac{6}{8}$; $5\frac{3}{4} - 4\frac{1}{4}$; $1\frac{4}{5} + 3\frac{2}{5}$; $5\frac{6}{10} + 1\frac{1}{2}$.

Challenge Have students create addition and subtraction exercises for rounding using combinations of mixed numbers and decimal amounts.

Multilevel Strategies

❶ Preproduction
Have students point to or say the mixed numbers on the number line.

Writing Encourage students to mark mixed numbers on the number line.

❷ ❸ Early Production and Speech Emergence
Ask students to name the rounded numbers aloud.

Writing Have students list all the rounded numbers on the number line.

❹ ❺ Intermediate and Advanced Fluency
Ask students to explain the rounding process using the number line.

Writing Have students make a list of the steps used in estimating sums and differences.

Name _____

Number Lines for Rounding

Show the following problems on the number lines: $\frac{7}{8} + 3\frac{6}{8}$; $5\frac{3}{4} - 4\frac{1}{4}$; $1\frac{4}{5} + 3\frac{2}{5}$; and $5\frac{6}{10} + 1\frac{1}{2}$.

1.

1   2   3   4   5   6   7   8   9   10

2.

1   2   3   4   5   6   7   8   9   10

3.

1   2   3   4   5   6   7   8   9   10

4.

1   2   3   4   5   6   7   8   9   10

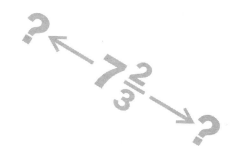

Problem Solving (sidebar, vertical)

Problem Solving
Reading for Math

SKILL: Choose an Operation
Model the skill using a word problem such as the following:

 Read

It was a very wet summer in Miami. $8\frac{3}{4}$ inches of rain fell in July, $9\frac{1}{4}$ inches fell in August, and $8\frac{1}{2}$ inches fell in September. How much rain fell altogether?

 Plan

I can add to find out the total rainfall during the summer.

 Solve

$8\frac{3}{4} + 9\frac{1}{4} + 8\frac{1}{2} = 26\frac{1}{2}$

$26\frac{1}{2}$ inches of rain fell during the months of July, August, and September.

Look Back

Is my answer reasonable?
Yes. If I rounded the numbers I would get $9 + 9 + 9 = 27$. So $26\frac{1}{2}$ is reasonable.
How did I know what operation to use?
The word "altogether" is a key word that lets me know I should add.

Distribute **Math Center Card 6A** to students.

Math Center Card

Reading for Math Skill
CHOOSE AN OPERATION • VERY SMALL ANIMALS INDIVIDUAL

The smallest rodent in the world is the northern pygmy mouse. This mouse's head and body measure $1\frac{7}{16}$ inches and its tail measures $2\frac{1}{4}$ inches.

The smallest primate in the world is the pygmy mouse lemur. This lemur's head and body measure $2\frac{1}{8}$ inches and its tail measures $5\frac{7}{16}$ inches.

Source: The Guinness Book of Records 2000

Answer these questions about these 2 animals. Explain how you decided whether to add or subtract.

1. How long is the northern pygmy mouse from the tip of its nose to the end of its tail?

2. How much longer is the pygmy mouse lemur's tail than the northern pygmy mouse's head and body?

3. How much shorter is the pygmy mouse lemur's head and body than the northern pygmy mouse's tail?

4. Write 2 questions that can be answered using the above information. Write 1 question that uses addition and 1 question that uses subtraction.

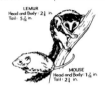

LEMUR
Head and Body: $2\frac{1}{8}$ in.
Tail: $5\frac{7}{16}$ in.

MOUSE
Head and Body: $1\frac{7}{16}$ in.
Tail: $2\frac{1}{4}$ in.

Math Center Card, Grade 5, Unit 6, 6A

STRATEGY: Write an Equation
Model the skill using a word problem such as the following:

 Read

Sid's class performed a play for the whole school. They practiced for $1\frac{1}{2}$ hours every day. They practiced for a total of 12 hours before the performance. How many days did they practice before the performance?

 Plan

I can write an equation to find the answer.

 Solve

Think: I know how many hours they practiced in all. I know how many hours each day. I can divide to find the answer.
$12 \div 1\frac{1}{2} = 12 \div \frac{3}{2} = 12 \times \frac{2}{3} = 8$
Sid's class practiced for 8 days.

 Look Back

Does my answer make sense?
Yes. I can multiply to check.
$8 \times 1\frac{1}{2} = 8 \times \frac{3}{2} = \frac{24}{2} = 12$

Distribute **Math Center Card 6B** to students.

Math Center Card

Problem Solving: Strategy
WRITE AN EQUATION • RADIO FRACTIONS PARTNERS

Write an equation to help you answer each question below. The first one is done for you. Use guess and check to help you find each missing number. Work with a partner.

1. A radio announcer has to fill 5 minutes of air time. If she plays a song that will last $3\frac{1}{4}$ minutes, how much time does she have left to fill?

   Think: $3\frac{1}{4} + \_\_ = 5$

   Try: $1\frac{1}{2}$
   $3\frac{1}{4} + 1\frac{1}{2}$
   $3\frac{1}{4} + 1\frac{1}{2} = 4\frac{3}{4}$

   Try: $1\frac{3}{4}$
   $3\frac{1}{4} + 1\frac{3}{4} = 4\frac{4}{4} = 5$

2. An announcer has $8\frac{1}{2}$ minutes to play a song, commercials, and read the weather. If she needs $1\frac{1}{2}$ minutes to read the weather, how long does she have for the song and commercials? Write an equation.

3. Two radio announcers have a morning radio show together. They have 15 minutes to play some songs, read the news, play commercials, and talk with each other. If the songs take $7\frac{1}{2}$ minutes, the commercials take $1\frac{1}{2}$ minutes, and the news takes 5 minutes, how long do they have to talk?

4. Write and solve your own problem. Share it with other students in the class.

Math Center Card, Grade 5, Unit 6, 6B

Assessment Checklist

	STUDENT NAMES												
SCHOOL:													
TEACHER: **SCHOOL YEAR:**													
Mark: + = Mastery √ = Satisfactory – = Needs Improvement													
LEVEL OF LANGUAGE PROFICIENCY (1–5)													
MATH OBJECTIVES													
• Add fractions and mixed numbers.													
• Identify and use addition properties with fractions.													
• Subtract fractions and mixed numbers.													
• Estimate sums and differences of mixed numbers.													
ESL/TESOL LISTENING/SPEAKING													
Demonstrate knowledge through application in a variety of contexts.													
Follow oral and written directions.													
Gather information orally and in writing.													
Interpret information presented visually.													
Listen to, speak, and write about subject matter.													
Participate in full-class and pair discussions.													
ESL/TESOL READING													
Read about subject matter information.													
Apply basic reading comprehension skills.													
Follow written directions, implicit and explicit.													
ESL WRITING													
Write to demonstrate comprehension.													
Write using spelling patterns and targeted English vocabulary.													

 **by Dinah Zike**

1 **Preproduction**
- Did students write the unit vocabulary?
- Did they copy the definitions?

2 **3** **Early Production and Speech Emergence**
- Did students label the tables correctly?
- Did they write the Vocabulary words?
- Did they copy the definitions?

4 **5** **Intermediate and Advanced Fluency**
- Did students write definitions for the unit vocabulary?
- Did they use correct spelling and grammar?

Add Fractions and Mixed Numbers	Like Denominators	Unlike Denominators
Fractions		
Mixed Numbers		

Subtract Fractions and Mixed Numbers	Like Denominators	Unlike Denominators
Fractions		
Mixed Numbers		

Planner

Multiply and Divide Fractions

LOG ON Visit **www.mmhmath.com**

Assessment
p. 131
• Assessment Checklist
• Foldables

Unit Activities		
• **Activity 1** Readiness Pattern Fractions, p. 118		• **Activity 3** Dare to Compare, p. 119
• **Activity 2** Biggest Is Best! p. 118		• **Activity 4** Model Division, p. 119

Lessons	Key Objectives	Vocabulary	Materials	Resources
READ TOGETHER "Matharena" by Vicki Young, pp. 116–117	**Math:** Multiply fractions and whole numbers. Add and subtract fractions. **ESL/TESOL:** Goal 2, Standards 2, 3.	cancels, consistent, distraction, invert, leftover, persistent, resistant, satisfaction		
UNIT WARM-UP Understanding Multiplying Fractions p. 120	**Math:** Multiply fractions and whole numbers. **ESL/TESOL:** Goal 1, Standard 2. Goal 2, Standard 2.	factors, fraction, mixed number, product, times, whole number	counters	**Overhead Manipulatives**
LESSON 1 Fractions and Whole Numbers pp. 122–123	**Math:** Multiply fractions and whole numbers. Estimate products of fractions and whole numbers. **ESL/TESOL:** Goal 2, Standards 1, 2.	compatible numbers, denominator, estimate, fraction, improper fraction, numerator	counters	Learning Resource 25
LESSON 2 Multiply Fractions pp. 124–125	**Math:** Multiply a fraction by a fraction. **ESL/TESOL:** Goal 2, Standard 2.	Associative Property, denominator, diagram, numerator	counters, crayons, egg cartons	Learning Resource 26
LESSON 3 Multiply Mixed Numbers pp. 126–127	**Math:** Multiply mixed numbers and whole numbers. Multiply fractions and mixed numbers. **ESL/TESOL:** Goal 2, Standard 1.	Distributive Property of Multiplication, improper fraction, mixed number	markers, pencils	Learning Resource 27 Teacher Tool 10
LESSON 4 Dividing Fractions pp. 128–129	**Math:** Divide fractions, mixed numbers, and whole numbers. **ESL/TESOL:** Goal 1, Standard 3. Goal 2, Standard 2.	dividend, divisor, quotient, reciprocal	calculators, rulers	Learning Resource 28
PROBLEM SOLVING p. 130 • Skill: Solve Multi-Step Problems • Strategy: Make an Organized List	Use skills and strategies to solve problems.			**Math Center Cards 7A, 7B**

English Vocabulary

Dear Family: Please help your child practice the key vocabulary words for this unit.

denominator the number below the bar in a fraction; the part of the fraction that tells how many equal parts are in the whole

fraction a number that names part of a whole or part of a group

greatest common factor (GCF) the greatest common factor of two or more numbers is the greatest whole number that is a common factor of the numbers

numerator the number above the bar in a fraction

round to find the nearest value of a number based on a given place

See **Math at Home Family Guide** for additional math vocabulary, activities, and games in English, Spanish, and Haitian Creole.

Vocabulario en español

Estimados familiares: Por favor ayuden a su hijo/a a practicar las palabras del vocabulario de esta unidad.

denominador número que se escribe debajo de la raya de una fracción; indica el total de partes iguales

fracción número que representa una parte de un todo o de un grupo

máximo común divisor el máximo común divisor de dos o más números es el mayor número entero que es factor común de los números

numerador número que se escribe sobre la raya de una fracción

redondear encontrar el valor más cercano a un número según el valor posicional dado

Vokabilè an kreyòl

Chè paran: Tanpri ede pitit la pratike mo vokabilè nan seksyon sa a.

denominatè nimewo ki anba liy nan yon fraksyon; pati fraksyon ki di kombyen pati egal ki gen nan yon gwo

fraksyon yon nimewo ki eksprime on pati nan yon nimewo ou byen nan yon gwoup

pi gwo faktè komen se pi gwo nimewo antye ki se yon faktè pou nimewo yo

nimeratè nimewo ki anlè ba fraksyon an

awondi kalkile valè ki pi pwòch on nimewo ak pozisyon chif yo

Matharena

by Vicki Young

 45 minutes

Math Objectives
- Multiply fractions and whole numbers.
- Add and Subtract Fractions.

ESL/TESOL Descriptors
- Listen to, speak, read, and write about subject matter information.
- Practice new language.

Reading Skill
- Main Idea and Supporting Details.

Vocabulary
cancels, consistent, distraction, invert, leftover, persistent, resistant, satisfaction

Before Reading

Build Background/Oral Language
If possible, play the original song "Macarena" and teach the dance to students.

Point to the title of the song, "Matharena." Underline the word *math*. Say: **Now we're going to learn a math song about fractions.** List the math operations and vocabulary mentioned in the song. Tell students to listen for them as you read the text.

During Reading

- Slowly read the text aloud. Track the words as you do so.
- Challenge children to raise their hands when they hear you say each operation word.
- As students become familiar with the song, invite them to chime in and say the last word of each line with you. Illustrate by pointing to the first three lines and saying: *resistant, consistent, persistent.*

Phonological/Phonemic Awareness
Write and say the words *fraction* and *action.* Underline the letters *–tion.* Emphasize the sound they make in combination and have students repeat. Return to the song and invite volunteers to identify other words with the same sound. *(satisfaction, distraction)*

After Reading

Distribute copies of the song to each student. Encourage them to box the word *math* every time they see it. Then challenge them to circle all the math words they can find. *(fractions, multiplying, factor, dividing, adding, common denominators, numerators)*

Music Sing the "Matharena" to the music. Invite students to perform the dance as they sing with you.

Assessment

Observe students' ability to recognize the math words in the song. See Assessment Checklist on page 131.

Multilevel Strategies

1 Preproduction
Say: **Show me the word multiplying.** Guide students to find this word in the lyrics of the song.

Writing Invite students to write this word and its operational sign.

2 3 Early Production and Speech Emergence
Point to the word *multiplication* in the song and ask: **Which operation is this?**

Writing Encourage students to write the names of all of the operations in the song.

4 5 Intermediate and Advanced Fluency
Say: **Name the operation words in the song.**

Writing Challenge students to write a multiplication sentence for you to solve.

Matharena

Lyrics by Vicki Young
Melody: "Macarena"

Math is FUN so don't be resistant,
Just learn the rules, the rules are consistent.
And most important, you must be persistent!
Do the matharena!

Don't give up when you work with fractions.
Look at the problem and decide on your action.
With the right answer, you'll feel the satisfaction.
Do the matharena!

Multiplying fractions, you can cancel if you factor,
As long as factors match that's what you're after.
The leftover factors must show up in your answer!
Do the matharena!

When you're dividing, invert the second fraction.
Go to verse three and work without distraction.
If every factor cancels, the answer "1" requires no action.
Do the matharena!

Adding fractions, get common denominators.
Multiply by missing factors to get the numerators.
Add numerators only, NOT denominators.
Do the matharena!

Activities

Activities

Readiness

ACTIVITY 1

INDIVIDUAL

Pattern Fractions

YOU NEED

crayons

markers

- Here are two ways to show the same multiplication sentence:

$\frac{1}{4} \times 16 = 4$. One fourth of the 16 shapes = 4 triangles.

What other multiplication sentence could you write for these two patterns?

- Draw patterns to show these multiplication problems. Use triangles, circles, trapezoids, hexagons, squares, or rectangles. Write a complete sentence for each.

1. $\frac{1}{5} \times 20$ **2.** $\frac{4}{5} \times 25$ **3.** $\frac{1}{7} \times 21$ **4.** $\frac{3}{7} \times 35$

5. $\frac{3}{8} \times 24$ **6.** $\frac{3}{4} \times 12$ **7.** $\frac{2}{3} \times 15$ **8.** $\frac{2}{3} \times 27$

Multiply Whole Number by a Fraction

ACTIVITY 2

PARTNERS

Biggest Is Best!

YOU NEED

spinner (0–9)

- Each player spins four times to get four numbers. (For zero, spin again.) Use your four digits to write two fractions. Record the digits as shown below.

$$\frac{\square}{\square} \times \frac{\square}{\square}$$

Find the product.

- The player with the greater product scores 1 point. Play until one partner reaches 7 points.

Variation 1: The player with the lower product scores 1 point.

Variation 2: The player with the product closer to $\frac{1}{2}$ scores 1 point.

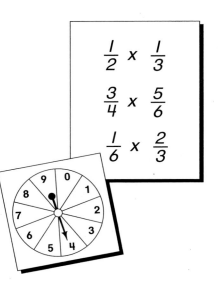

Multiply a Fraction by a Fraction

Game Zone

ACTIVITY 3

SMALL GROUP

Dare to Compare

YOU NEED

index cards

- **Group Leader:** You need an odd number of players for this game. Choose three or five students to play. Give each player index cards.

- **Each Player:** Write down a fraction on one of your cards. Do not show your number until everyone is ready. When all of the players show their cards, work together to put them in order from least to greatest. The player who has written the middle value wins the point. Any players who write equivalent fractions lose one point.

- The player who first scores 5 points wins.

Multiply Fractions

- ✂

ACTIVITY 4

INDIVIDUAL

Model Division

- Here's a way to show division of a whole number by a unit fraction. For example: $4 \div \frac{1}{3}$. Draw rectangles for the whole number, in this case, 4 rectangles.

Draw thirds in each rectangle. The total number of $\frac{1}{3}$ units is the quotient.

- Here is how to divide a fraction by another fraction. For example, $\frac{4}{10} \div \frac{2}{10}$. Draw $\frac{4}{10}$, that is four $\frac{1}{10}$ units. How many groups of $\frac{2}{10}$ are there? Use circles to show $\frac{4}{10} \div \frac{2}{10} = 2$ groups.

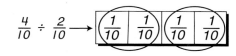

- Use models to show the following:

1. $6 \div \frac{1}{4}$ **2.** $4 \div \frac{1}{6}$ **3.** $7 \div \frac{1}{5}$

4. $5 \div \frac{1}{7}$ **5.** $\frac{4}{9} \div \frac{1}{9}$ **6.** $\frac{6}{8} \div \frac{2}{8}$ **7.** $\frac{4}{5} \div \frac{2}{5}$

Divide Fractions

Warm-Up

20 minutes

▶ **Key Strategy**
Use manipulatives

▶ **Format**
Whole class and small groups

▶ **Math Vocabulary**
factors, fraction, mixed number, product, times, whole number

▶ **Daily Vocabulary**
panda, zoo

▶ **Resource**
Overhead Manipulatives: Counters

▶ **Materials**
counters

LOG ON Visit **www.mmhmath.com** to find printable **Vocabulary Cards** that help build academic language.

Understanding Multiplying Fractions

Math Objective	ESL/TESOL Descriptors
■ Multiply fractions and whole numbers.	■ Describe, read about, or participate in a favorite activity. ■ Demonstrate knowledge through application in a variety of contexts.

Activate Prior Knowledge Draw two columns on the board. In the left column, list the words **whole number,** *improper fraction,* **mixed number,** and **fraction.** In the right column, write examples of each, in a different order. Call volunteers up to the board to match the words to the examples. Read aloud words and have students repeat them.

• Write subtraction and addition sentences with mixed numbers and like and unlike denominators; review how to add and subtract fractions. Then say: *We have added and subtracted fractions and mixed numbers. Now we are going to multiply them.*

Hands-on Lesson Elicit from students their experiences at zoos. Say: *Here is a story problem about a zoo. A zoo has 8 panda bears and wants to send $\frac{1}{4}$ of them to another zoo.*

• Divide students into small groups. Distribute counters to each group. Ask students to imagine that the counters are the pandas. Have them find $\frac{1}{4}$ of 8. You may want to use Counters from **Overhead Manipulatives** to model the problem.

• Guide students in separating 8 counters into 4 groups. Then ask: *How many pandas are in each group?* Elicit the answer of 2, or $\frac{1}{4}$ of 8. Tell students they have just multiplied using a fraction. Ask a volunteer to write the multiplication sentence: $\frac{1}{4} \times 8 = 2$.

• Remind students that the word *of* in a problem with fractions tells us to multiply. Say: *The problem said the zoo wants to send $\frac{1}{4}$ of the 8 pandas. That means $\frac{1}{4}$ times eight.* Here $\frac{1}{4}$ and 8 are the **factors,** and 2 is the **product.**

Multilevel Strategies

❶ Preproduction
Have students move the counters for their group.

❷❸ Early Production and Speech Emergence
Invite students to name the number in each group of counters.

❹❺ Intermediate and Advanced Fluency
Have students explain separating 8 counters into 4 groups of 2 to find $\frac{1}{4}$ of 8.

Procedure: Help students make these Foldables to write vocabulary words and definitions throughout the unit. Encourage students to use the Foldables as a study guide.

 **by Dinah Zike**

Half-Book

1. Provide each student with a sheet of paper. Have students fold the sheet in half like a hot dog, then fold the sheet again, 1" from the top.

2. Help your students unfold their papers and draw lines along the folds.

3. Have your students label the columns of their Foldables Half-Books.

Labels may include:

$\frac{2}{3}$ x 15

Step 1: Write the whole number as a fraction.
$\frac{2}{3}$ x $\frac{15}{1}$
Step 2: Multiply the numerators. Then multiply the denominators.
$\frac{2}{3}$ x $\frac{15}{1}$ = $\frac{30}{3}$
Step 3: Simplify.
$\frac{30}{3}$ = 10

Multiplying whole numbers by a fraction	Multiplying a fraction by a fraction

4. As your students work through the unit, have them take notes and record main ideas in the columns of their charts.

$\frac{2}{3}$ x $\frac{1}{4}$

Step 1: Multiply the numerators.
$\frac{2}{3}$ x $\frac{1}{4}$ = $\frac{2}{}$
Step 2: Multiply the denominators.
$\frac{2}{3}$ x $\frac{1}{4}$ = $\frac{2}{12}$
Step 3: Simplify.
$\frac{2}{12}$ = $\frac{1}{6}$

 **by Dinah Zike**

Half-Book

1. Provide each student with a sheet of paper. Have students fold the sheets in half like a hot dog, then fold the sheet again, 1" from the top.

2. Help your students unfold their papers and draw lines along the folds.

3. Have your students label the columns of their Foldables Half-Books.

Labels may include:

$4 \div \frac{1}{2}$

$\frac{1}{2} \bigm| \frac{1}{2}$ $\frac{1}{2} \bigm| \frac{1}{2}$

$\frac{1}{2} \bigm| \frac{1}{2}$ $\frac{1}{2} \bigm| \frac{1}{2}$

$4 \div \frac{1}{2} = 8$

Dividing whole numbers by a fraction	Dividing a fraction by a fraction

4. As your students work through the unit, have them take notes and record main ideas in the columns of their charts.

$\frac{3}{4} \div \frac{1}{8}$

Divide Using Reciprocals:
Step 1: Find the reciprocal of the divisor.
$\frac{1}{8} \diagdown \frac{8}{1}$
Step 2: Multiply by the reciprocal of the divisor.
$\frac{3}{4} \div \frac{1}{8} = \frac{3}{4}$ x $\frac{8}{1}$
Step 3: Simplify.

$\frac{3}{\underset{1}{4}}$ x $\frac{\overset{2}{8}}{1} = \frac{3}{1}$ x $\frac{2}{1} = \frac{6}{1} = 6$

Lesson 1

  45 minutes

▶ **Key Strategy**
Use manipulatives

▶ **Format**
Whole class and
small groups

▶ **Math Vocabulary**
compatible numbers,
denominator, estimate,
fraction, improper fractions,
numerator, round

▶ **Daily Vocabulary**
draw, number line

▶ **Resource**
Learning Resource 25

Materials
• counters

Assessment

Check students' mastery of
multiplying fractions as they
complete the lesson. See page
131 for Assessment Checklist.
Remind students to work on
their Foldables.

Home Connection

Have students ask their family
members to help them multiply
a fraction of something at home,
such as $\frac{1}{2}$ the number of books
on a shelf or boxes in the
kitchen cabinet. Have them
share the results with the class.

Fractions and Whole Numbers

Math Objectives	**ESL/TESOL Descriptors**
■ Multiply fractions and whole numbers. ■ Estimate products of fractions and whole numbers.	■ Follow oral and written directions, implicit and explicit. ■ Demonstrate knowledge through application in a variety of contexts.

Activate Prior Knowledge Review the problem students worked out in the Warm-Up lesson. Ask: *How did we find out how much is $\frac{1}{2}$ of 8 pandas?* (*by using counters*) Say: *Now let's look at other ways to multiply by fractions.*

Hands-on Lesson Write 4×2 on the board and draw a number line from 1–8 with lines for every half. Have a volunteer help you count out 4 twos and mark the line. Point out that the product of multiplying by whole numbers is a larger number. (8) Have students copy your examples and record them in their journals.

• Write $4 \times \frac{1}{2}$ on the board and ask another student to count 4 halves. Elicit that the product of multiplying by fractions is a smaller number (2). Explain that when you multiply a number by a fraction, the product is less than the whole-number factor.

• Say: *Now let's multiply some larger numbers with fractions. We can estimate to help get the answer.*

• Distribute Learning Resource 25: Cookie Fractions. Read the problem together and help students to find a **compatible number,** a number that can be easily divided and multiplied, to help them to estimate. After they estimate, work through the process of multiplying a whole number and a fraction. Review how to convert the whole number to an **improper fraction** by making 1 the denominator. Then have them multiply **numerators** and **denominators.**

Challenge Ask students to create word problems with fractions of whole numbers and illustrate them.

Multilevel Strategies

❶ Preproduction
Ask: *Which number is your estimate?*

Writing Encourage students to write the numeral and word for the estimate.

❷ ❸ Early Production and Speech Emergence
Have students tell their estimates and answers. Ask: *Was your estimate close?*

Writing Have students write the estimates and actual numbers.

❹ ❺ Intermediate and Advanced Fluency
Ask: *How did you estimate that number?*

Writing Ask students to write the steps to estimate products.

Name _____

Cookie Fractions

There are 32 cookies. Six people will eat them. They can each have $\frac{1}{6}$ of the cookies. How many cookies will each person get?

Estimate $\frac{1}{6}$ of 32. About how many cookies will each person get?

1. Find a number that is close to 32 and compatible with 6.

_____

2. Divide the compatible number by 6. _____

Now multiply $\frac{1}{6} \times 32$ to find the exact answer.

3. Change 32 to an improper fraction. _____

4. Write the new multiplication sentence. _____

5. Multiply numerators and denominators. _____

6. Divide to simplify the answer. _____

Lesson 3

45 minutes

▶ **Key Strategy**
Use charts and graphs

▶ **Format**
Whole class and individual

▶ **Math Vocabulary**
Distributive Property of Multiplication, improper fraction, mixed number

▶ **Daily Vocabulary**
box, top, wrapping paper

▶ **Resources**
Learning Resource 27
Teacher Tool 10

Materials
• markers
• pencils

Assessment

Check students' mastery of fractions as they complete the lesson. See Assessment Checklist on page 131. Remind students to work on their Foldables.

Home Connection

Have students find things at home that have mixed fractions they can multiply (for example, doubling recipes). Students can make a list and create and solve multiplication sentences. Invite students to share their lists and problems with the class.

Multiply Mixed Numbers

Math Objectives	**ESL/TESOL Descriptors**
■ Multiply mixed numbers and whole numbers.	■ Follow oral and written directions, implicit and explicit.
■ Multiply fractions and mixed numbers.	■ Gather information orally and in writing.

Activate Prior Knowledge Bring a box and hold up some wrapping paper. Say: *I have a box to wrap. I have $1\frac{1}{2}$ feet of wrapping paper. The top of the box uses $\frac{1}{4}$ of the paper. How much paper does the top use?* Invite a student to write the multiplication sentence, $1\frac{1}{2} \times \frac{1}{4}$. Ask: *What kind of numbers are these?* Elicit that one is a **mixed number** and the other is a fraction. Ask: *Will you get a larger number or a smaller number if you multiply a mixed number by a fraction?* (The product will be smaller than the mixed number. You only need part of the wrapping paper for the top of the box).

Hands-on Lesson Discuss how to multiply a mixed number by a fraction. Explain what is an **improper fraction.** Ask a student to change the mixed number into an improper fraction ($1\frac{1}{2} = \frac{3}{2}$). Then ask other students to write the new sentence ($\frac{3}{2} \times \frac{1}{4}$) and solve.

• Show another way to do the same problem, using the **Distributive Property of Multiplication:** $1\frac{1}{2} \times \frac{1}{4}$ becomes $(1 \times \frac{1}{4}) + (\frac{1}{2} \times \frac{1}{4}) = \frac{1}{4} + \frac{1}{8} = \frac{3}{8}$. Distribute fraction strips (Teacher Tool 10) to pairs and have them show the new multiplication sentence with the strips.

• Distribute Learning Resource 27: Multiplying at the Zoo. The problem requires multiplying mixed numbers by whole numbers. Students can use the Distributive Property, or convert the whole numbers and mixed numbers to fractions. Divide students into groups to complete the page, showing their work. (Answers for 1, starting 200: Next year, 300; Year 2, 450; Year 3, 675)

Challenge Have students create and solve mixed-number multiplications using 2-digit whole numbers.

Multilevel Strategies

1 **Preproduction**
Ask students to point to or say the improper fraction.

Writing Have students write the numerals and the word for an improper fraction.

2 **3** **Early Production and Speech Emergence**
Ask students to name the mixed number and the fraction.

Writing Invite students to write a multiplication sentence using mixed numbers.

4 **5** **Intermediate and Advanced Fluency**
Have students explain two ways to multiply mixed numbers.

Writing Encourage students to write the steps for one way to multiply mixed numbers.

Name _____

Cookie Fractions

There are 32 cookies. Six people will eat them. They can each have $\frac{1}{6}$ of the cookies. How many cookies will each person get?

Estimate $\frac{1}{6}$ of 32. About how many cookies will each person get?

1. Find a number that is close to 32 and compatible with 6.

_____

2. Divide the compatible number by 6. _____

Now multiply $\frac{1}{6} \times 32$ to find the exact answer.

3. Change 32 to an improper fraction. _____

4. Write the new multiplication sentence. _____

5. Multiply numerators and denominators. _____

6. Divide to simplify the answer. _____

Lesson 2

35 minutes

▶ **Key Strategy**
Use visuals

▶ **Format**
Whole class and individual

▶ **Math Vocabulary**
Associative Property, diagram, denominator, model, numerator, shaded section, double shaded

▶ **Daily Vocabulary**
recipe

▶ **Resource**
Learning Resource 26

Materials
- counters
- crayons
- egg cartons

Assessment

Check students' mastery of fraction multiplication as they complete the lesson. See Assessment Checklist on page 131. Remind students to work on their Foldables.

Home Connection

Have students use a model to solve a fraction multiplication sentence with family members and tell the class how they solved it.

Multiply Fractions

Math Objective	**ESL/TESOL Descriptors**
■ Multiply a fraction by a fraction.	■ Represent information visually. ■ Listen to, speak, read, and write about subject matter information.

Activate Prior Knowledge Review compatible numbers. Hold up the recipe from Unit 6 (p. 105, Learning Resource 21). Read: $\frac{3}{4}$ *of a cup of brown sugar.* Say: *I want to make $\frac{1}{2}$ of the recipe. How much sugar do I need?* Elicit that you can multiply fractions to find the answer.

Hands-on Lesson Ask a student to write the multiplication sentence for the recipe problem: $\frac{1}{2} \times \frac{3}{4} =$ ____. Have students multiply the **numerators** and then the **denominators**. Ask: *How is multiplying fractions different than adding them?* Explain that you don't need to find a common denominator. When adding, we only add numerators, but when multiplying, we multiply the numerators and then denominators (even with like denominators). Point out that when you multiply two fractions, the product is smaller than both fractions. To show the **Associative Property,** have students multiply $\frac{3}{4} \times \frac{1}{2}$ and ask if the product is the same.

- Explain that we can also use **models** to multiply fractions. Divide students into groups. Distribute egg cartons and counters. Write $\frac{1}{2} \times \frac{1}{6}$. Ask a student to cover up $\frac{1}{2}$ of the egg carton with a piece of paper. Another student puts counters in $\frac{1}{6}$ of the uncovered cups. Ask: *What fraction of the 12 cups have counters?* ($\frac{1}{12}$)

- Distribute Learning Resource 26: Multiplying Fractions. Have students color $\frac{2}{3}$ of the **diagram.** Now have them show $\frac{3}{4} \times \frac{2}{3}$ by coloring three of the four parts in the **shaded section** with another color. Three out of the six total boxes are **double shaded,** so the answer is $\frac{3}{6}$ (or $\frac{1}{2}$ in simplest form).

Challenge Have students write a fraction word problem and show how to solve it using a picture and an equation.

Multilevel Strategies

❶ Preproduction
Say: *Show me $\frac{1}{2} \times \frac{1}{6}$ with the egg carton.*

Writing Invite students to write a multiplication sentence.

❷ ❸ Early Production and Speech Emergence
Ask: *What multiplication sentence does this model show?*

Writing Have them write several multiplication sentences as you say them.

❹ ❺ Intermediate and Advanced Fluency
Have students explain how to multiply fractions.

Writing Challenge students to write the steps of multiplying fractions.

Name _____

Multiplying Fractions

Color $\frac{2}{3}$ of the rectangles. Then color $\frac{3}{4}$ of $\frac{2}{3}$ with another color.

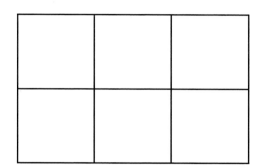

$$\frac{2}{3} \times \frac{3}{4} = \underline{\hspace{2cm}}$$

Color $\frac{3}{4}$ of the rectangles. Then color $\frac{1}{2}$ of $\frac{3}{4}$ with another color.

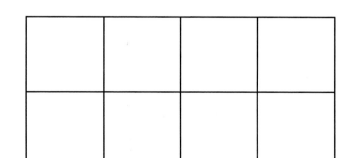

$$\frac{1}{2} \times \frac{3}{4} = \underline{\hspace{2cm}}$$

Lesson 3

 45 minutes

▶ **Key Strategy**
Use charts and graphs

▶ **Format**
Whole class and individual

▶ **Math Vocabulary**
Distributive Property of Multiplication, improper fraction, mixed number

▶ **Daily Vocabulary**
box, top, wrapping paper

▶ **Resources**
Learning Resource 27
Teacher Tool 10

Materials
- markers
- pencils

Assessment

Check students' mastery of fractions as they complete the lesson. See Assessment Checklist on page 131. Remind students to work on their Foldables.

Home Connection

Have students find things at home that have mixed fractions they can multiply (for example, doubling recipes). Students can make a list and create and solve multiplication sentences. Invite students to share their lists and problems with the class.

Multiply Mixed Numbers

Math Objectives	**ESL/TESOL Descriptors**
■ Multiply mixed numbers and whole numbers.	■ Follow oral and written directions, implicit and explicit.
■ Multiply fractions and mixed numbers.	■ Gather information orally and in writing.

Activate Prior Knowledge Bring a box and hold up some wrapping paper. Say: *I have a box to wrap. I have $1\frac{1}{2}$ feet of wrapping paper. The top of the box uses $\frac{1}{4}$ of the paper. How much paper does the top use?* Invite a student to write the multiplication sentence, $1\frac{1}{2} \times \frac{1}{4}$. Ask: *What kind of numbers are these?* Elicit that one is a **mixed number** and the other is a fraction. Ask: *Will you get a larger number or a smaller number if you multiply a mixed number by a fraction?* (The product will be smaller than the mixed number. You only need part of the wrapping paper for the top of the box).

Hands-on Lesson Discuss how to multiply a mixed number by a fraction. Explain what is an **improper fraction.** Ask a student to change the mixed number into an improper fraction ($1\frac{1}{2} = \frac{3}{2}$). Then ask other students to write the new sentence ($\frac{3}{2} \times \frac{1}{4}$) and solve.

- Show another way to do the same problem, using the **Distributive Property of Multiplication:** $1\frac{1}{2} \times \frac{1}{4}$ becomes $(1 \times \frac{1}{4}) + (\frac{1}{2} \times \frac{1}{4}) = \frac{1}{4} + \frac{1}{8} = \frac{3}{8}$. Distribute fraction strips (Teacher Tool 10) to pairs and have them show the new multiplication sentence with the strips.

- Distribute Learning Resource 27: Multiplying at the Zoo. The problem requires multiplying mixed numbers by whole numbers. Students can use the Distributive Property, or convert the whole numbers and mixed numbers to fractions. Divide students into groups to complete the page, showing their work. *(Answers for 1, starting 200: Next year, 300; Year 2, 450; Year 3, 675)*

Challenge Have students create and solve mixed-number multiplications using 2-digit whole numbers.

Multilevel Strategies

❶ Preproduction
Ask students to point to or say the improper fraction.

Writing Have students write the numerals and the word for an improper fraction.

❷❸ Early Production and Speech Emergence
Ask students to name the mixed number and the fraction.

Writing Invite students to write a multiplication sentence using mixed numbers.

❹❺ Intermediate and Advanced Fluency
Have students explain two ways to multiply mixed numbers.

Writing Encourage students to write the steps for one way to multiply mixed numbers.

Name _____

Multiplying at the Zoo

Write the number of animals for each year.

A zoo has 200 animals. Each year it will add $1\frac{1}{2}$ times the number from the year before. How many animals will there be the third year? What if the zoo started with 120? 80? 40?

NOW	YEAR 1	YEAR 2	YEAR 3
200			
120			
80			
40			

Show your work

Lesson 4

 45 minutes

▶ **Key Strategy**
Use charts and graphs

▶ **Format**
Whole class and student pairs

▶ **Math Vocabulary**
dividend, divisor, quotient, reciprocal

▶ **Daily Vocabulary**
inches, ruler

▶ **Resource**
Learning Resource 28

Materials
- calculators
- rulers

Assessment

Check students' mastery of fractions as they complete the lesson. See Assessment Checklist on page 131. Remind students to work on their Foldables.

Home Connection

Encourage students to find fractions in magazines and in supermarket flyers. Encourage them to use those fractions in division sentences for the class to solve.

Dividing Fractions

Math Objective	**ESL/TESOL Descriptors**
■ Divide fractions, mixed numbers, and whole numbers.	■ Practice new language. ■ Compare and contrast information.

Activate Prior Knowledge Review math vocabulary such as *improper fraction, mixed number,* and *Distributive Property.* Draw a circle and divide it into 4 parts. Ask: **How many parts are there?** Ask students to make a multiplication sentence about the picture. ($4 \times \frac{1}{4} = 1$) Then ask them to make a division sentence. ($4 \div 1 = \frac{1}{4}$) Remind students that multiplication and division are related operations.

Hands-on Lesson Review the vocabulary of division. Write a division sentence and ask volunteers to identify the **dividend, divisor,** and **quotient.**

- Distribute rulers and Learning Resource 28. Review the $\frac{1}{4}, \frac{1}{2}, \frac{1}{8}$ inch markings on rulers. Each marking is a fraction of one inch.

- Divide the class into pairs. Ask them to use their rulers to complete the problems. For example, students will count out how many $\frac{1}{2}$-inch increments there are in 7 inches. Have them use the first line on the sheet as a guide.

- Ask: **How are all the dividends the same?** *(All are whole numbers.)* **Are all the divisors the same?** *(Some are fractions and some are mixed numbers.)* **How do the quotients compare to the dividends?** *(All are greater.)*

- Take one of the division sentences from the page and show how to solve it without using the ruler. Discuss how to make **reciprocals,** one of two numbers whose product is 1, by switching the numerator and the denominator (for example, $\frac{1}{8}$ is the reciprocal of $\frac{8}{1}$). Ask students to find the reciprocal of each divisor on their page. To divide by a fraction, we multiply by its reciprocal. Demonstrate with one of the sentences: $2 \div \frac{1}{2} = 2 \times \frac{2}{1} = 4$.

Cultural Link Ask students to show division steps used in most Spanish-speaking countries.

Multilevel Strategies

1 Preproduction
Have students show you the dividend and the divisor on their rulers.

Writing Ask students to fill in the empty spaces as their partner says the numbers.

2 3 Early Production and Speech Emergence
Ask: **What is the reciprocal of $\frac{1}{8}$?**

Writing Have students label a division sentence.

4 5 Intermediate and Advanced Fluency
Ask: **How do you make a reciprocal fraction?**

Writing Ask students to write an example of a reciprocal.

Name _____

Fractions Rule

Fill in the blanks.

How Many	Dividend	Dividend	Quotient	Division Sentence
$\frac{1}{2}$ inch in 2 inches	2	$\frac{1}{2}$	4	$2 \div \frac{1}{2} = 4$
$\frac{1}{2}$ inch in 7 inches				
$\frac{1}{4}$ inch in 3 inches				
$\frac{3}{4}$ inch in $3\frac{3}{4}$ inches				
$\frac{1}{4}$ inch in $1\frac{1}{2}$ inches				

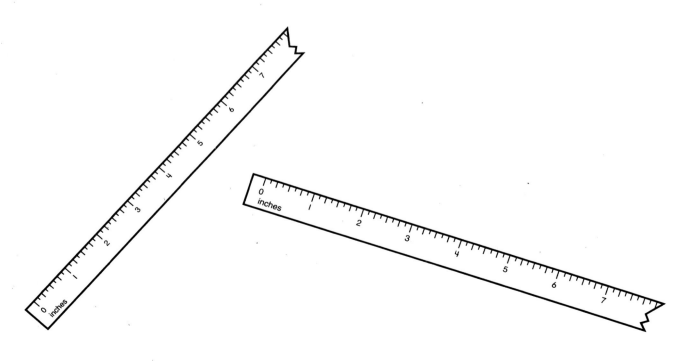

Problem Solving
Reading for Math

Read → Plan → Solve → Look Back

Remind students of
the basic steps
of problem solving.

SKILL: Solve Multi-Step Problems
Model the skill using a word problem such as:

 Read

Jenny makes 15 brownies in each batch. She can bake 3 batches a day. She promised to have 250 brownies to sell at the fair. If she bakes for 5 days, will she have enough?

 Plan

First I can multiply to find how many brownies she makes a day. Then I can multiply to find how many brownies she can make in 5 days.

 Solve

3 x 15 = 45. Jenny can make 45 brownies a day. 45 x 5 = 225. Jenny promised 250 brownies. She can make 225 brownies in 5 days. She will not have enough brownies to keep her promise.

 Look Back

Does my answer make sense? Yes.

Distribute **Math Center Card 7A** to students.

Math Center Card 7A

Reading for Math Skill

SOLVE MULTI-STEP PROBLEMS • WALKING HOME

Students at P.S. 10 can either join the band or play sports after school. Of the 30 students in Mr. Gutierrez's class, ⅓ are in the band and ⅖ play sports. The rest of the students are not in an after-school activity.

Of the students who do an activity, ⅓ walk home. The other ⅔ ride a bus.

How many students walk home after their activities?

1. Make a plan. Write the steps needed to solve this problem.

2. Follow your plan to solve the problem.

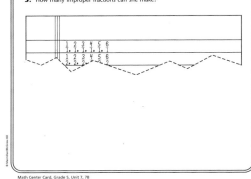

? ? ?

Math Center Card, Grade 5, Unit 7, 7A

STRATEGY: Make an Organized List
Model the strategy using a word problem such as:

 Read

Freda has red, blue, green, and yellow beads. She wants to make friendship pins. Each pin will have 3 beads of 2 colors. She wants every pin to be different. How many different pins can she make?

 Plan

I can make an organized list to see all the combinations. I will put the doubles first to help me organize.

 Solve

red, red, blue; red, red, green; red, red, yellow; blue, blue, red; blue, blue, green; blue, blue, yellow; green, green, red; green, green, blue; green, green, yellow; yellow, yellow, red; yellow, yellow, blue; yellow, yellow, green
Freda can make 12 different pins.

 Look Back

How can I be sure I found all the combinations? I can look at the organized list.

Distribute **Math Center Card 7B** to students.

Math Center Card 7B

Problem Solving: Strategy

MAKE AN ORGANIZED LIST • NUMBER CUBE FRACTIONS

You need: a red number cube and a white number cube (optional)

Maggie is using 2 number cubes to make fractions. She tosses a red number cube and a white number cube. She writes the red number as the numerator and the white number as the denominator.

Make an organized list to help you answer the questions below. List all of the fractions that Maggie can make with the 2 number cubes; then, go through the list to answer the questions.

1. How many proper fractions can she make?

2. How many fractions can she make that are equal to 1?

3. How many improper fractions can she make?

Math Center Card, Grade 5, Unit 7, 7B

Assessment Checklist

	STUDENT NAMES										
SCHOOL:											
TEACHER:　　　**SCHOOL YEAR:**											
Mark: + = Mastery ✓ = Satisfactory – = Needs Improvement											
LEVEL OF LANGUAGE PROFICIENCY (1–5)											
MATH OBJECTIVES											
• Multiply fractions, mixed numbers, and whole numbers.											
• Estimate products of fractions and whole numbers.											
• Multiply a fraction by a fraction.											
• Divide fractions, mixed numbers, and whole numbers.											
ESL/TESOL LISTENING/SPEAKING											
Compare and contrast information.											
Describe, read about, or participate in a favorite activity.											
Follow oral and written directions, implicit and explicit.											
Listen to, speak, read, and write about subject matter information .											
Practice new language.											
Demonstrate knowledge through application in a variety of contexts.											
ESL/TESOL READING											
Read about subject matter information.											
Apply basic reading comprehension skills.											
Follow written directions, implicit and explicit.											
ESL WRITING											
Write to demonstrate comprehension.											
Write using spelling patterns and targeted English vocabulary.											

 **by Dinah Zike**

❶ Preproduction
- Did students write the unit vocabulary?
- Did they copy the definitions?

❷❸ Early Production and Speech Emergence
- Did students label the tabs correctly?
- Did they wrtie the unit vocabulary?
- Did they copy the definitions?

❹❺ Intermediate and Advanced Fluency
- Did students write definitions for the unit vocabulary?
- Did they use correct spelling and grammar?

Multiplying whole numbers by a fraction	Multiplying a fraction by a fraction

Dividing whole numbers by a fraction	Dividing a fraction by a fraction

Planner

Measurement

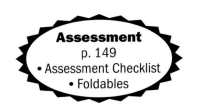

Unit Activities	• **Activity 1** Readiness Name That Time, p. 136	• **Activity 3** Measure Race, p. 137
	• **Activity 2** Let's Measure, p. 136	• **Activity 4** Metric Stairs, p. 137

Lessons	Key Objectives	Vocabulary	Materials	Resources
READ TOGETHER "Measuring," pp. 134–135	**Math:** Convert units of measurement. **ESL/TESOL:** Goal 2, Standard 2.	carat, coral, culture, gem, gram, measure, metric, unit, weight	coffee can, pictures of gemstone jewelry, scissors	Graphic Organizer 2
UNIT WARM-UP Understanding Measurement p. 138	**Math:** Choose appropriate units of measurement. Convert units of measurement. **ESL/TESOL:** Goal 1, Standard 3.	capacity, length, mass, temperature, time, weight	bottles, calendars, clocks, containers, measuring cups	Teacher Tools 12, 13, 15
LESSON 1 Time pp. 140–141	**Math:** Convert and compute units of time. Find elapsed time. **ESL/TESOL:** Goal 2, Standard 2.	elapsed time	brass fasteners, cardboard, glue, pen, pencil, scissors	Learning Resource 29 Teacher Tool 12
LESSON 2 Customary Measurement pp. 142–143	**Math:** Choose appropriate units, estimate and measure. Convert customary units. **ESL/TESOL:** Goal 2, Standard 1.	cup, fluid ounce, feet/ foot, gallon, inch, mile, nonstandard, ounce, pint, pound, quart, yard	class objects, measuring cups, ruler, scale, yardstick	Learning Resource 30
LESSON 3 Metric Measurement pp. 144–145	**Math:** Choose appropriate metric units of length and mass. Convert metric units. **ESL/TESOL:** Goal 2, Standard 2.	centimeter, gram, kilogram, kilometer, liter, mass, metric, milliliter, millimeter	classroom objects, metric ruler, metric scale, meter stick	Learning Resource 31 Teacher Tools 13 and 15
LESSON 4 Measure Temperature pp. 146–147	**Math:** Convert units of temperature. Compare and order integers. **ESL/TESOL:** Goal 2, Standard 2.	Celsius, degree, Fahrenheit, integer, negative number, positive number	Celsius and Fahrenheit thermometers, pencils or pens	Learning Resource 32
PROBLEM SOLVING p. 148 • Skill: Check for Reasonableness • Strategy: Draw a Diagram	Use skills and strategies to solve problems.			**Math Center Cards 8A, 8B**

English Vocabulary

Dear Family: Please help your child practice the key vocabulary words for this unit.

capacity the amount the inside of a container can hold, measured in units of liquid measure

degree (˚) a unit for measuring temperature

direct measure a way to obtain the measure of an object by using measuring devices

elapsed time the amount of time that passes from the start of an activity to the end of the activity

indirect measure the measurement of an object through the known measure of another object

integer a positive or negative whole number or 0

mass the amount of matter in an object

negative number a number less than 0

opposite integers two different integers that are the same distance from 0 on a number line

positive number a number greater than 0

Vocabulario en español

Estimados familiares: Por favor ayuden a su hijo/a a practicar las palabras del vocabulario de esta unidad.

capacidad la cantidad que puede contener un recipiente, expresado en unidades de medida de líquidos

grado (˚) unidad usada para medir la temperatura

medición directa una forma de medir un objeto mediante el uso de instrumentos de medición

tiempo transcurrido tiempo que pasa desde el principio hasta el fin de una actividad

medición indirecta medición de un objeto usando la medida conocida de otro objeto

entero número entero positivo o negativo ó 0

masa cantidad de materia que contiene un objeto

número negativo número menor que 0

enteros opuestos dos enteros diferentes que están a la misma distancia de 0 en una recta numérica

número positivo número mayor que 0

Vokabilè an kreyòl

Chè paran: Tanpri ede pitit la pratike mo vokabilè nan seksyon sa a.

kapasite kantite yon veso ka kenbe, lè-w mezire nan mezi an likid

degre (˚) yon inite mezi tanperati

vrè mezi yon fason pou jwenn mezi yon bagay lè-w itilize yon enstriman mezi

entèval kantite tan ki pase depi koumansman ak finisman yon aktivite

mezi endirèk mezire yon bagay ak mezi yon lòt bagay ou konnen

nimewo pwen yon nimewo antye pozitf osnon negatif osnon 0

volim kantite matyè nan yon bagay

nimewo negatif yon nimewo ki pi piti pase 0

nimewo pwen opoze de pwen diferan ki gen menm distans sot nan zewo nan liy nimewote-a

nimewo pozitif pi gwo pase 0

Measuring

 45 minutes

Math Objective
- Convert units of measurement.

ESL/TESOL Descriptors
- Listen to, speak, read, and write about subject matter information.
- Ask and answer questions.

Reading Skill
- Compare and Contrast.

Vocabulary
carat, coffee, coral, gems, gram, jewel, measure, metric, unit, weight

Before Reading

Build Background/Oral Language
Invite a student to hold a paper clip in one hand, a book in the other. Ask: **Which item is heavier?** Invite the class to describe how the student came to his/her decision. Ask: **Are there other ways to find out which item weighs more?** Explain that a scale could be used.

During Reading

- As you read, clarify the meanings of vocabulary words. Hold up a picture of gemstone jewelry and explain that the gem can be measured in *carats*.

- Allow students to hold a coffee can. Ask them to imagine how heavy a *sack* of coffee is. Distinguish that heavy objects are measured in kilograms, light objects are measured in grams.

Phonological/Phonemic Awareness
Write and say: ***Equivalent, carat, sack, kilogram.*** Identify the sound these words share. (*/k/*) Circle the letter(s) in each word that make this sound. (*q, c, ck, k*) Find similar words in the reading.

After Reading

Draw a word web (Graphic Organizer 2). Ask students to identify the main idea of the text and write *Measuring Weight* in the center circle. Guide students to describe the ways weight is measured in the reading. Add *seeds, carat, kilogram, gram* to the outer circles of the web. Invite students to add other units of measure they know.

Art Pass out magazines, scissors, glue. Have students cut out pictures of objects that look heavy or light. Show one piece of chart paper labeled *Kilograms,* another labeled *Grams.* Help the class to glue their items to the paper based on their unit of measure.

Assessment

Observe students in group activities. See Assessment Checklist on page 149.

Multilevel Strategies

1 Preproduction
Ask: **What measurement would you use to describe this?** Show students a picture of a gemstone and have them point to the word *carat* on the chart.

Writing Encourage students to draw and label a gemstone and its unit of measurement.

2 3 Early Production and Speech Emergence
Ask: **What unit of measurement would you use to describe a sack of coffee?** Encourage children to respond *kilogram.*

Writing Invite students to write each unit of measurement they learned about in the text.

4 5 Intermediate and Advanced Fluency
Say: **Name the units of measurement we read about. Name an item you can describe with each measurement.**

Writing Ask children to complete this sentence: *A (_) can be measured in (_).*

Measuring

In the Middle East the first units of measure came from the plant world. Seeds were a popular unit of weight. The Arabic word *qirat* (KEY-raht) means the seed of the coral tree. *Qirats* were used for thousands of years to measure the weight of precious gems. Today, we say *carat*. A carat is still the unit of measure by weight for jewels. In 1913, jewelers around the world agreed that a carat would be equivalent to 200 milligrams.

Special units of weight have been used in many cultures for measuring particular products. For example, in Costa Rica a *saco de café* (SAH-co day CAH-fay), or sack of coffee, was equivalent to 69 kilograms. Today, most products around the world are measured using the metric units of gram and kilogram.

Activities

ACTIVITY 1

PARTNERS

Name That Time

YOU NEED
construction paper
scissors

- Work together to make a model clock. Draw and cut out a clock face and two clock hands.

- **Player 1:** Set a time on the clock. Fill in the blank in the following statement to state a word problem to Player 2:

"It is now (time set on clock). I have just spent _____ hours and _____ minutes (*some activity such as cleaning my room, doing homework, or reading a book*). What time was it when I began the activity?"

- **Player 2:** Use the clock to calculate the time Player 1 began the activity. Set the clock at that time.

- Player 2 gets one point if correct. Switch roles and play again. Play ten rounds. The player with the most points wins. If there is a tie, continue playing until one player wins.

© Macmillan/McGraw-Hill

Time

ACTIVITY 2

SMALL GROUP

Let's Measure

YOU NEED
metric ruler
metric measuring tape

- **As a Group:** With partners, choose ten objects in the room to measure, for example, a book, a pencil, a desk, or a stapler. Use the *nearest measure*. For example, *the nearest millimeter* for the pencil and *the nearest centimeter* for the desk.

- **Individually:** Silently estimate the length, width, or height of each object. Write your estimates down.

- Measure the ten objects with your partners. Determine the difference between the actual measurement and your estimate for each object. The student whose estimate is closest to the actual measurement of an object scores one point. The student with the most points wins.

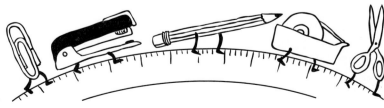

© Macmillan/McGraw-Hill

Explore Metric Length

ACTIVITY 3

PARTNERS

Measure Race

- Copy the game board as shown. Make sure your playing pieces can fit in each box.

- Take turns rolling the number cube. Move the number of spaces shown on the cube. Name an item that should be measured in that unit. If you can't name an item, you lose a turn.

- The first player to reach the end wins.

- As a challenge, after rolling the number cube, name an item whose capacity or mass would be about the number you rolled.

YOU NEED

number cube

2 different colored cubes or counters

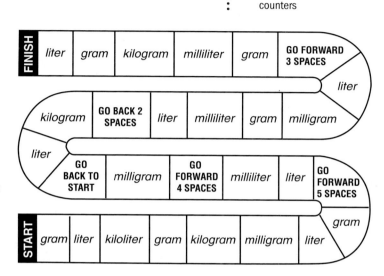

Metric Capacity and Mass

✂ -

ACTIVITY 4

PARTNERS

Metric Stairs

- Prepare the cards and spinner. Spin the spinner for the basic unit. Choose a card for the prefix of the basic unit.

- Toss the number cube. This is your starting measurement.

- Now choose another card for another prefix. Rewrite the starting measurement with the new unit.

- Switch roles. Continue for 10 turns.

Example:

You spin *meter*.

You choose *deci*.

You toss a 4.

You choose *kilo*.

So, 4 dm = 0.0004 km.

YOU NEED

6 index cards labeled with prefixes *kilo-, hecto-, deka-, deci-, centi-,* and *milli-*

spinner labeled *gram, meter, liter*

number cube

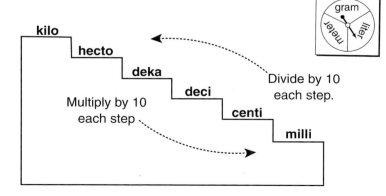

Metric Conversions

Understanding Measurement

 **25 minutes**

▶ **Key Strategy**
Use realia

▶ **Format**
Whole class

▶ **Math Vocabulary**
capacity, length, mass, temperature, time, weight

▶ **Daily Vocabulary**
bottles, containers, signs

▶ **Resources**
Teacher Tools 12, 13, 15

▶ **Materials**
calendars, clocks and watches, food and drink containers, liter bottles, measuring cups, measuring tape, meter sticks, quart containers, rulers, scales, thermometers, yardsticks

---

Math Objectives	**ESL/TESOL Descriptors**
■ Choose appropriate units of measurement.	■ Practice new language.
■ Convert units of measurement.	■ Actively connect new information to information previously learned.

Activate Prior Knowledge Hold up a ruler. Ask: *What can I measure with this? (length of objects)* Point to the wall clock. Ask: *What do we measure with a clock? (time, hours, minutes)* Hold up a measuring cup. Ask: *What does this measure? (how much liquid)* Also ask about a scale and a thermometer.

Hands-on Lesson On the board, list the types of measurements, and words that describe each: **length** (how long), **capacity** (how much), **weight/mass** (how heavy), **time** (how many minutes or hours), and **temperature** (how many degrees). Have volunteers write the five category words on separate signs to place on five desks.

● On a table, set up measuring tools of all kinds, randomly mixed, including measuring cups, rulers, meter sticks and yardsticks, measuring tape, scales, thermometers, clocks, watches, calendars. You may want to include Teacher Tools 12 (Analog Clockface), 13 (ruler), and 15 (Metric Measuring Tape).

● Have students in groups come up in turn to the measuring tool table. Each student picks one item and moves it to one of the five measurement desks. After sorting, name the tools in the five categories, with students' help.

● Display food and drink containers and discuss some the units of measurement students may know. For example, soda comes in liters, milk comes in quarts, flour is measured in pounds and grams, gas for cars is measured in gallons. Compare some of the measures, such as a liter to a quart, which measure almost the same amount. Pass around the containers for students to read labels and compare sizes.

Multilevel Strategies

① Preproduction
Ask students to point to the categories as you name them.

② ③ Early Production and Speech Emergence
Encourage students to read the category signs aloud.

④ ⑤ Intermediate and Advanced Fluency
Invite students to read the categories and name the matching measuring tools.

 Visit **www.mmhmath.com** to find printable **Vocabulary Cards** that help build academic language.

Procedure: Help students make these Foldables to write vocabulary words and definitions throughout the unit. Encourage students to use the Foldables as a study guide.

by Dinah Zike

Layered-Look Book

1. Provide each student with two sheets of paper. Have students roll up the bottom edges of the paper. Stop them 1" from the top edges.

2. When all the tabs are the same size, have students crease the papers to hold the tabs in place. Help your students staple along the fold and direct them to label the tabs accordingly.

3. Students can use their Foldables Layered-Look Books to take notes as they progress through the lessons and then use them to review the skills learned.

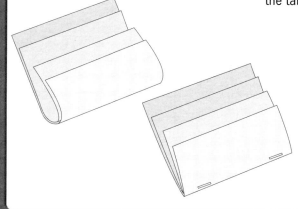

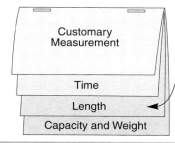

Customary Measurement

Time

Length

Capacity and Weight

Labels may include:

1 foot (ft) = 12 inches (in.)
1 yard (yd) = 36 inches (in.)
1 yard (yd) = 3 feet
1 mile (mi) = 5,280 feet
1 mile (mi) = 1,760 yards

by Dinah Zike

Layered-Look Book

1. Provide each student with two sheets of paper. Have students roll up the bottom edges of the paper. Stop them 1" from the top edges.

2. When all the tabs are the same size, have students crease the paper to hold the tabs in place. Help your students staple along the fold and direct them to label the tabs accordingly.

3. Students can use their Foldables Layered-Look Books to take notes as they progress through the lessons and then use them to review the skills learned.

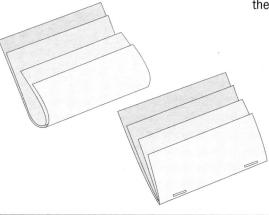

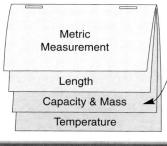

Metric Measurement

Length

Capacity & Mass

Temperature

Labels may include:

1 metric cup (c) = 250 mL
1 liter (L) = 1,000 mL = 100 cL
1 kilogram (Kg) = 1,000 grams (g)

Lesson 1

45 minutes

▶ **Key Strategy**
Use manipulatives

▶ **Format**
Whole class and individual

▶ **Math Vocabulary**
elapsed time

▶ **Daily Vocabulary**
clock, minute hand, second hand

▶ **Resources**
Learning Resource 29
Teacher Tool 12

Materials
- brass fasteners
- cardboard or heavy stock paper
- glue
- pen, pencil
- scissors

Assessment

Check students' mastery of telling time as they complete activity. See Assessment Checklist on page 149. Remind students to work on their Foldables.

Home Connection

Have students record times from their daily home schedules (i.e., wake-up time, dinner time, etc.) and share them with the class.

Time

Math Objectives	ESL/TESOL Descriptors
■ Convert and compute with units of time. ■ Find elapsed time.	■ Interpret information presented visually. ■ Listen to, speak, read, and write about subject matter information.

Activate Prior Knowledge Show a clock. Write 12:00 midnight on the board and have students count around the clock (1 A.M., 2 A.M., etc.). Stop at noon, write 12 noon, and continue with 1 P.M. and so on.

Hands-on Lesson Distribute Teacher Tool 12: Analog Clockface. Have students assemble clocks with second and minute hands. Review seconds and minutes. Skip count around the clock by 5-, 10-, 15- and 30-minute intervals.

- Draw a clock on the board and set the hands to a time, for example, 6:30 P.M. Have students set their clocks to that time. Write 6:30 P.M. on the board. Ask: **What do you do at this time?** Review the ways to say the time: **six thirty, half past six, or half past the hour.** Review a quarter past and a quarter to the hour.

- Write times on the board and have students say the times and set their clocks.

- Ask: **How many minutes are there in an hour and a half? Two hours? Three hours?** Elicit 90, 120, and 180 minutes.

- Write the start and end times of your school day. Ask: **How much time is there between the beginning and the end of the school day?** Distribute Learning Resource 29: Keeping Time and ask students to suggest beginning and end times of various activities. Have them calculate each **elapsed time.**

- Point out that the clocks we use are 12-hour clocks. Some students may be familiar with military time, which uses a 24-hour clock.

- Ask: **How many hours are there in a day? Days in a week? Months in a year?** Have students help make a chart of equivalent units of time.

Cultural Link Invite students to bring in examples of calendars or clocks from ancient cultures.

Multilevel Strategies

1 Preproduction
Name a time and have students set their clocks accordingly.

Writing Ask students to write a time that you set on the clock.

2 3 Early Production and Speech Emergence
Set a time and ask: **What time is it?**

Writing Invite students to write the time you say.

4 5 Intermediate and Advanced Fluency
Have students set clocks for each other and ask and answer: **What time is it? It is ___.**

Writing Encourage students to write times in several ways.

Name _____

Keeping Time

Write the start and end times of three activities.
Then write the elapsed time of the activity and the
elapsed time between activities.

1.

ACTIVITY	START TIME	END TIME	ELAPSED TIME
	◯ _____	◯ _____	Amount of time spent on activity

Elapsed time between end of Activity 1 and start of Activity 2:

_____

2.

ACTIVITY	START TIME	END TIME	ELAPSED TIME
	◯ _____	◯ _____	Amount of time spent on activity

Elapsed time between end of Activity 2 and start of Activity 3:

_____

3.

ACTIVITY	START TIME	END TIME	ELAPSED TIME
	◯ _____	◯ _____	Amount of time spent on activity

Lesson 2

 45 minutes

▶ **Key Strategy**
Use realia

▶ **Format**
Whole class and small groups

▶ **Math Vocabulary**
capacity, cup, direct and indirect measures, feet/foot, fluid ounce, gallon, inch, length, mile, nonstandard, ounce, pint, pound, quart, weight, yard

▶ **Daily Vocabulary**
center, measuring cup, scale, tape measure

▶ **Resource**
Learning Resource 30

Materials
- classroom objects
- inch rulers
- measuring cups
- paper clips
- scale (customary units)
- unsharpened pencils
- yardsticks

Assessment

Check students' mastery of measurement as they complete the lesson. See Assessment Checklist on page 149.

Home Connection

Have students record the measurements of five items at home and present them to the class.

Customary Measurement

Math Objectives	**ESL/TESOL Descriptors**
■ Choose appropriate units, estimate and measure.	■ Follow oral and written directions, implicit and explicit.
■ Convert customary units of measurement.	■ Select different media to help understand language.

Activate Prior Knowledge Divide students into groups. To each group distribute paper clips, unsharpened pencils, inch rulers, and yardsticks. Assign objects for groups to measure with each of these four tools. They might measure the height of a chair, the width of the door, the length of a piece of chalk, or the length of the classroom.

Hands-on Lesson Have groups compare the measurements they made with the **nonstandard** units, or **indirect measures** (for example, measurements in paper clips) to the standard measurements (or **direct measures**) used, such as those with the inch rulers or yardsticks.

- Write the words **length, capacity,** and **weight** on the board. Hold up standard measuring tools such as measuring cups, rulers, and scale, and have students help you decide if they are measuring tools for length, weight, or capacity.

- Have students help you generate a list of units of measurement for each category: length in **inches, feet, yards, miles;** weight in **ounces, and pounds;** and capacity in **cups, pints, quarts, gallons,** and **fluid ounces.**

- Divide students into three groups. Distribute Learning Resource 30: Our Customary Measurements. Set up three centers for measuring length, capacity, and weight, and assign each group to one center. Have them estimate and then measure common classroom objects, and record the tools, the estimates, and the measurements. When students finish measuring, rotate groups so that all groups visit all three centers.

Challenge Have students create word problems using the measurements they took of classroom objects.

Multilevel Strategies

1 Preproduction
Name an object and have students show you the measurement they made.

Writing Invite students to write their measurements.

2 3 Early Production and Speech Emergence
Ask: *How long was the (desk)? How much did the (book) weigh?*

Writing Encourage students to write the tools and measurements.

4 5 Intermediate and Advanced Fluency
Have students read their lists of measurements aloud.

Writing Ask students to write about their measurements in full sentences.

Name _____

Our Customary Measurements

Fill in the table with your estimates and actual measurements.

OBJECT	MEASURING TOOL	ESTIMATED MEASUREMENT	ACTUAL MEASUREMENT

Lesson 3

 45 minutes

▶ **Key Strategy**
Use realia

▶ **Format**
Whole class and small groups

▶ **Math Vocabulary**
capacity, centimeter, decimeter, gram, kilogram, kilometer, length, liter, mass, meter, metric, milliliter, millimeter

▶ **Daily Vocabulary**
meter stick, metric scale

▶ **Resources**
Learning Resource 31
Teacher Tools 13 and 15

Materials
- classroom objects to measure
- metric ruler
- metric scale
- meter stick

Assessment

Check students' mastery of measurement as they complete the lesson. See Assessment Checklist on page 149. Remind students to work on their Foldables.

Home Connection

Have students measure household objects in metric units and share their measurements with the class.

Metric Measurement

Math Objectives	**ESL/TESOL Descriptors**
▪ Choose appropriate metric units of length and mass. ▪ Convert metric units of measurement.	▪ Demonstrate knowledge through application in a variety of contexts. ▪ Retell information.

Activate Prior Knowledge Hold up a meter stick. Have students examine metric rulers. Ask: *How is the metric ruler divided? (by tens) Is a ruler divided the same way?* Point out that most of the world uses the metric system, but in the U.S. we use both metric and customary measurements.

Hands-on Lesson List metric measurement vocabulary of **length, capacity,** and **mass**. Discuss the meaning, and pronunciation of *millimeter, centimeter, decimeter, meter, kilometer, milliliter, liter, gram, and kilogram.* Point out the prefixes *deci-, centi-, milli-,* of *deci*meter, *centi*meter, *milli*meter and how they represent 10, 100, and 1,000. Students may know other words that use these prefixes *(cent, centipede, dime, decimal, decade, million).* Hold up objects to measure and ask students which unit is appropriate.

- Divide students into small groups and distribute Learning Resource 31: Our Metric Measurements. Create three centers for measuring length, capacity, and mass. Have groups rotate to measure classroom objects. At each center, have students write estimated measurements, list tools, and record measurements.

- Compare metric and customary units. Distribute rulers (Teacher Tools 13 and 15) and have students compare inches to centimeters. Elicit that there are about $2\frac{1}{2}$ (2.54) centimeters in an inch. Have groups compare pound and kilogram weights. Have them lift and compare an ounce and a gram weight.

Cultural Link Encourage students to bring in imported products from their native countries labeled in metric units.

Multilevel Strategies

❶ Preproduction
Have students point to the names of the units as you say them.

Writing Have students write the name of a unit of measurement.

❷❸ Early Production and Speech Emergence
Ask students to name the units of measurement.

Writing Encourage students to write a phrase about a customary and metric unit of their choice.

❹❺ Intermediate and Advanced Fluency
Ask students why they chose certain units.

Writing Ask students to write sentences about their measurements.

Name _____

Our Metric Measurements

Fill in the table with your estimates and actual measurements.

OBJECT	MEASURING TOOL	ESTIMATED MEASUREMENT	ACTUAL MEASUREMENT

Lesson 4

 35 minutes

▶ **Key Strategy**
Use visuals

▶ **Format**
Whole class and small groups

▶ **Math Vocabulary**
Celsius, degree, Fahrenheit, integer, negative number, positive number

▶ **Daily Vocabulary**
map, thermometer, weather

▶ **Resource**
Learning Resource 32

Materials
- Celsius and Fahrenheit thermometers
- pencils or pens

Assessment

Check students' mastery of measurement as they complete the lesson. See Assessment Checklist on page 149. Remind students to work on their Foldables.

Home Connection

Encourage students to measure the temperature outside their home in Celsius and Fahrenheit for several days and share the records with the class. Make sure students have thermometers at home.

Measure Temperature

Math Objectives	ESL/TESOL Descriptors
■ Convert units of temperature. ■ Compare and order integers.	■ Listen to, speak, read, and write about subject matter information. ■ Actively connect new information to information previously learned.

Activate Prior Knowledge Prepare a winter hat, scarf, and gloves. Put on the hat to pantomime that it's cold. Show thermometers for Fahrenheit and Celsius. Then show that it's getting colder and colder by putting on the scarf and gloves. Ask: **What is happening to the temperature?** *(It is going down.)*

Hands-on Lesson Discuss the **Fahrenheit** (F) and **Celsius** (C) systems, named after their inventors. Talk about the similarities between systems. Both measure temperature in **degrees.** Both show cold and hot temperatures. On both scales, there are numbers **(integers)** to measure degrees. On both scales, there are **negative numbers** (below zero) and **positive numbers** (above zero). Elicit student responses.

● Compare the Fahrenheit and Celsius scales. Point out that water freezes at 32°F and 0°C. Water boils at 212°F and 100°C. Write these temperatures and ask: **What is the difference between Fahrenheit and Celsius?** Elicit that the scales use different units of measurement. Fahrenheit is customary in the United States, while Celsius is used worldwide.

● Distribute Learning Resource 32: What's the Temperature? Have students convert temperatures from °C to °F or °F to °C by using both sides of the thermometer. Then have them use the approximate formulas to see how close they get.

Answers (in actual conversions): **2.** –47°F, **3.** –26°C, **4.** –73°F, **5.** –29°C, **7.** –28°C, **8.** 43°F, **9.** –6°C, **10.** –69°F

Challenge Have groups collect temperature data and make a poster called Worldwide Temperatures to display in the classroom.

Multilevel Strategies

❶ Preproduction
Have students point to the negative and positive temperatures.

Writing Encourage them to write negative and positive temperatures.

❷ ❸ Early Production and Speech Emergence
Have students read negative and positive temperatures on both scales.

Writing Invite students to list temperatures when it is hot, warm, or cold.

❹ ❺ Intermediate and Advanced Fluency
Ask: **What is the temperature today? Tell me in Fahrenheit and in Celsius.**

Writing Have students write a sentence describing the temperature and how it feels.

Name _____

What's the Temperature?

Write the temperatures in Fahrenheit or Celsius.

CONVERTING TEMPERATURES	
°C → °F (approximate)	°F → °C (approximate)
Double the °C and add 30	Subtract 30 from °F and divide by 2

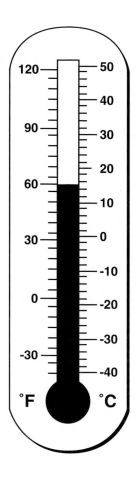

PLACE	AVERAGE HIGH TEMPERATURE IN SUMMER	
	°F	°C
1. Miami, Florida	87°F	30°C
2. Barrow, Alaska	_____	8°C
3. Sydney, Australia	79°F	_____
4. Mexico City	_____	22°C
5. South Pole	−21°F	_____

PLACE	AVERAGE HIGH TEMPERATURE IN WINTER	
	°F	°C
6. Miami, Florida	_____	17°C
7. Barrow, Alaska	−20°F	_____
8. Sydney, Australia	_____	6°C
9. Mexico City	43°F	_____
10. South Pole	_____	−56°C

UNIT 8

Problem Solving

Problem Solving
Reading for Math

Remind students of the basic steps of problem solving.

SKILL: Check for Reasonableness
Model the skill using a word problem such as:

 Read Paul plans to bring juice for the picnic. He needs 40 cups of juice so everyone can have 2 cups. He has 6 quarts of juice. Does he have enough?

 Plan I can add to find out how many cups are in 6 quarts.

 Solve **Think:** There are 2 cups in a pint. There are 2 pints in a quart. There are 4 cups in a quart. I can add. $4 + 4 + 4 + 4 + 4 + 4 = 24$. There are 24 cups in 6 quarts. Paul does not have enough.

 Look Back I can count on by 4s until I get to 40. … 28, 32, 36, 40. Paul needs 10 quarts to have 2 cups for each person.

Distribute **Math Center Card 8A** to students.

Math Center Card 8A

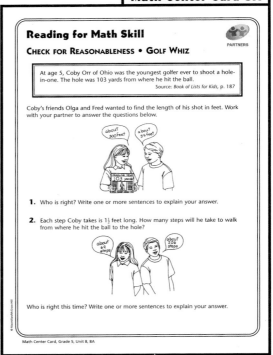

STRATEGY: Draw a Diagram
Model the strategy using a word problem such as:

 Read There are 5 singers on the radio show. Each singer gets 3 minutes to sing a song. The DJ talks for 2 minutes between each song. How long is the show if the DJ also talks for 5 minutes before the first song and after the last song?

 Plan I can draw a diagram to show the times.

 Solve I'll use one symbol for the DJ's time and another symbol for the singers' time.

5 ③ 2 ③ 2 ③ 2 ③
2 ③ 5

I can add the □s: $5 + 2 + 2 + 2 + 2 + 5 = 18$
The DJ talked for 18 minutes. I can add the ○s: $3 + 3 + 3 + 3 + 3 = 15$. The singers sang for 15 minutes. I can add to find how many minutes in all. $18 + 15 = 33$. The radio show was 33 minutes long.

 Look Back How can I check? I can add all the numbers again a different way.
$5 + 3 + 2 + 3 + 2 + 3 + 2 + 3 + 2 + 3 + 5 = 33$

Distribute **Math Center Card 8B** to students.

Math Center Card 8B

Assessment Checklist

	STUDENT NAMES											
SCHOOL:												
TEACHER: **SCHOOL YEAR:**												
Mark: + = Mastery ✓ = Satisfactory – = Needs Improvement												
LEVEL OF LANGUAGE PROFICIENCY (1–5)												
MATH OBJECTIVES												
• Convert and compute units of time.												
• Find elapsed time.												
• Choose appropriate units and estimate and measure.												
• Convert customary and metric units of measurement.												
• Choose appropriate metric units of length, and mass.												
• Compare and order integers.												
ESL/TESOL LISTENING SPEAKING												
Actively connect new information to information previously learned.												
Follow oral and written directions, implicit and explicit.												
Intepret information presented visually.												
Listen to, speak, read, and write about subject matter information.												
Practice new language.												
Select different media to help understand language.												
ESL/TESOL READING												
Read about subject matter information.												
Apply basic reading comprehension skills.												
Follow written directions, implicit and explicit.												
ESL WRITING												
Write to demonstrate comprehension.												
Write using spelling patterns and targeted English vocabulary.												

Foldables by Dinah Zike

1 Preproduction
- Did students write the unit vocabulary?
- Did they copy the definitions?

2 3 Early Production and Speech Emergence
- Did students label the tabs correctly?
- Did they write the vocabulary words?
- Did they copy the definitions?

4 5 Intermediate and Advanced Fluency
- Did students write definitions for the unit vocabulary?
- Did they use correct spelling and grammar?

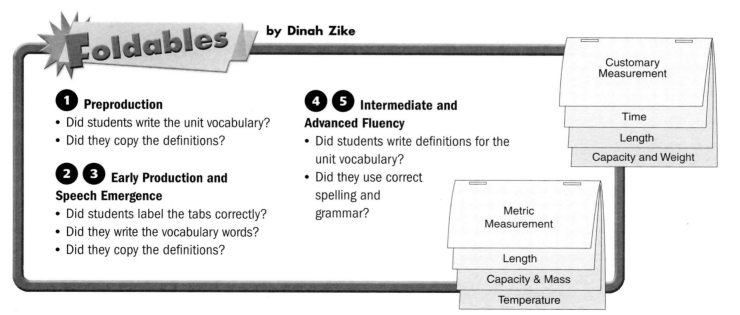

Customary Measurement

Time

Length

Capacity and Weight

Metric Measurement

Length

Capacity & Mass

Temperature

Planner

Algebra Expressions and Equations

Assessment
p. 167
• Assessment Checklist
• Foldables

LOG ON Visit **www.mmhmath.com**

Unit Activities		
• **Activity 1** Readiness Detective Work, p. 154		• **Activity 3** Expression Exploration, p. 155
• **Activity 2** Missing Numbers, p. 154		• **Activity 4** Musical Math, p. 155

Lessons	Key Objectives	Vocabulary	Materials	Resources
READ TOGETHER "For Any Equation" by Michael Garin, pp. 152–153	**Math:** Explore equations. **ESL/TESOL:** Goal 1, Standards 1, 2.	forget, oatmeal, parenthesis, rolling, screaming, sink, tantrum		Graphic Organizer 2
UNIT WARM-UP Understanding Algebraic Expressions p. 156	**Math:** Write equations. Write algebraic expressions. **ESL/TESOL:** Goal 1, Standards 2, 3.	algebraic expression, equation, evaluate, inverse operation, variable	glue, scissors, sports magazines	
LESSON 1 Order of Operations pp. 158–159	**Math:** Evaluate expressions. Use the proper order of operations. **ESL/TESOL:** Goals 1, 2; Standards 1, 1.	algebraic expression, evaluate, order of operations	crayons or markers	Learning Resource 33
LESSON 2 Graphing Functions pp. 160–161	**Math:** Represent and solve problems with tables, graphs, and functions. **ESL/TESOL:** Goal 2, Standard 1.	axis, coordinate, expression, function, ordered pair, origin	pens or pencils	Learning Resource 34 Teacher Tool 1
LESSON 3 Variables pp. 162–163	**Math:** Solve addition and subtraction equations. Write algebraic expressions. **ESL/TESOL:** Goal 2, Standard 1.	equation, inverse operations, solution, variable	counters, pencils, markers or crayons	Learning Resource 35 **Overhead Manipulatives**
LESSON 4 Inverse Operations pp. 164–165	**Math:** Evaluate expressions. Use inverse operations. **ESL/TESOL:** Goal 1, Standards 1, 3.	inverse operations	pens, pencils	Learning Resource 36 **Overhead Manipulatives**
PROBLEM SOLVING p. 166 • Skill: Use Graphs to Identify Relationships • Strategy: Make a Graph	Use skills and strategies to solve problems.			**Math Center Cards 9A, 9B**

See **Math at Home Family Guide** for additional math vocabulary, activities, and games in English, Spanish, and Haitian Creole.

English Vocabulary

Dear Family: Please help your child practice the key vocabulary words for this unit.

algebraic expression a variable by itself or a combination of one or more variables, one or more operations, and possibly one or more numbers

axis a horizontal or vertical number line on a graph

coordinate one of two numbers in an ordered pair

equation a mathematical statement with an equal sign in it

function a relationship in which one quantity depends on another quantity

inverse operations operations that can undo each other

order of operations the agreed-upon order for performing operations

ordered pair a pair of numbers that gives the location of a point on a coordinate graph or grid

origin the point on a coordinate graph where the vertical axis meets the horizontal axis

variable a symbol used to represent a number or numbers

Vocabulario en español

Estimados familiares: Por favor ayuden a su hijo/a a practicar las palabras del vocabulario de esta unidad.

expresión algebraica la que contiene una o más variables, una o más operaciones, y probablemente uno o más números

eje recta numérica horizontal o vertical en una gráfica

coordenada cada uno de los dos números en un par ordenado

ecuación expresión matemática con un signo de igual

función relación en la que una cantidad depende de otra cantidad

operaciones inversas operaciones que se anulan entre sí

orden de las operaciones el orden acordado para realizar operaciones

par ordenado par de números que da la ubicación de un punto en una gráfica de coordenadas o cuadrícula

origen el punto en una gráfica de coordenadas en el que se encuentran el eje vertical y el eje horizontal

variable símbolo que se usa para representar un número o un grupo de números

Vokabilè an kreyòl

Chè paran: Tanpri ede pitit la pratike mo vokabilè nan seksyon sa a.

ekspresyon aljebrik yon varyab poukont li osnon yon konbinezon youn osnon plizyè varyab, youn osnon plizyè operasyon, e petèt youn osnon plizyè nimewo

aks yon liy nimewote orizontal osnon vètikal nan yon desen

kowòdone youn osnon de nimewo nan yon pè done

ekwasyon yon deklarasyon matematik ak yon siy egal ladan'l

fonksyon relasyon kote yon kantite depann de yon lòt

kantite

operasyon envès operasyon ki ka defèt youn lòt

lòd operasyon lòd pou rezoud operasyon

pè done yon pè nimewo ki bay kote yon pwen ye nan yon desen kowodone osnon yon grafik osnon youn kadriye

orijin pwen nan yon desen kowòdone kote aks vetikal la rankontre aks orizontal la

varyab senbòl itilize pou reprezante yon nimewo osnon plizyè nimewo

© Macmillan/McGraw-Hill

For Any Equation

by Michael Garin

 25 minutes

Math Objective
- Explore equations.

ESL/TESOL Descriptors
- Use nonverbal communication in social interactions.
- Express personal needs, feelings, and ideas.

Reading Skill
- Recognize Cause and Effect.

Vocabulary
forget, oatmeal, parenthesis, rolling, screaming, sink, tantrum

Before Reading

Build Background/Oral Language
Look at the title and the illustration and predict what the poem is about. Ask: **What math operations are in equations?** Elicit *addition*, *subtraction*, *multiplication*, and *division*.

Ask: **What are emotions?** Elicit that emotions are feelings, such as *happy*, *sad*, *mad*. Ask: **What makes you feel happy (sad/mad)?** Hand out

Graphic Organizer 2: Word Web. Have students put *Emotions* in the center and fill it in.

As you read the poem, ask students to listen for equations and for words that describe emotions.

During Reading

- Read the poem through once without stopping as students track text. Reread the poem slowly with students repeating each line. Encourage them to ask about new or difficult words.
- Divide the class into two groups and ask them to read alternate verses in unison.

Phonological/Phonemic Awareness
Write the words *right* and *fight* on the board. Say the words aloud and have students repeat. Elicit that the *i* is long and the *gh* is silent. Brainstorm other words with this spelling, such as *light*, *might*, *tight*, *sight*, and *night*.

After Reading

Ask: **What equations were in the poem?** Have volunteers write and solve them. Ask: **What emotion words were in the poem?** Write responses on the board. Ask: **Why does the person in the poem feel mad and sad?** (*The problem is very hard.*) Have students make index cards with pictures of emotions.

Drama Group students and have each group act out a verse of the poem as you read it.

Assessment

Observe fluency as students read the poem aloud. See Assessment Checklist on page 167.

Multilevel Strategies

1 Preproduction
Say: **Show me what being mad looks like.**

Writing Encourage students to write words with a long *i* and silent *-gh*.

2 3 Early Production and Speech Emergence
Ask: **Do I look mad or sad?**

Writing Invite students to write a sentence using a word from the list with a long *i* and silent *-gh*.

4 5 Intermediate and Advanced Fluency
Say: **Tell me about feeling mad.**

Writing Have a group write their own poem using one or more words from the list with a long *i* and silent *-gh*.

For Any Equation

by Michael Garin

*Do you sometimes face an equation and
think that you will never solve it? This poem will help.*

This problem is very hard.
You will never get it.
You can try. You can cry.
You might as well forget it.

In one of the parenthesis
Are numbers you must add.
Like $2 + 2$ or $5 + 1$
That will make you mad.

In the other parenthesis
Are numbers to subtract
Like $5 - 1$ or $4 - 2$.
Now you're feeling sad.

Now multiply exponentially
Like $3 \times 3 \times 3 \times 3$
(that's 3 to the fourth, or more).
Don't you feel like screaming
And rolling on the floor?

And now divide what's OUTSIDE
Like maybe 3 into 9.
What is that you're saying?
You are feeling fine.

You answered the equation.
You say you got it right.
You didn't have a tantrum.
You didn't have a fight.

You didn't throw your oatmeal
Into the kitchen sink.
I guess the answer really is
You are smarter than you think.

Activities

Readiness

PARTNERS

ACTIVITY 1

Detective Work

Be a math detective. Find which numbers fit each clue.

1. $n + 13.5$ is greater than 20

2. $10 - x$ is between 3 and 5

3. $y - 3$ is less than 5.5

4. $v + 7$ is between 15 and 17

4	5.2	6.8
8.4	9.25	11.1

Create a clue for your partner. Exchange clues and solve.

See answers on p. 293.

Explore Addition and Subtraction Expressions

© Macmillan/McGraw-Hill

PARTNERS

ACTIVITY 2

Missing Numbers

- Each partner does problems 1–2. Compare your solutions.

1. Tim's aunt is 45 years older than he is. Write an expression with a variable to stand for Tim's age or his aunt's age. Spin the spinner for possible ages for Tim. Solve for two possible ages for Tim.

2. Write questions for this expression: $257 + n$. Spin twice to get n. Then solve.

- Make up your own questions that can be solved with variable expressions. Have your partner write the variable expressions and solve for two different values.

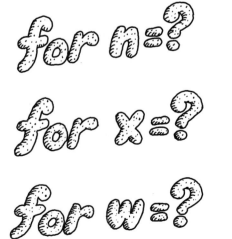

© Macmillan/McGraw-Hill

Addition Equations

Game Zone

ACTIVITY 3

PARTNERS

Expression Exploration

Write one expression on each index card.

$4 \times n$ $n \times 8$ $n \div 2$ $n \div 4$

© Macmillan/McGraw-Hill

YOU NEED
- 4 index cards
- number cube
- calculator

- Mix up the cards.

- Toss a number cube twice to make a decimal in the form ☐.☐. This decimal represents n.

- Choose a card. Evaluate the expression on the card for your decimal.

- Your partner uses a calculator to check. If your answer agrees, scores 1 point.

- Take turns.

- The winner is the first player to get 8 points.

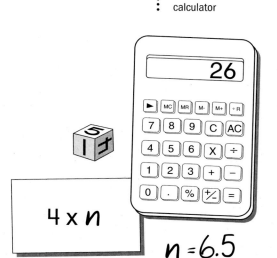

$4 \times n$

$n = 6.5$

Multiplication and Division Equations

✂

ACTIVITY 4

PARTNERS

Musical Math

Spin the spinner. If you get 0, spin again. Solve the problem letting the number represent n.

Maria had n songs to play at the piano recital. Joey had $n \times 2$ songs, but Milo had only $n - 1$ songs. If each song takes 3 minutes to play, how many minutes will they play?

Try again by:

- spinning again for a new number.

- write the expressions again for Joey and Milo.

© Macmillan/McGraw-Hill

YOU NEED
- spinner (0-9)

Two-Step Equations

Understanding Algebraic Expressions

 25 minutes

▶ **Key Strategy**
Use realia

▶ **Format**
Whole class and small groups

▶ **Math Vocabulary**
algebraic expression, equation, evaluate, inverse operation, variable

▶ **Daily Vocabulary**
collage, parentheses, players, sports

▶ **Materials**
glue, scissors, sports magazines

Math Objectives	**ESL/TESOL Descriptors**
■ Write equations.	■ Share social and cultural traditions.
■ Write algebraic expressions.	■ Use context to construct meaning.

Activate Prior Knowledge Initiate a discussion on team sports and the number of players needed for each team. Write student suggestions on the board for example, a basketball team has 5 players. Show some magazine pictures of sports.

Hands-on Lesson Have groups work together make a sports collage by gluing pictures in groups that belong to a specific sport. Tell them they can move the pictures within a group but not separate them from that group, in order to keep the collage organized.

● When finished, explain that numbers can also be arranged in groups and orders to make problems easier to solve. Ask a student volunteer to show his or her sports collage. Say: *We are going to write an equation for this collage.* Model how to use parentheses to group different kinds of sports players together, and then add them. For example, write: *(2 basketball players from team A + 4 basketball players from team B) + (9 baseball players) = 15 total players.*

● Model writing an **algebraic expression** for a word problem on the board. Say: *A basketball team scored 62 points in a game. We know that 4 of the players scored 48 points. How many points did the fifth player score?* Explain that we don't know how many points the fifth player scored, so this is an unknown or **variable.** Help students write an algebraic expression: $48 + y = 62$. Now help them **evaluate** the expression for y. Explain that you can use the **inverse operation** (in this case, subtraction) to solve. $(62 - 48 = y; y = 14)$

● Encourage groups to write a word problem using their collages and exchange them with other groups to solve.

Multilevel Strategies

❶ Preproduction
Have students point to a variable in an algebraic expression.

❷❸ Early Production and Speech Emergence
Ask students to name the variable in an algebraic expression.

❹❺ Intermediate and Advanced Fluency
Ask students to read an algebraic expression and say which term is the variable.

 LOG ON Visit **www.mmhmath.com** to find printable **Vocabulary Cards** that help build academic language.

Procedure: Help students make these Foldables to write vocabulary words and definitions throughout the unit. Encourage students to use the Foldables as a study guide.

 **by Dinah Zike**

Four-Door Book

1. Provide each student with a large sheet of paper. Have them fold it like a shutter fold. Next, fold the paper in half like a hamburger.

2. Help your students open the fold and cut along the inside fold lines to form four tabs. They can label the tabs as illustrated.

3. As students work through the unit, have them take notes and record main ideas under the four tabs of their Foldables Four-Door Books.

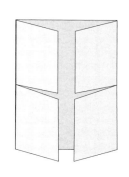

Labels may include:

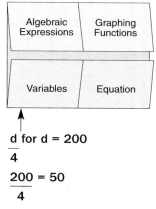

| Algebraic Expressions | Graphing Functions |
| Variables | Equation |

$\dfrac{d \text{ for } d = 200}{4}$

$\dfrac{200}{4} = 50$

A variable is a symbol used to represent a number or numbers.

 **by Dinah Zike**

Four-Door Book

1. Provide each student with a large sheet of paper. Have them fold it like a shutter fold. Next, fold the paper in half like a hamburger.

2. Help your students open the fold and cut along the inside fold lines to form four tabs. They can label the tabs as illustrated.

3. As students work through the unit, have them take notes and record main ideas under the four tabs of their Foldables Four-Door Books.

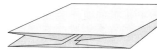

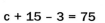

Labels may include:

A solution of an equation is the number that makes the equation a true statement when it is substituted for the variable.

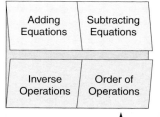

| Adding Equations | Subtracting Equations |
| Inverse Operations | Order of Operations |

$c + 15 - 3 = 75$

Use inverse operations to isolate the variable.

$c + 15 - 3 + 3 = 75 + 3$

$c + 15 = 78$

$c + 15 - 15 = 78 - 15$

$c = 63$

Don't forget to check your answer by substituting 63 for c.

Lesson 1

45 minutes

▶ **Key Strategy**
Use visuals

▶ **Format**
Whole class and student pairs

▶ **Math Vocabulary**
algebraic expression, evaluate, order of operations

▶ **Daily Vocabulary**
baseball, box, calculator, football, parentheses

▶ **Resource**
Learning Resource 33

Materials
• crayons or markers

Assessment

Check students' mastery of division as they complete the lesson. See Assessment Checklist on page 167. Remind students to work on their Foldables.

Home Connection

Ask students to work with a family member to think of everyday division problems. Ask students to share the problem with the class.

Order of Operations

Math Objectives	ESL/TESOL Descriptors
▪ Evaluate expressions. ▪ Use the proper order of operations.	▪ Share and request information. ▪ Follow oral and written directions.

Activate Prior Knowledge Initiate a discussion about buying a number of items, such as school supplies. Ask students for suggestions of school supplies, such as notebooks, pencils, markers, rulers. Write suggestions on the board.

Hands-on Lesson Pose a school-supplies problem to the class. Say: *Sari bought 5 pencils at $0.50 each and 2 notebooks at $1.10 each. How much did she spend?* Explain that the best way to do a word problem is to turn each part of it into an **algebraic expression.** Say: *We'll use the letter* p *for the cost of a pencil and the letter* n *for the cost of a notebook. Sari spent* 5p *on pencils and* 2n *on notebooks.* 5p *and* 2n *are algebraic expressions.* Write the expressions, equation, and solution on the board.

$$5p + 2n = \text{Total Spent}$$
$$5 \times \$0.50 = \$2.50; \ 2 \times \$1.10 = \$2.20$$
$$\$2.50 + \$2.20 = \$4.70$$

• Discuss when things are done in a certain order. For example, students wake up, get out of bed, and then brush their teeth. Explain the **order of operations** used in mathematics: do the operations in parentheses first; multiply and divide from left to right; add and subtract. Model how to **evaluate** the following expression and use order of operations to solve: $(7 \times 6) + (5 \times 4) = 62$.

• Distribute Learning Resource 33 and have pairs of fluent and nonfluent students solve using order of operations. *(The answer is 56 balls in all.)*

Challenge Encourage students to write an expression and use order of operations to solve the school-supplies problem above.
$(5 \times \$0.50) + (2 \times \$1.10) + (2 \times \$0.95) = \$6.60$)

Multilevel Strategies

❶ Preproduction
Ask students to point to the expression.

Writing Ask them to write the symbols used in an expression.

❷❸ Early Production and Speech Emergence
Ask students to read the expression for the school-supplies problem aloud.

Writing Have students write the expression.

❹❺ Intermediate and Advanced Fluency
Ask students to tell you the first order of operation.

Writing Have students write an expression using parentheses.

Name _____

Order of Operations!

Read this word problem and work with your partner to solve it.

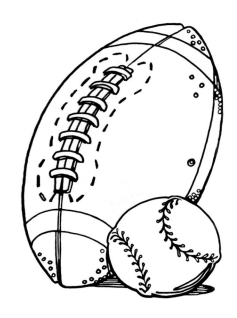

Mr. Johnson bought some new sports equipment for the school. He bought 7 boxes of baseballs and 4 boxes of footballs. Every box of baseballs holds 6. Two of the boxes of footballs hold 5 and two other boxes hold 2. How many balls did Mr. Johnson buy in all?

Look at this **expression** to help you solve the problem. Fill in your answer in the blank.

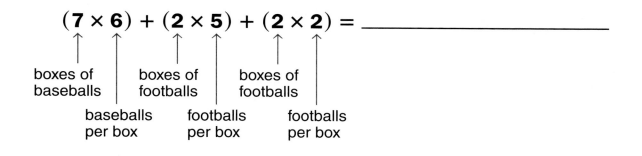

$$(7 \times 6) + (2 \times 5) + (2 \times 2) = \underline{\hspace{3cm}}$$

boxes of baseballs

boxes of footballs

boxes of footballs

baseballs per box

footballs per box

footballs per box

Lesson 2

45 minutes

▶ **Key Strategy**
Use visuals

▶ **Format**
Whole class and pairs

▶ **Math Vocabulary**
axis, coordinate, expression, function, ordered pair, origin

▶ **Daily Vocabulary**
unique

▶ **Resources**
Learning Resource 34
Teacher Tool 1

Materials
• pens or pencils

Assessment

Check students' mastery of algebraic functions as they complete the lesson. See Assessment Checklist on page 167.
Remind students to work on their Foldables.

Home Connection

Have students collect data at home (such as numbers of family members with red shirts), organize it on a plot, and share it with the class.

Graphing Functions

Math Objective	ESL/TESOL Descriptors
■ Represent and solve problems with tables, graphs, and functions.	■ Participate in full-class, group, and pair discussions.
	■ Ask and answer questions.

Activate Prior Knowledge Distribute three identical coins to every student, using Teacher Tool 1 or manipulatives. Ask a student to stand and hold up the coins. Ask: *How many coins do you see?* (3) Ask additional students to stand and hold up coins. Each time, ask: *How many coins are there now? If ten students are standing, how many coins would be showing?* ($10 \times 3 = 30$)

Hands-on Lesson Write 3s on the board. Say: *Every student has three coins. The expression 3s represents the number of coins. 3s means three times the number of students.*

• Draw a three-column chart on the board labeled s, c, Ordered Pairs. Call students one at a time to stand in front and hold up the coins. Show a volunteer how to enter the data in the table as students and coins accumulate. Draw the axes of a line graph on the board. Point out the horizontal **axis** and label it *number of students (s)*. Point out the vertical **axis** and label it *numbers of coins (c)*. Identify the **origin** (0, 0). Explain that in an **ordered pair** the first **coordinate** indicates units to the right of the origin; the second coordinate indicates units above the origin.

• Demonstrate how to plot the ordered pairs on the graph. Explain that the s value goes first. Say: *This graph shows a function. The function is c = 3s. Every value of s has a unique value of c.* Invite a volunteer to draw a line through the ordered pairs.

• Distribute Learning Resource 34: Graphing to student pairs. Challenge them to write ordered pairs for each place and to complete the sheet.

Challenge Have student pairs write and graph a function that shows how much they would have if they saved $6.50 a week for 20 weeks.

Multilevel Strategies

1 Preproduction
Have students point to an ordered pair on a graph.

Writing Have them draw a picture of what the ordered pair represents.

2 3 Early Production and Speech Emergence
Have students read the ordered pairs used in their graph.

Writing Have them write a phrase about the function on the graph.

4 5 Intermediate and Advanced Fluency
Have students explain how to answer word problems using ordered pairs.

Writing Have students write a sentence about what the ordered pair shows.

Name _____

Graphing

Maria and Fred wash 2 cars every hour. Finish the table. Use the table to make a graph. Connect the points with a line.

H	C	ORDERED PAIR
1	2	(1,2)
2	4	
3	6	
4		
5		

H = number of hours   *C* = number of cars washed

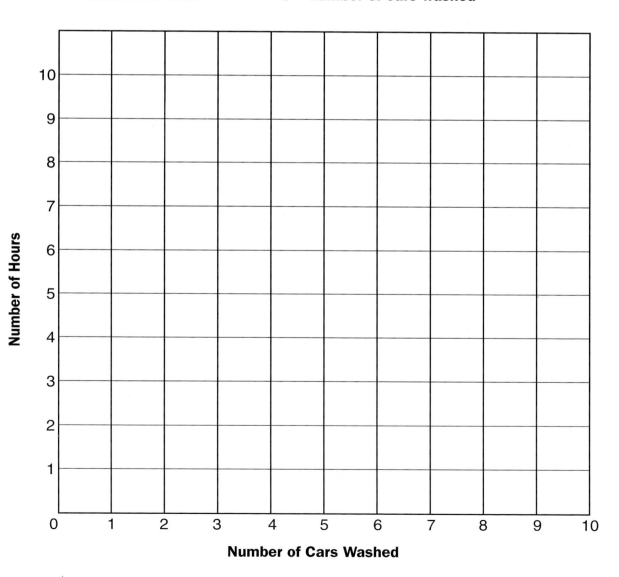

Number of Hours

Number of Cars Washed

Lesson 3

45 minutes

▶ **Key Strategy**
Use manipulatives

▶ **Format**
Whole class and pairs

▶ **Math Vocabulary**
equation, inverse
operations, solution,
variable

▶ **Daily Vocabulary**
unknown

▶ **Resources**
Learning Resource 35
Overhead Manipulatives:
Counters
Teacher Tool 5

Materials
- counters (red and yellow)
- pencils
- markers or crayons
  (red and yellow)

Assessment

Check students' mastery of
algebra as they complete the
lesson. See Assessment
Checklist on page 167.
Remind students to work on
their Foldables.

Home Connection

Have students play the variable
game at home with family
members, using household
objects for counters.

Variables

Math Objectives	ESL/TESOL Descriptors
■ Solve addition and subtraction equations.	■ Request and provide clarification.
■ Write algebraic expressions.	■ Participate in full-class, group, and pair discussions.

Activate Prior Knowledge Write $50 + 15 = 65$ on the board. Then
substitute x for one of the addends: $50 + x = 65$. Elicit suggestions on how to
solve, for example, count up or subtract.

Hands-on Lesson Tell students they are going to play a game to find
something unknown. In math, it's called a **variable** because it can change.

- Pair fluent and nonfluent speakers. Distribute Teacher Tool 5: Two-Color
  Counters, and have pairs cut out and color half of the counters red, the other
  half yellow.

- Write on the board the algebraic expression: $5 + x =$ ___. Have pairs model the
  5 with red counters. One partner puts counters of both colors in the cup, shakes
  it, spills them out, then puts the yellow counters next to the 5 red ones.

- Have the other partner write the sentence for the counters, substituting the
  yellow counters for the variable $(5 + 4 = 9)$. Have them write the **solution.**

- Then provide a subtraction sentence with a variable for groups to work on, such as
  $5 - r =$ ___. Tell students that subtraction is the **inverse operation** to addition.

- Use Counters from **Overhead Manipulatives** to model.

- Distribute Learning Resource 35: Variable Counters to each pair. Prompt students
  to put a handful of red and yellow counters in the cup, shake, and spill them out.
  One partner counts the total number of counters, and the other counts the number
  of yellow counters. Then, they work together to solve the equation to figure out the
  number of red counters. Students will follow similar procedures for parts 2 and 3
  on the Learning Resource. Circulate among student pairs and ask them to tell you
  how they solve the **equations** for $R, Y,$ and T.

Challenge Have students create addition and subtraction examples using two
variables, then exchange with classmates to solve.

Multilevel Strategies

1 Preproduction
Ask students to point to
each variable as you
name it.

Writing Invite students to
write an expression as you
say it.

**2 3 Early Production
and Speech Emergence**
Ask students to name each
variable as you point to it.

Writing Encourage
students to write an
expression with a variable.

**4 5 Intermediate
and Advanced Fluency**
Have students read an
addition equation with an
algebraic expression.

Writing Have students
write and solve a
subtraction equation with
an algebraic expression.

Name _____

Variable Counters

Take some red and yellow counters. Put them in a cup.
Spill them out.

Y = YELLOW   R = RED   T = TOTAL

1.   Count the total. Count the yellows. How many <u>reds</u> are there?
R = T − Y

R	T	Y

2.   Count the total. Count the reds. How many <u>yellows</u> are there?
Y = T − R

Y	T	R

3.   Count the yellows. Count the reds. What's the <u>total</u>?
T = R + Y

T	R	Y

Lesson 4

 45 minutes

▶ **Key Strategy**
Use visuals

▶ **Format**
Whole class and pairs

▶ **Math Vocabulary**
inverse operations

▶ **Daily Vocabulary**
counter

▶ **Resources**
Learning Resource 36
Overhead Manipulatives:
Counters
Teacher Tool 5

Materials
- pens
- pencils

Assessment

Check students' mastery of algebra as they complete the lesson. See Assessment Checklist on page 167. Remind students to work on their Foldables.

Home Connection

Have students take home a copy of Learning Resource 36 to solve with a family member. Family members can suggest other numbers as well. Bring results to share with the class.

Inverse Operations

Math Objectives	ESL/TESOL Descriptors
▪ Evaluate expressions.	▪ Share and request information.
▪ Use inverse operations.	▪ Listen to and imitate how others use English.

Activate Prior Knowledge Review the term *variable* with students and have them practice writing expressions with variables.

Hands-on Lesson Distribute Teacher Tool 5: Two-Color Counters. Have students write the following equation and model how to solve: $d + 9 = 15$. Introduce the idea of using **inverse operations** to solve. First, have students count out fifteen counters. Then have them subtract 9 of the counters. Ask: *How many counters are left over?* (6 counters left over; d = 6) Rewrite as a subtraction sentence. (15 − 9 = d; d = 6) You may want to use Counters from **Overhead Manipulatives** to model.

- Model using inverse operations with multiplication and division sentences. Write on the board: $6 \times d = 36$. Ask for student suggestions on how to use the inverse operation of division. Rewrite the sentence as $36 \div 6 = d$; d = 6.

- Pair fluent and nonfluent speakers. Distribute Learning Resource 36: Inverse Operations. Tell pairs they are going to play a game using inverse operations. Counters should be used to help solve the problems.

- Have pairs play until all five problems have been solved. Then have them exchange their work and have a class discussion about the ways pairs chose to solve each problem.

Challenge Have students write problems for their partners to solve using inverse operations.

Multilevel Strategies

① Preproduction
Ask students to read an answer to an addition problem.

Writing Ask students to copy an addition problem.

② ③ Early Production and Speech Emergence
Ask: *What is the inverse operation of addition?* (subtraction)

Writing Have students write the inverse operation of $8 \times A = 32$. ($32 \div 8 = A$)

④ ⑤ Intermediate and Advanced Fluency
Ask: *How can you solve a multiplication problem with a variable using inverse operations?* (use division)

Writing Ask students to write the steps of solving the problem.

Name _____

Inverse Operations

Solve the following problems using inverse operations.

1. $d + 8 = 12$

Write the inverse operation: _____

$d =$ _____

2. $f + 9 = 24$

Write the inverse operation: _____

$f =$ _____

3. $g + 34 = 126$

Write the inverse operation: _____

$g =$ _____

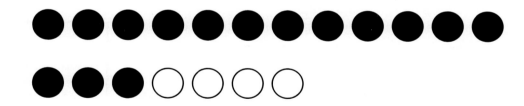

4. $d \div 3 = 4$

Write the inverse operation: _____

$d =$ _____

5. $f \div 6 = 36$

Write the inverse operation: _____

$f =$ _____

UNIT 9

Problem Solving

Problem Solving

Reading for Math

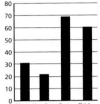

Read → Plan → Solve → Look Back

Remind students of the basic steps of problem solving.

SKILL: Use Graphs to Identify Relationships

Model the skill using a word problem such as:

 Read

The soccer club voted on which food to serve at the awards ceremony. Which food got twice as many votes as pizza? Use the graph to answer the question.

 Plan

I can compare the bars to find the answer.

 Solve

Think: I can eliminate hot dogs, because they got fewer votes than pizza. Pizza got 30 votes. $30 + 30 = 60$. Chicken got 60 votes. Chicken got twice as many votes as pizza.

 Look Back

Does my answer make sense?
Yes. The only other food is pasta with 70 votes. 70 is more than twice 30.

Distribute **Math Center Card 9A** to students.

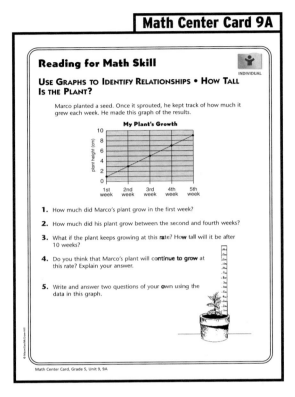

Math Center Card 9A

Reading for Math Skill

USE GRAPHS TO IDENTIFY RELATIONSHIPS • HOW TALL IS THE PLANT?

Marco planted a seed. Once it sprouted, he kept track of how much it grew each week. He made this graph of the results.

My Plant's Growth

1. How much did Marco's plant grow in the first week?
2. How much did his plant grow between the second and fourth weeks?
3. What if the plant keeps growing at this rate? How tall will it be after 10 weeks?
4. Do you think that Marco's plant will continue to grow at this rate? Explain your answer.
5. Write and answer two questions of your own using the data in this graph.

Math Center Card, Grade 5, Unit 9, 9A

STRATEGY: Make a Graph

Model the strategy using a word problem such as:

 Read

Kita surveyed the class for favorite pets. She made a tally chart to show the results of the survey. How can she show the results so they can be more easily interpreted?

Dogs ||||| ||||| ||||| |
Cats ||||| ||||| ||||| ||||| |||
Hamsters ||||| ||

 Plan

I can make a bar graph.

 Solve

Think: The lowest vote was 7, the highest 23. I can make a graph with a scale that has intervals of 5.

Look Back

Does my graph show all of the information? Yes.

Distribute **Math Center Card 9B** to students.

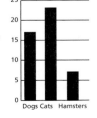

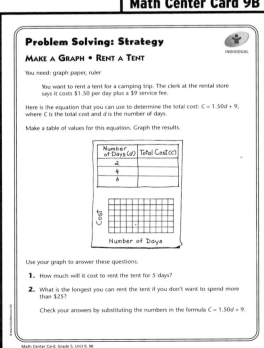

Math Center Card 9B

Problem Solving: Strategy

MAKE A GRAPH • RENT A TENT

You need: graph paper, ruler

You want to rent a tent for a camping trip. The clerk at the rental store says it costs $1.50 per day plus a $9 service fee.

Here is the equation that you can use to determine the total cost: $C = 1.50d + 9$, where C is the total cost and d is the number of days.

Make a table of values for this equation. Graph the results.

Number of Days (d)	Total Cost (C)
2	
4	
6	

Use your graph to answer these questions.

1. How much will it cost to rent the tent for 5 days?
2. What is the longest you can rent the tent if you don't want to spend more than $25?

Check your answers by substituting the numbers in the formula $C = 1.50d + 9$.

Math Center Card, Grade 5, Unit 9, 9B

Assessment Checklist

	STUDENT NAMES								
SCHOOL:									
TEACHER: **SCHOOL YEAR:**									
Mark: + = **Mastery** √ = **Satisfactory** – = **Needs Improvement**									
LEVEL OF LANGUAGE PROFICIENCY (1–5)									
MATH OBJECTIVES									
• Evaluate expressions.									
• Use the proper order of operations.									
• Represent and solve problems with tables, graphs, and functions.									
• Solve addition and subtraction equations.									
• Write algebraic expressions and equations.									
• Use inverse operations.									
ESL/TESOL LISTENING/SPEAKING									
Express personal needs, feelings, and ideas.									
Share and request information.									
Participate in full-class, group, and pair discussions.									
Ask and answer questions.									
Listen to and imitate how others use English.									
ESL/TESOL READING									
Read about subject matter information.									
Apply basic reading comprehension skills.									
Follow written directions, implicit and explicit.									
ESL WRITING									
Write to demonstrate comprehension.									
Write using spelling patterns and targeted English vocabulary.									

 **Foldables** by Dinah Zike

1 Preproduction
- Did students write the unit vocabulary?
- Did they copy the definitions?

2 3 Early Production and Speech Emergence
- Did students label the tabs correctly?
- Did they write the vocabulary words?
- Did they copy the definitions?

4 5 Intermediate and Advanced Fluency
- Did students write definitions for the unit vocabulary?
- Did they use correct spelling and grammar?

Algebraic Expressions	Graphing Functions
Variables	Equation

Adding Equations	Subtracting Equations
Inverse Operations	Order of Operations

UNIT 10

Planner

Geometry

Assessment
p. 185
• Assessment Checklist
• Foldables

Visit **www.mmhmath.com**

Unit Activities
• **Activity 1** Readiness Folding Figures, p. 172
• **Activity 2** Angle Search, p. 172
• **Activity 3** Race to the Center, p. 173
• **Activity 4** Congruent Concentration, p. 173

Lessons	Key Objectives	Vocabulary	Materials	Resources
READ TOGETHER "Shapes," by Shel Silverstein, pp. 170–171	**Math:** Describe and classify geometric figures. **ESL/TESOL:** Goal 2, Standard 3.	kerplunk, passing, picked, rectangular, rolling, shack, struck, wounded		
UNIT WARM-UP Understanding Geometry p. 174	**Math:** Describe and classify geometric figures. **ESL/TESOL:** Goal 1, Standard 3.	angle, circle, parallel lines, rectangle, square, triangle	checkerboard, glue, magazines, poster paper, scissors	
LESSON 1 Angles and Lines pp. 176–177	**Math:** Measure, draw, and classify angles. **ESL/TESOL:** Goal 2, Standard 1.	angle, degree, endpoint, intersecting lines, line, parallel lines	glue, protractors, toothpicks	Learning Resource 37
LESSON 2 Triangles and Quadrilaterals pp. 178–179	**Math:** Describe and classify geometric figures. Find the unknown angles of a figure. **ESL/TESOL:** Goal 2, Standard 1.	closed figure, congruent, open figure, parallelogram, rhombus, trapezoid	colored markers, protractor, rulers	Learning Resource 38 Teacher Tool 14
LESSON 3 Circles pp. 180–181	**Math:** Identify the center and the diameter of a circle. **ESL/TESOL:** Goal 2, Standard 1.	center, central angle, chord, circle, compass, diameter, radius	beads, beans and small pasta, compass, ruler	Learning Resource 39
LESSON 4 Congruence, Symmetry, and Transformation pp. 182–183	**Math:** Identify congruent and similar figures. Identify transformations. **ESL/TESOL:** Goal 1, Standard 1.	congruent figures, glide, reflection, rotation, similar figures, slide, transformation	paper or plastic shapes, ruler	Learning Resource 40 Teacher Tools 7 and 14
PROBLEM SOLVING p. 184 • Skill: Draw a Diagram • Strategy: Find a Pattern	Use skills and strategies to solve problems.			**Math Center Cards 10A, 10B**

See **Math at Home Family Guide** for additional math vocabulary, activities, and games in English, Spanish, and Haitian Creole.

English Vocabulary

Dear Family: Please help your child practice the key vocabulary words for this unit.

acute angle an angle with a measure of less than 90°

congruent figures figures that have the same shape and size

corresponding parts matching parts of congruent or similar figures

obtuse angle an angle with measure greater than 90° and less than 180°

parallelogram a quadrilateral in which both pairs of opposite sides are parallel

right angle an angle that measures 90°

similar figures figures that have the same shape, but not the same size

Vocabulario en español

Estimados familiares: Por favor ayuden a su hijo/a a practicar las palabras del vocabulario de esta unidad.

ángulo agudo ángulo que mide menos de 90°

figuras congruentes figuras que tienen la misma forma y tamaño

partes correspondientes partes que coinciden en figuras similares o congruentes

ángulo obtuso ángulo que mide más de 90° y menos de 180°

paralelogramo cuadrilátero en el cual ambos pares de lados opuestos son paralelos.

ángulo recto ángulo que mide 90°

figuras semejantes figuras que tienen la misma forma, pero no necesariamente el mismo tamaño

Vokabilè an kreyòl

Chè paran: Tanpri ede pitit la pratike mo vokabilè nan seksyon sa a.

ang egi yon ang ki pi piti pase 90°

fòm parèy ki gen menm fòm ak menm mezi

pati egal pati ki koresponn osnon menm

ang obti yon ang ki mezire plis pase 90° e mwens pase 180°

paralelogram yon kwadrilatè kote de pè kote opoze yo paralèl

ang dwa yon ang ki mezire 90°

fòm similè fòm ki gen menm fòm pa menm mezi

Shapes

by Shel Silverstein

 25 minutes

Math Objective
- Describe and classify geometric figures.

ESL Objectives
- Apply basic reading comprehension skills.
- Represent information visually.

Reading Skill
- Recall story details, including character and setting.

Vocabulary
kerplunk, passing, picked, rectangular, rolling, shack, struck, wounded

Before Reading

Build Background/Oral Language

- Say the title of the poem. Ask: **What shapes can you think of?** Have volunteers draw the shapes on the board and write their names.

- Say: **Kerplunk!** as you drop something on the floor. Explain that this is a "sound" word. Discuss with students other "sound" words such as *boom, ping, clang, thwack,* and *so on.*

During Reading

- Point to the shapes on the board and pantomime action as you read.

- Reread line by line and have students repeat. Then read in unison.

Phonological/Phonemic Awareness

Write the word *square* on the board. Say /sk/, **square,** and have students repeat. Draw a 3-column chart. Write *sq, sk, sc* at the top of each column. Brainstorm words with the /sk/ sound and write them in the appropriate column (**sq:** *squeeze, squid, squad, squirrel, squash;* **sc:** *scoop, scorpion, score, scarf, scare, scuba;* **sk:** *ski, sky, skip, skirt, skate, skeleton*).

After Reading

Ask: **What happened to the square?** Encourage students to explain what happened in their own words. Pair students to read the poem aloud to each other.

Drama Have students recite and role-play the poem for the class. Students can draw large shapes and use them as costumes.

Assessment

Observe fluency as students recite the poem aloud. See Assessment Checklist on page 185.

Multilevel Strategies

1 Preproduction
Have students point to words from the poem as you say them.

Writing Have students illustrate a /sk/ word.

2 3 Early Production and Speech Emergence
Have students read a line from the poem.

Writing Have students write and illustrate a phrase using a /sk/ word.

4 5 Intermediate and Advanced Fluency
Ask students to read aloud the whole poem.

Writing Have a group write and illustrate a sentence using two /sk/ words.

Shapes

by Shel Silverstein

A square was sitting quietly

Outside his rectangular shack

When a triangle came down—*kerplunk!*—

And struck him in the back.

"I must go to the hospital,"

Cried the wounded square,

So a passing rolling circle

Picked him up and took him there.

Readiness

ACTIVITY 1

INDIVIDUAL

Folding Figures

Fold and cut a square piece of paper to make the following shapes. The challenge is to make the shape without drawing the figure first.

1. triangle

2. octagon

3. pentagon

4. hexagon

5. star

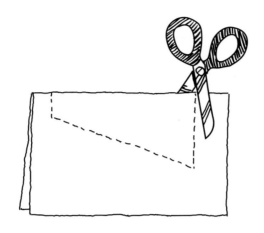
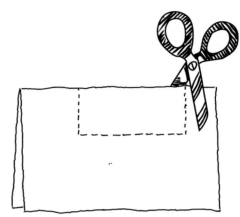

YOU NEED
scissors
paper

Basic Geometric Ideas

ACTIVITY 2

PARTNERS

Angle Search

- Take turns.

- Flip a penny. Heads = 1. Tails = 0. This number will be the first digit of your 3-digit angle measure. (If your first digit is 0, then your angle will be a 2-digit number.)

- Spin the spinner two times. Use these numbers for the second and third digits of your angle measure.

- Find the angle as *acute, obtuse, right,* or *straight*.

- Using only a ruler, estimate and draw an angle with that number of degrees.

- Measure the angle with a protractor.

- Find the difference between your estimate and the measure. Keep a running sum of the differences.

- Play five rounds. The player with the lower total wins.

YOU NEED
penny
spinner (0–9)
straightedge ruler
protractor (Teacher Tool 13)

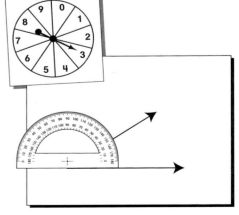

Explore Naming and Measuring Angles

© Macmillan/McGraw-Hill

UNIT
10

Activities

Game Zone

ACTIVITY 3

SMALL GROUP

Race to the Center

- Make a game board like the one shown. Draw 7 columns and 7 rows to make 49 squares in all.

- Each player cuts out one triangle that fills half a square. Write your initials inside the triangle.

- Make 4 cards for each of the 3 commands in the picture. Shuffle them and place them facedown in a pile.

- Place your triangle in one corner of the game board.

- Take turns. Pick a card on each turn, and move your triangle. If it is not possible to move, you lose your turn.

- The first player to reach the exact center of the board wins.

YOU NEED
scissors
12 index cards

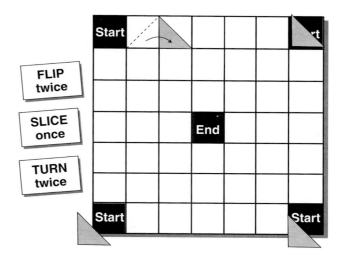

Triangles

✂ -

ACTIVITY 4

PARTNERS

Congruent Concentration

- Draw 5 geometric figures, each on a different card. Make 5 triangles and your partner makes 5 quadrilaterals. Copy the figures carefully on another card to make a congruent figure for each shape.

- Mix up the 20 cards and spread them out facedown on the table. Take turns turning over two cards at a time. If you make a match, put both congruent figures faceup in front of you and take another turn. If you do not make a match, turn the cards facedown.

- The player with more cards when all the cards are matched wins.

YOU NEED
20 index cards (or slips of paper)

Congruence and Similarity

Understanding Geometry

⏱ 20 minutes

▶ **Key Strategy**
Use visuals

▶ **Format**
Whole class and small groups

▶ **Math Vocabulary**
angle, circle, parallel lines, rectangle, right angle, square, triangle

▶ **Daily Vocabulary**
diamond, names of classroom objects

▶ **Materials**
checkerboard, crayons or markers, glue, magazines, poster paper, scissors

---

Math Objective	**ESL/TESOL Descriptors**
▪ Describe and classify geometric figures.	▪ Practice new language. ▪ Use context to construct meaning.

Activate Prior Knowledge Ask students what kinds of sports they like to play. Discuss field games like soccer, football, and baseball and indoor games like basketball. Have students describe the shape of the fields *(rectangles* and *diamonds),* and the markings and shapes on the fields: yard lines, end zones, half circle goalie areas. Ask volunteers to draw some of these geometric shapes on the board.

Hands-on Lesson Hold up a checkerboard. Point out that the board is made up of squares. Squares are made up of **right angles** and **parallel lines.** Draw a right angle on the board. Compare parallel lines to train tracks that run side by side. They are always the same distance apart and never meet.

● Discuss other geometric shapes: **circles, triangles, squares, rectangles.** Draw and label the shapes on the board.

● Play the game "I Spy" with the class using clues that name or describe geometric shapes. Model the game by saying: *I spy something in the classroom that is round and has hands.* Have students guess. *(Is it a clock?)* Then give another clue. For example, *I spy a rectangle you can see through.* (a window) Then give students a chance to give the clues.

● Divide students into groups of fluent and nonfluent speakers. Distribute materials to each group. Have groups work together to find as many shapes as they can in magazines and draw ones they find in the classroom. Have them label their shapes.

● Have groups share their work with the class. Compile the shape collections into a class book.

Multilevel Strategies

① Preproduction
Say: *Show me a rectangle in the classroom.*

② ③ Early Production and Speech Emergence
Have students name the shapes they found as a group.

④ ⑤ Intermediate and Advanced Fluency
Encourage students to name and describe shapes.

 LOG ON Visit **www.mmhmath.com** to find printable **Vocabulary Cards** that help build academic language.

Procedure: Help students make these Foldables to write vocabulary words and definitions throughout the unit. Encourage students to use the Foldables as a study guide.

Foldables

by Dinah Zike

Three-Fold Pocket Book

1. Provide each student with a large sheet of paper. Have students fold a 3" tab along the long edge of the sheet. Fold this folded paper into thirds to create a three-pocket booklet.

2. Help your students glue or staple the ends of the pockets closed. Have them label the pockets as illustrated.

3. Students can use their Three-Fold Pocket Books by taking notes on the 3" × 5" index cards and storing them inside the appropriate pockets. At the

end of the unit, students can use their Three-Fold Pocket Books to review.

Notecards may include:

An angle is formed by two rays with the same endpoint.

Angles | Triangles | Quadrilaterals

This is
∠ XYZ

Foldables

by Dinah Zike

Three-Fold Pocket Book

1. Provide each student with a large sheet of paper. Have students fold a 3" tab along the long edge of the sheet. Fold this folded paper into thirds to create a three-pocket booklet.

2. Help your students glue or staple the ends of the pockets closed. Have them label the pockets as illustrated.

3. Students can use their Three-Fold Pocket Books by taking notes on 3" × 5" index cards and storing them inside the appropriate pockets. At the end

of the unit, students can use their Three-Fold Pocket Books to review.

Notecards may include:

A diameter is a chord that passes through the center of a circle. A radius is a line segment that connects the center to a point on the circle. The plural of radius is radii.

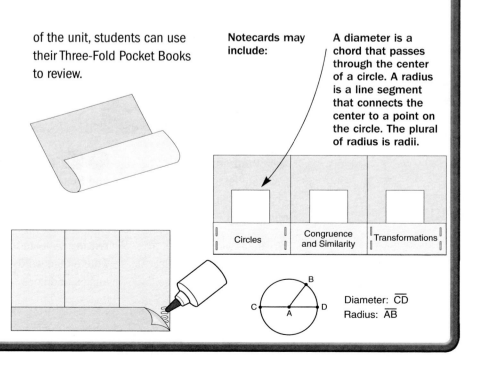

Circles | Congruence and Similarity | Transformations

Diameter: $\overline{CD}$
Radius: $\overline{AB}$

 35 minutes

▶ **Key Strategy**
Use visuals

▶ **Format**
Whole class and small groups

▶ **Math Vocabulary**
angle (acute, obtuse, right, straight), degree, endpoint, intersecting lines, line, line segment, parallel lines, perpendicular lines, protractor, ray

▶ **Daily Vocabulary**
glue, pencils, toothpicks

▶ **Resource**
Learning Resource 37

Materials
- glue
- protractors
- toothpicks

Assessment

Check students' mastery of geometry as they complete the lesson. See Assessment Checklist on page 185.

Home Connection

Have students look through newspapers and magazines at home to find examples of angles and lines. Ask them to bring in their examples to share with the class.

Angles and Lines

Math Objective	**ESL/TESOL Descriptors**
■ Measure, draw, and classify angles.	■ Follow oral and written directions, implicit and explicit
	■ Participate in full-class, group, and pair discussions.

Activate Prior Knowledge Point to circles, triangles, rectangles, and squares in the classroom, such as window or door frames. Ask students to tell you the names of the shapes. Then ask them to show you the the **parallel lines** and **right angles** in the rectangles and squares.

Hands-on Lesson Ask students to compare the angles in a rectangle and acute triangle. Identify the **acute angle.** Draw right and acute angles on the board. Measure them with a **protractor.** Write the number of **degrees.** Elicit that a right angle has 90°, and an acute angle has less than 90°. Draw an **obtuse angle** *(larger than 90°)* and a **straight angle** *(180°)* and compare and measure them.

- Draw **rays, lines,** and **line segments** on the board. Ask: *What is the difference between these?* Point out the arrows on the line that show that it goes on forever in both directions. Point out the one **endpoint** in the ray and the two endpoints on the line segment.

- Distribute Learning Resource 37: Angles and Lines. Name the angles again and ask students to find each one on the page. Repeat with parallel lines. Point out that these lines never cross, or intersect. Then have them find the **intersecting lines,** including **perpendicular lines.** Point out the 90° angle created by perpendicular lines.

- Divide students into groups and distribute toothpicks, glue, and protractors. Have students measure the angles and label the lines and angles. Then they can glue the toothpicks over the models.

Challenge Have students create a design of angles and lines and show the measurements.

Multilevel Strategies

❶ Preproduction
Have students point to the angles and lines as you name them.

Writing Invite students to draw and label an angle.

❷ ❸ Early Production and Speech Emergence
Have students name the lines and angles.

Writing Ask students to write all the words for angles and lines.

❹ ❺ Intermediate and Advanced Fluency
Say: *Tell me about these lines and angles.*

Writing Encourage students to write sentences comparing angles.

Name _____

Angles and Lines

Glue toothpicks over each angle. Choose words from the word box to label each angle. Measure the degree of each angle with a protractor and write it on the line.

perpendicular lines   parallel lines right angle   intersecting lines obtuse angle   acute angle straight angle

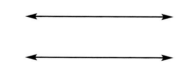

_____   _____

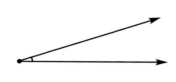

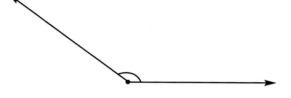

_____   _____

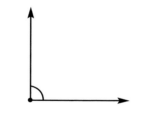

_____   _____

_____

Lesson 2

35 minutes

▶ **Key Strategy**
Use visuals

▶ **Format**
Whole class and pairs

▶ **Math Vocabulary**
closed figure, congruent, open figure, parallelogram, quadrilateral, rectangle, polygon, rhombus, trapezoid, triangle (acute, equilateral, isosceles, obtuse, right, scalene)

▶ **Daily Vocabulary**
diamond, kite

▶ **Resources**
Learning Resource 38
Teacher Tool 14

Materials
• colored markers
• protractor
• rulers

Assessment

Check students' understanding of geometric shapes as they complete the lesson. See Assessment Checklist on page 185. Remind students to work on their Foldables.

Home Connection

Ask students to find examples of figures around their homes, list them, and share the list with the class.

Triangles and Quadrilaterals

Math Objectives	**ESL/TESOL Descriptors**
■ Describe and classify geometric figures.	■ Participate in full-class, group, and pair discussions.
■ Find the unknown angles of a figure.	■ Request information and assistance.

Activate Prior Knowledge Ask students to draw a triangle, and 8, and a letter Z. Then ask them to mark a starting place of each and trace the shape with their finger. Ask: *What is different about these three figures?*

Hands-on Lesson Name the type of figures students drew. The 8 and the triangle are **closed figures.** They start and end at the same place. The triangle is also a **polygon** because it is made up lines that do not cross. The Z is an **open figure** because it starts and ends at different points.

• Distribute Learning Resource 38: Triangles and Quadrilaterals. Ask: *Are these figures open figures or closed figures? Are they polygons?*

• Discuss the angles in each triangle. **Acute triangles, right triangles,** and **obtuse triangles** are named for those type of angles. Have students measure and add the three angles in each triangle. The total degrees in each is always 180°.

• Discuss the sides of the triangles. The **equilateral triangle** has three **congruent** sides with the same size and shape; the **isosceles** has two congruent sides; and the **scalene** has none.

• Now look at the **quadrilaterals** (polygons with four sides and four angles). Point out which lines are parallel and congruent in each figure.

• Have students complete and label the figures on their Learning Resource.

• Ask students to cut shapes from Teacher Tool 14: Tangram Shapes. Have groups mix all the shapes and then sort them into triangles and quadrilaterals. Have groups color and glue the shapes to make a class book or bulletin board display.

Challenge Have students create word problems from the characteristics of their figures. For example, *What figure has four sides that are the same length?*

Multilevel Strategies

❶ Preproduction
Say: *Show me a (trapezoid).*

Writing Invite students to draw the shape you name.

❷❸ Early Production and Speech Emergence
Have students name the figures.

Writing Encourage students to write phrases about a figure.

❹❺ Intermediate and Advanced Fluency
Ask students to describe several figures.

Writing Challenge students to write sentences comparing two figures.

Name _____

Triangles and Quadrilaterals

Trace over the figures with a marker. Use one color for triangles and another color for quadrilaterals. Use the word box and write the name of each figure.

acute triangle	isosceles triangle	scalene triangle
obtuse triangle	equilateral triangle	right triangle
square	rhombus	trapezoid
rectangle	parallelogram	

 35 minutes

▶ **Key Strategy**
Use visuals

▶ **Format**
Whole class and small groups

▶ **Math Vocabulary**
center, central angle, chord, circle, compass, diameter, radius

▶ **Daily Vocabulary**
decoration, design, label

▶ **Resource**
Learning Resource 39

Materials
- beads, beans, and small pasta
- compasses (1 per group)
- ruler

Assessment

Check students' mastery of algebra as they complete the lesson. See page 185 for Assessment Checklist. Remind students to work on their Foldables.

Home Connection

Have students construct a circle at home using household items. They should label the parts of the drawing (radius, chord, and diameter). Encourage them to bring their drawings to class.

Circles

Math Objective
- Identify the center and the diameter of a circle.

ESL/TESOL Descriptors
- Follow oral and written directions, implicit and explicit.
- Ask and answer questions.

Activate Prior Knowledge Ask a student to draw a **circle** on the board. Draw perpendicular lines through the **center** and point to the four right angles. Ask: *How many degrees is each of these angles?* (90°) Ask students to add 90 four times to find out the total number of degees in a circle (360°).

Hands-on Lesson Distribute Learning Resource 39: Circles. Ask students to trace, from point **C** to point **D**, the **diameter** of the circle. Have them measure the diameter and note that it goes through the center of the circle. Then ask them to identify and measure the **radius.** Elicit that the radius is $\frac{1}{2}$ of the diameter. Say: *Find the chord from point E to point F, and the central angle formed by the radii AD and AB.* Read the sentences and ask students to complete the page.

- Display a **compass** and describe how to use it to draw circles of varying sizes. Explain that students will use their compasses to create circles; and then will decorate and label their circles.

- Divide the class into groups and distribute materials. Draw a key on the board like the one below as an example of what students will do. Students may choose any decoration for each part of the circle.

  KEY: black beads = radius; pasta = diameter; beans = chord

- When groups finish designing circles, have them make keys like the one above, and write measurements of the parts of their circles (*for example:* Our circle. The radius = 3 inches, etc.). Display the circles around the classroom.

Challenge Have students create word problems about circles. For example: *The diameter of a circle is 6 inches. What is its radius?*

Multilevel Strategies

❶ Preproduction
Say: *Show me the (radius) of your circle.*

Writing Encourage students to write the letters of the radius.

❷❸ Early Production and Speech Emergence
Ask students to name the chord of a circle.

Writing Invite students to write all the parts of the circle.

❹❺ Intermediate and Advanced Fluency
Ask students to tell the class about their circles.

Writing Have students write sentences about their circles.

Name _____

Circles

Fill in the blanks with the names for the parts of the circle.
Measure.

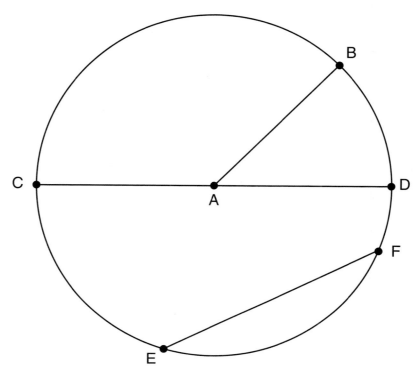

1. The name of the _____ is AB.

2. The length is _____.

3. The name of the _____ is CD.

4. The length is _____.

5. The name of the _____ is EF.

6. The length is _____.

 35 minutes

▶ **Key Strategy**
Use manipulatives

▶ **Format**
Whole class and pairs

▶ **Math Vocabulary**
congruent figures, corresponding parts, glide reflection, reflection (flip), rotation (turn), similar figures, transformation, translation (slide)

▶ **Daily Vocabulary**
grid, shapes

▶ **Resources**
Learning Resource 40
Teacher Tools 7 and 14

Materials
• paper or plastic shapes
• ruler

Assessment

Check students' mastery of geometry as they complete the lesson. See Assessment Checklist on page 185. Remind students to work on their Foldables.

Home Connection

Have students ask family members to help them identify congruent and similar shapes in their homes and list them to share with the class.

Congruence, Symmetry, and Transformation

Math Objectives
- Identify congruent and similar figures.
- Identify transformations.

ESL/TESOL Descriptors
- Share and request information.
- Listen to and imitate how others use English.

Activate Prior Knowledge Draw big and small rectangles and triangles. Point to two at a time, asking: *Are these figures the same?* Elicit that they are the same shape, but different sizes. Or they may be the same size and shape.

Hands-on Lesson Point to two figures identical in size and shape. Say: *These are* **congruent figures** *because they have the same shape and size.* Point to two different size rectangles and explain that they are **similar figures** because they have the same shape but not the same size.

- Distribute Teacher Tool 14: Tangram Shapes. Have students identify, cut out, and pair the triangles that are similar and those that are congruent.

- Distribute Learning Resource 40: Similar and Congruent to student pairs. Have students match the congruent and similar shapes. Point out that the angles have to be exactly the same for shapes to be congruent.

- Have students look at the bottom of the page. Talk about how congruent figures look if we change their position. Ask students to look at three **transformations** on the page: **translation (slide), rotation (turn),** and **reflection (flip).**

- Divide students into pairs. Distribute Teacher Tool 7: 10 × 10 Grid and paper or plastic shapes. Have students choose a figure. Ask them to show the three transformations of their figure on the grids, by tracing around the figure, moving it, and tracing again. Have them label and color their transformations.

Challenge Have students make translations, reflections of irregular shapes.

Multilevel Strategies

1 Preproduction
Have students point to congruent figures.

Writing Invite students to draw a pair of similar figures and label them.

2 3 Early Production and Speech Emergence
Ask: *Are these shapes congruent, or are they similar?*

Writing Ask students to write phrases about congruent figures. *(same shape, same size)*

4 5 Intermediate and Advanced Fluency
Invite students to describe what makes a figure congruent.

Writing Ask students to write sentences telling what makes shapes congruent or similar.

Name _____

Similar and Congruent

Draw a black line to connect similar figures. Draw a red line to connect the congruent figures.

Circle the word that describes the picture.

B B

reflection

rotation

translation

B ꞟ

translation

reflection

rotation

B ꟼ

rotation

reflection

translation

 UNIT 10

Problem Solving

Remind students of the basic steps of problem solving.

Problem Solving
Reading for Math

SKILL: Draw a Diagram
Model the skill using a word problem such as:

 Read

Patrick has 18 violet plants. He wants to plant them in a border around his garden. His garden is 3 feet by 4 feet. If he plants the violets 6 inches apart, how many more plants will he need to have enough to go all the way around?

 Plan

I can draw a diagram to show the garden.

 Solve

Think: 1 foot = 12 inches

4 feet

3 feet

$24 - 18 = 6$. Patrick needs 6 more plants.

 Look Back

Does my answer make sense? Yes. How can I check? I can think that each 4-foot side will have 8 plants. Each 3-foot side will have 6 plants. $8 + 8 + 6 + 6 = 28$. There are 4 corners. $28 - 4 = 24$.

Distribute **Math Center Card 10A** to students.

Math Center Card 10A

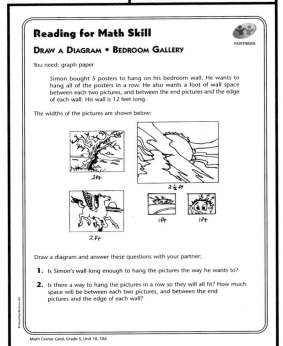

Reading for Math Skill

DRAW A DIAGRAM • BEDROOM GALLERY

You need: graph paper

Simon bought 5 posters to hang on his bedroom wall. He wants to hang all of the posters in a row. He also wants a foot of wall space between each two pictures, and between the end pictures and the edge of each wall. His wall is 12 feet long.

The widths of the pictures are shown below:

Draw a diagram and answer these questions with your partner:

1. Is Simon's wall long enough to hang the pictures the way he wants to?

2. Is there a way to hang the pictures in a row so they will all fit? How much space will be between each two pictures, and between the end pictures and the edge of each wall?

Math Center Card, Grade 5, Unit 10, 10A

STRATEGY: Find a Pattern
Model the strategy using a word problem such as:

 Read

Craig has to buy seats for the next performance in the Little Theater. 72 people from his drama school plan to attend. He knows there are 15 seats in a row. How many rows will his group sit in?

 Plan

I can make a table.

 Solve

I can show rows in one row and seats in the next.

rows	1	2	3	4	5
seats	15	30	45	60	75

Craig's group will sit in 5 rows.

 Look Back

Does my answer make sense? Yes. How can I check? I can guess and check. $15 \times 3 = 45$. Too low. $15 \times 5 = 75$. That's enough.

Distribute **Math Center Card 10B** to students.

Math Center Card 10B

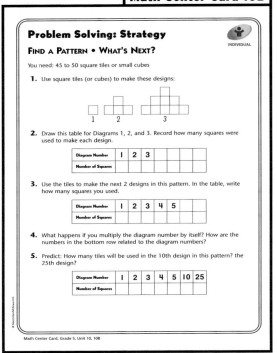

Problem Solving: Strategy

FIND A PATTERN • WHAT'S NEXT?

You need: 45 to 50 square tiles or small cubes

1. Use square tiles (or cubes) to make these designs:

    1   2   3

2. Draw this table for Diagrams 1, 2, and 3. Record how many squares were used to make each design.

Diagram Number	1	2	3	
Number of Squares				

3. Use the tiles to make the next 2 designs in this pattern. In the table, write how many squares you used.

Diagram Number	1	2	3	4	5
Number of Squares					

4. What happens if you multiply the diagram number by itself? How are the numbers in the bottom row related to the diagram numbers?

5. Predict: How many tiles will be used in the 10th design in this pattern? the 25th design?

Diagram Number	1	2	3	4	5	10	25
Number of Squares							

Math Center Card, Grade 5, Unit 10, 10B

Assessment Checklist

	STUDENT NAMES												
SCHOOL:													
TEACHER: **SCHOOL YEAR:**													
Mark: + = Mastery √ = Satisfactory – = Needs Improvement													
LEVEL OF LANGUAGE PROFICIENCY (1–5)													
MATH OBJECTIVES													
• Describe and classify geometric figures.													
• Measure, draw, and classify angles.													
• Identify congruent and similar figures.													
• Identify the center and the diameter of a circle.													
• Identify transformations.													
ESL/TESOL LISTENING/SPEAKING													
Follow oral and written directions, implicit and explicit.													
Listen to and imitate how others use English.													
Participate in full-class, group, and pair discussions.													
Practice new language.													
Request information and assistance.													
Share and request information.													
Use context to construct meaning.													
ESL/TESOL READING													
Read about subject matter information.													
Apply basic reading comprehension skills.													
Follow written directions, implicit and explicit.													
ESL WRITING													
Write to demonstrate comprehension.													
Write using spelling patterns and targeted English vocabulary.													

  **by Dinah Zike**

1 Preproduction
• Did students write the unit vocabulary?
• Did they copy the definitions?

2 **3** Early Production and Speech Emergence
• Did students label the tabs correctly?
• Did they write the vocabulary words?
• Did they copy the definitions?

4 **5** Intermediate and Advanced Fluency
• Did students write definitions for the unit vocabulary?
• Did they use correct spelling and grammar?

Angles   Triangles   Quadrilaterals

Circles   Congruence and Similarity   Transformations

Planner

Planner

Perimeter and Area

Visit www.mmhmath.com

Assessment
p. 203
• Assessment Checklist
• Foldables

Unit Activities		
• **Activity 1** Readiness Mapping Areas, p. 190	• **Activity 3** Estimating Circumference, p. 191	
• **Activity 2** Words and Triangles, p. 190	• **Activity 4** Fencing the Farm, p. 191	

Lessons	Key Objectives	Vocabulary	Materials	Resources
READ TOGETHER "A Square Story" by Michael Garin, pp. 188–189	**Math:** Find perimeter and area. **ESL/TESOL:** Goal 2, Standard 3; Goal 1, Standard 3.	area, care, each, every, inside, limit, plainly, pride		Graphic Organizer 4
UNIT WARM-UP Understanding Perimeter p. 192	**Math:** Find perimeter of a rectangle. **ESL/TESOL:** Goal 1, Standard 3; Goal 1, Standard 1.	perimeter	crayons or markers	
LESSON 1 Perimeter of Polygons pp. 194–195	**Math:** Find perimeter of regular and irregular figures. **ESL/TESOL:** Goal 2, Standard 2.	formula, perimeter,	construction paper, glue, pencils, rulers, scissors	Learning Resource 41 Teacher Tools 8 and 9
LESSON 2 Area of a Rectangle pp. 196–197	**Math:** Find area of rectangles. **ESL/TESOL:** Goal 2, Standard 1; Goal 1, Standard 3.	area, formula, square units, width	rulers	Learning Resource 42 Teacher Tool 8
LESSON 3 Parallelograms and Triangles pp. 198–199	**Math:** Find area of rectangles, triangles, and parallelograms. **ESL/TESOL:** Goal 2, Standard 2.	area, base, formula, height of a parallelogram	rulers, scissors	Learning Resource 43
LESSON 4 Trapezoids and Circles pp. 200–201	**Math:** Find perimeter and area of irregular figures. Find circumference of circles. **ESL/TESOL:** Goal 2, Standard 3.	area, base, circumference, formula, height	rulers, scissors, string	Learning Resource 44 Teacher Tools 6 and 13
PROBLEM SOLVING p. 202 • Skill: Distinguish Between Perimeter and Area • Strategy: Simpler Problem	Use skills and strategies to solve problems.			**Math Center Cards 11A, 11B**

See **Math at Home Family Guide** for additional math vocabulary, activities, and games in English, Spanish, and Haitian Creole.

English Vocabulary

Dear Family: Please help your child practice the key vocabulary words for this unit.

area the number of square units needed to cover the inside of a figure

base a side of a polygon, usually the one at the bottom

circumference the distance around a circle

compound figure a shape that is made up of two or more shapes

formula an equation with at least two variables, showing how one variable depends on the other variable or variables

height of a parallelogram the length of a line segment from one side of the parallelogram to the side parallel to it, drawn perpendicular to both of the sides

perimeter the distance around a closed figure

square unit a unit for measuring area, such as a square inch or a square centimeter

Vocabulario en español

Estimados familiares: Por favor ayuden a su hijo/a a practicar las palabras del vocabulario de esta unidad.

área número de unidades cuadradas necesarias para cubrir el interior una figura

base lado de un polígono, por lo regular el de la parte inferior

circunferencia contorno de un círculo

figura compuesta figura que está formada por dos o más figuras

fórmula ecuación con por lo menos dos variables, que expresa cómo una variable depende de otra variable o variables

altura de un paralelogramo longitud de un segmento de recta que va desde un lado de un paralelogramo hasta el lado paralelo a éste, y que es perpendicular a ambos lados

perímetro longitud del contorno de una figura cerrada

unidad cuadrada unidad para medir el área, como la pulgada cuadrada o el centímetro cuadrado

Vokabilè an kreyòl

Chè paran: Tanpri ede pitit la pratike mo vokabilè nan seksyon sa a.

sifas kantite inite kare ou bezwen pou kouvri anndan yon fòm

baz pati yon poligon, trè souvan s–ak anba a

sikonferans distans otou yon sèk

fòm konpoze yon fòm ki fèt ak de osnon plizyè fòm

fòmil yon ekwasyon ak o mwens de varyab, ki montre

kouman yon varyab depann de youn osnon plizye varyab

otè yon paralelogram mezi liy yon segman soti nan yon kote paralelogram nan pou rive kote paralel li a, li fòme yon liy pepandikilè de kote yo

perimèt distans otou yon fòm ki fèmen

mèt kare yon inite pou mezire kote, pa egzanp pye kare osnon santimèt

A Square Story

by Michael Garin

 25 minutes

Math Objective
- Find perimeter and area.

ESL Objectives
- Connect new information to information previously learned.
- Use context to construct meaning.

Reading Skill
- Summarize.

Vocabulary
area, care, each, every, inside, limit, plainly, pride

Before Reading

Build Background/Oral Language
Look at the title and the illustration. Predict what the poem is about.

Draw a rectangle and label length and width. Ask: **How can I find the area?** Invite a volunteer to measure the sides and find the area. Ask: **How can I find the perimeter?** Repeat the activity.

During Reading
- Read the poem through once without stopping as students track the text.
- Reread the poem slowly with students repeating each line. Encourage them to ask about new or difficult words.
- Read the poem in unison.

Phonological/Phonemic Awareness
Write *length* and *width* on the board. Underline *th*. Say the unvoiced /*th*/ sound. Say: /*th*/ **length** /*th*/ **width.** Brainstorm other words with the same sound, list them on the board and practice them. (*breath, with, thumb, thick, thanks, through, path, north, south, moth*)

After Reading

Hand out the Graphic Organizer 4: Main Idea and Supporting Details. Ask students to **summarize** the main idea of the poem. (*to find out how big the square is*) Ask students to write the question in the large box and fill in the other boxes with the directions for finding the perimeter and area.

Art Have students draw a verse of the poem and label their illustration. Fluent speakers may choose to use speech bubbles.

Assessment

Observe fluency as students read the poem. See Assessment Checklist on page 203.

Multilevel Strategies

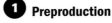

1 Preproduction
Ask students to point to words from the poem as you say them.

Writing Have students write or copy /*th*/ words as you say them.

2 3 Early Production and Speech Emergence
Ask students to read a line aloud from the poem.

Writing Invite students to write a phrase using a /*th*/ word.

4 5 Intermediate and Advanced Fluency
Ask students to read aloud the whole poem.

Writing Encourage students to write a few sentences using /*th*/ words.

A Square Story

by Michael Garin

*Here is a story to help you figure out
the area—and the perimeter—of any square you meet.*

"How big a square are you?"
Asked Marta to the square.
"If you mean my area—
Multiply with care.
My length times my width
And may I say with pride,
In square units you will get
the area inside."

"But if you want perimeter,"
(he didn't want to limit her).
"Add up each and every side
And you will plainly see
The distance around my figure
Is the perimeter of me."

Activities

Readiness

PARTNERS

ACTIVITY 1

Mapping Areas

YOU NEED
graph paper a political map of the United States

- Look at a map of the United States. Find the states of Colorado, Kansas, North Dakota, South Dakota, and Wyoming. They are almost rectangles.

- Work with a partner to draw a pretend rectangular country on graph paper. Divide it into rectangular and square states. Make the states different sizes. You and your partner fill up all of your pretend country. Name each state and find its area. List the states in order of increasing area. What do you notice about the sum of the state areas?

WYOMING   NORTH DAKOTA   COLORADO   KANSAS

Area of Rectangles

INDIVIDUAL

ACTIVITY 2

Words and Triangles

- Find the area of each triangle. Write down and group together the letters of those triangles with the same area. Rearrange the letters in each group to form a word. Then rearrange the words to form a sentence about math.

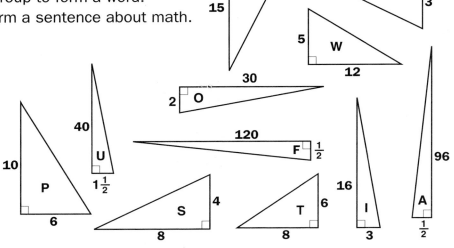

See answers on p. 293.

Explore Area of Triangle

© Macmillan/McGraw-Hill

Activities

Game Zone

ACTIVITY 3

SMALL GROUP

Estimating Circumference

- **As a group:** Find 10 circular objects in the room, for example, a wastebasket, clock, or a cup. With your partners, decide on a *nearest measure* for the circumference of each object. For example, describe the circumference of the wastebasket to the *nearest centimeter*.

- **Individually:** Estimate the circumference of each object. Write your estimates down. (Hint: Try estimating the diameter of the object first.)

- Measure the 10 objects with your partners. Determine the difference between the actual circumference and your estimate for each object. The player whose estimate is closest to the actual measurement of an object wins 1 point. The player with the most points wins.

YOU NEED
metric ruler
measuring tape

Explore Circumference of Circles

PARTNERS

ACTIVITY 4

Fencing the Farm

Estimate to solve. Work with your partner.

1. Farmer Dell has 1,000 km of fencing. Does he have enough to enclose his farm? Explain your reasoning.

2. What if he buys the land inside the dotted lines? He wants to use fencing to separate this area from the rest of his farm. How much more fencing will he need?

230 km

39 km

117 km

78 km

350 km

See answers on p. 293.

Perimeter of Polygons

© Macmillan/McGraw-Hill

Understanding Perimeter

▶ **Key Strategy**
Use manipulatives

▶ **Format**
Whole class and
small groups

▶ **Math Vocabulary**
perimeter

▶ **Daily Vocabulary**
offices, rooms

▶ **Materials**
crayons or markers

Math Objective	ESL/TESOL Descriptors
■ Find perimeter of a rectangle.	■ Practice new language. ■ Share and request information.

Activate Prior Knowledge Point to a corner of the room. Elicit from students that the corners come together at right angles. Discuss the fact that rooms are almost always rectangles or squares and have four right angles.

Hands-on Lesson Draw a floor plan of the classroom on the board with students. Draw the desks, bookcases, tables, doors, window, chalkboards, chairs, rugs, etc. Where appropriate, use other shapes, such as circles for globes.

• Discuss that a floor plan is a bird's-eye view of a room. You are looking down from above. Elicit the names of professionals that use floor plans in their work: decorators, architects, building managers, contractors, builders, and anyone who wants to rearrange furniture.

• Brainstorm different places floor plans are used, such as medical and dental offices, businesses, homes, theaters, hotels, sports arenas, and so on.

• Distribute materials to students in small groups. Ask each group to think of a place for which they will make a floor plan. They may combine their papers into one large floor plan if they desire, or they may work on different rooms in a house, theater and so on.

• When they are done, have them measure around the sides of their floor plans. Tell them to measure each of the four sides and then add up the total. Explain that they just measured the **perimeter** of their rooms. Define perimeter as the outside edge of a shape.

Multilevel Strategies

1 Preproduction
Invite students to trace their finger around the perimeter of their paper.

2 3 Early Production and Speech Emergence
Ask students to tell you what kind of room they designed.

4 5 Intermediate and Advanced Fluency
Encourage students to describe their floor plans.

LOG ON Visit **www.mmhmath.com** to find printable **Vocabulary Cards** that help build academic language.

Procedure: Help students make these Foldables to write vocabulary words and definitions throughout the unit. Encourage students to use the Foldables as a study guide.

 **by Dinah Zike**

Three-Tab Venn Diagram

1. Provide each student with a sheet of paper. Fold the paper in half like a hot dog. Then, fold into thirds.

2. Have your students draw two overlapping ovals and label them as illustrated.

3. Help your students cut the top layer along both fold lines to make three tabs.

4. As students work through the unit, have them take notes and record main ideas under the tabs of their Three-Tab Venn Diagram. Use main idea phrases, vocabulary words, lists, and examples.

Labels may include:

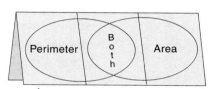

Perimeter is the distance around the outside of a closed figure.

Area is the number of square units needed to cover the inside of a figure.

 **by Dinah Zike**

Three-Tab Book

1. Provide each student with a sheet of paper. Fold the paper in half like a hot dog. Then, fold into thirds.

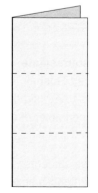 

2. Have your students label the tabs as illustrated.

3. Help your students cut the top layer along both fold lines to make three tabs.

4. As students work through the unit, have them take notes and record main ideas under the tabs of their Three-Tab Book. Use main idea phrases, vocabulary words, lists, and examples.

Labels may include:

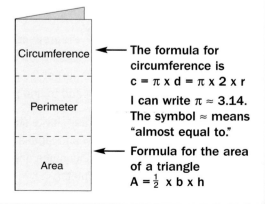

The formula for circumference is $c = \pi \times d = \pi \times 2 \times r$

I can write $\pi \approx 3.14$. The symbol $\approx$ means "almost equal to."

Formula for the area of a triangle $A = \frac{1}{2} \times b \times h$

⏱ **35 minutes**

▶ **Key Strategy**
Use charts and graphs

▶ **Format**
Whole class and individual

▶ **Math Vocabulary**
formula, perimeter

▶ **Daily Vocabulary**
around, edge, length, width

▶ **Resources**
Learning Resource 41
Teacher Tools 8 and 9

Materials
- construction paper
- glue/tape
- pencils
- rulers (inch, metric)
- scissors

Assessment

Check students' understanding of perimeter as they complete the lesson. See Assessment Checklist on page 203. Remind students to work on their Foldables.

Home Connection

Have students find the perimeter of a room in their house. Ask them to present their findings to the class.

Perimeter of Polygons

Math Objective	**ESL/TESOL Descriptors**
■ Find perimeter of regular and irregular figures.	■ Analyze, synthesize, and infer from information. ■ Represent and interpret information visually.

Activate Prior Knowledge Look together at the floor plans students made in the Warm-Up lesson. Say: *We measured around the edges of our rectangles. What did we measure?* (*perimeter*) Tell students that now you will find the **perimeter** of other shapes. Review names of geometric figures.

Hands-on Lesson Draw a quadrilateral with four different length sides and write numbers to show the lengths of the sides. Ask: *How do we find the perimeter?* Elicit that they have to add all four sides. Ask a volunteer to show this in a math sentence. Write the **formula** for the perimeter of a quadrilateral, $P = s_1 + s_2 + s_3 + s_4$. (Explain that s is for *side*).

- Ask: *What can the formula be for rectangles?* Show that since there are two equal lengths and widths, the formula is $P = 2l + 2w$. Then ask students to figure out a formula for squares and rhombuses. Elicit that there are 4 equal sides, so the formula is $P = 4s$. Also do triangles. ($P = s_1 + s_2 + s_3$)

- Distribute rulers and Learning Resource 41: Perimeter. Ask students to find the perimeters of the figures, using the written numbers. Then have students draw a figure on the grid and measure to find its perimeter in inches. Ask them to draw additional figures on grid paper (Teacher Tools 8 and 9: Graph Paper and Inch Graph Paper).

- Distribute construction paper to groups. Have each student make a different regular or irregular shape with as many sides as they want, taking up one sheet of paper. Have them find perimeters and figure out which shapes in the group have the longest and shortest perimeters.

Challenge Have students find the perimeter of a shape with 30 or 40 sides.

Multilevel Strategies

❶ Preproduction
Ask students to show you what part of the shape they add to find perimeter.

Writing Invite students to draw and label a shape with its name and perimeter.

❷ ❸ Early Production and Speech Emergence
Have students name a shape and its formula for perimeter.

Writing Encourage students to list the perimeter formulas they know for various shapes.

❹ ❺ Intermediate and Advanced Fluency
Ask students to explain the formula for perimeter of a square.

Writing Have students explain in sentences how they find perimeter.

41

Name _____

Perimeter

Use the measurements on the shapes to find the perimeter.

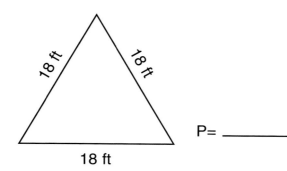

P= _____

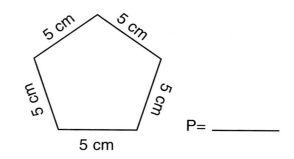

P= _____

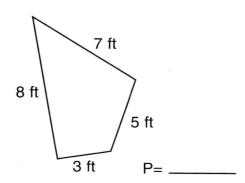

P= _____

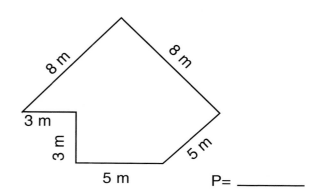

P= _____

Now draw your own polygon. Measure in centimeters and find the perimeter.

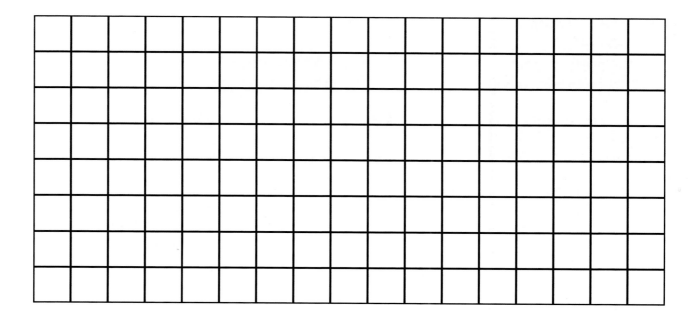

Lesson 2

35 minutes

▶ **Key Strategy**
Use charts and graphs

▶ **Format**
Whole class and pairs

▶ **Math Vocabulary**
area, formula, square units

▶ **Daily Vocabulary**
length, measure, object,
squares, units, width

▶ **Resources**
Learning Resource 42
Teacher Tool 8

Materials
• rulers

Assessment

Check students' mastery of
finding area as they complete the
lesson. See Assessment Checklist
on page 203. Remind students
to work on their Foldables.

Home Connection

Have students find the area of a
room at home. Ask them to
share their findings with the
class.

Area of a Rectangle

Math Objective	**ESL/TESOL Descriptors**
■ Find area of rectangles.	■ Participate in full-class, group, and pair discussions.
	■ Practice new language.

Activate Prior Knowledge Review the formulas for finding the perimeter of
squares and rhombuses, rectangles, quadrilaterals, and triangles. Say: ***You know
how to measure the perimeter—the outside edge of a figure. Now how do you
measure the space inside?***

Hands-on Lesson Ask when people might need to know the space, or **area,**
inside a room (for example, if you were buying a carpet or furniture).

● Distribute Teacher Tool 8: Graph Paper. Establish that each square is an inch.
Have students create a rectangle, measure and label the lengh and width, and
find the perimeter. Say: ***How do you find the area?*** Ask students to count the
squares inside the figure.

● Ask: ***What can the formula for area be? What is the best way to count the
squares more quickly?*** (*multiply*) Write the **formula** for area for a rectangle:
$A = lw$. (*area = length × width*) Explain that area is measured in **square units.** For
example, if the sides are measured in inches, the area is in square inches.

● Write the formula for area of a square: $A = s^2$. Remind students that the 2 is an
exponent which means to the power of 2. Say: ***Area = side squared.***

● Distribute Learning Resource 42: Perimeter and Area. Divide class into groups.
Have them find perimeter and the area of one of their squares by using formulas
and then counting squares to check themselves.

Challenge Ask students what happens to the area if you double the sides.

Multilevel Strategies

1 Preproduction
Have students point to the
letters in the formulas as
you say the words.

Writing Invite them to
draw and label the area of
a square.

**2 3 Early Production
and Speech Emergence**
Ask: ***What is the formula
for area of a square?***

Writing Encourage
students to write shapes
and their area formulas.

**4 5 Intermediate
and Advanced Fluency**
Ask students to explain
how to find area.

Writing Have students
write the steps for finding
area.

42

Name _____

Perimeter and Area

Choose one of the four squares. Measure to find its perimeter and area. Write your measurements on the square.

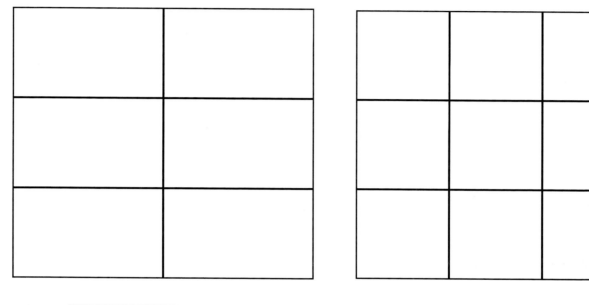

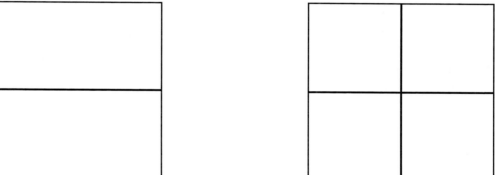

Write the formula for the perimeter of a square.

_____

 35 minutes

▶ **Key Strategy**
Use manipulatives

▶ **Format**
Whole class and pairs

▶ **Math Vocabulary**
area, base, formula, height
of a parallelogram

▶ **Daily Vocabulary**
half

▶ **Resource**
Learning Resource 43

Materials
- rulers
- scissors

Assessment

Check students' mastery of
finding area and perimeter as
they complete the lesson. See
Assessment Checklist on
page 203. Remind students to
work on their Foldables.

Home Connection

Encourage students to practice
finding the area of triangles and
rectangles at home with a family
member. Encourage them to
share their results with the class.

Parallelograms and Triangles

Math Objective	**ESL/TESOL Descriptors**
▪ Find area of rectangles, triangles, and parallelograms.	▪ Select, connect, and explain information.
	▪ Request information and assistance.

Activate Prior Knowledge Review the formulas for area of square and area
of a rectangle. Draw a triangle and a parallelogram on the board. Say: *You know
how to find the area for a rectangle or a square. How do we find the area of a
parallelogram or a triangle?*

Hands-on Lesson Ask students to find objects in the classroom that have the
same shape as those taught in this lesson. Divide students into pairs and
distribute scissors, rulers and Learning Resource 43: Rectangles, Triangles, and
Parallelograms.

- First have students identify each figure. Then have them cut out the rectangle at
  the bottom of the sheet and place it over the rectangle at the top to see that it is
  the same size. Next they cut it on the diagonal dotted line into two congruent
  triangles. Say: *What part of the rectangle is each triangle?* ($\frac{1}{2}$)

- Ask students to arrange the two triangles to form a parallelogram, on top of the
  one on the page. Say: *What can you tell me about the area of the rectangle and
  the parallelogram?* (*They are the same.*) *What about the area of one triangle?*
  (*It is half the area of the rectangle and the parallelogram.*)

- Point out the **base** and **height;** locate them on the figures. Write the *rectangle,
  parallelogram, triangle* on the board. Underneath each heading, write the **formula**
  for area: $A = l \times w$, $A = b \times h$, $A = \frac{1}{2}b \times h$. Explain the letters, and have students
  find them on their sheets. Then have them figure out the area of each figure
  using the formulas.

- Provide bases and heights for right triangles and parallelograms on the board
  and ask pairs to work together to find the areas using the two formulas.

Multilevel Strategies

1 **Preproduction**
Have students point to the
letters in the formulas as
you say the words.

Writing Invite them to
draw a triangle and write
the formula.

2 3 **Early Production
and Speech Emergence**
Have students say the
formula as you write them.

Writing Encourage
students to list the three
figures and their formulas.

4 5 **Intermediate
and Advanced Fluency**
Ask students to explain the
two formulas.

Writing Ask students to
write sentences telling the
steps of finding area.

Name _____

Rectangles, Triangles, and Parallelograms

Use these shapes to find area.

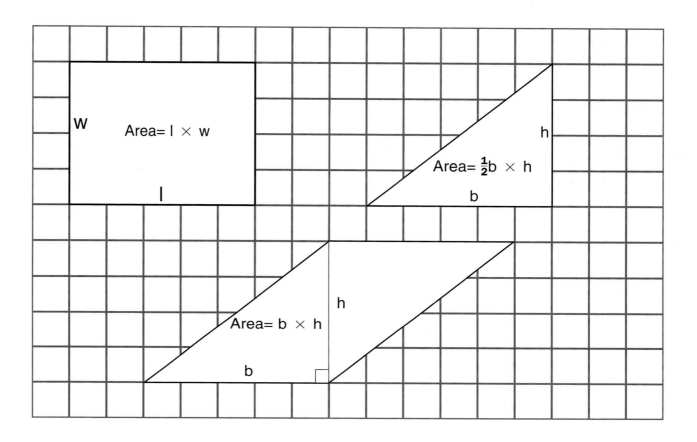

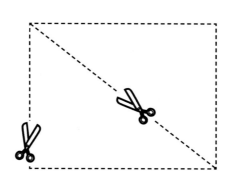

 45 minutes

▶ **Key Strategy**
Use visuals

▶ **Format**
Whole class and pairs

▶ **Math Vocabulary**
area, base, circumference, formula, height

▶ **Daily Vocabulary**
half

▶ **Resources**
Learning Resource 44
Teacher Tools 6 and 13

Materials
• rulers
• scissors
• string

Assessment

Check students' mastery of area and perimeter as they complete the lesson. See Assessment Checklist on page 203. Remind students to work on their Foldables.

Home Connection

Encourage students to find circles at home with family members, and find their circumference. Have them report their findings to the class.

Trapezoids and Circles

Math Objectives	**ESL/TESOL Descriptors**
■ Find perimeter and area of irregular figures.	■ Use context to construct meaning.
■ Find circumference of circles.	■ Select, connect, and explain information.

Activate Prior Knowledge Draw a parallelogram and review the formula for finding the area, $A = b \times h$. Mark its **height** and **base** and ask the class to find the **area.** Draw a trapezoid on the board. Explain that you can find the area of a trapezoid by using the **formula** for a parallelogram.

Hands-on Lesson Pair fluent and nonfluent students and distribute grid paper (Teacher Tool 6), scissors, and rulers (Teacher Tool 13). Have students draw and cut out two identical trapezoids. Turn one upside down and tape the side to the other trapezoid. Ask: *What shape is this now?* (*parallelogram*) Point out that the two figures have the same height, and the base equals the trapezoid's base a + base b. The area of one trapezoid will be equal to $\frac{1}{2}$ the area of this parallelogram, so the formula for the area of the trapezoid is: $A = \frac{1}{2} \times h \times (base\ a + base\ b)$.

• Distribute Learning Resource 44: Trapezoids and Circles. Have students find the area of the trapezoid.

• Now ask students to look at the circles on the page. Distribute string to pairs and ask them to cut string the length of the diameter, and then to cut another the length of the distance around the outside, the **circumference.** Ask them to compare the strings. The circumference is about three times the diameter. The actual number if you divide circumference by diameter $= $ pi, or π, which rounds to 3.14. Write the formula $C = \pi d$ or $C = 2\pi r$. Guide students to complete the page.

Cultural Link Ancient Greeks discovered and named *pi* (π), the number you get by dividing the circumference of a circle by its diameter (3.14156…).

Multilevel Strategies

1 Preproduction
As you read a formula, have students point to the letters.

Writing Invite them to write the formula for area of a trapezoid.

2 3 Early Production and Speech Emergence
Ask students to say the formula for area of a trapezoid.

Writing Encourage students to write the shape names and formulas they have learned for area.

4 5 Intermediate and Advanced Fluency
Ask students to explain how to find area of various shapes.

Writing Challenge students to write sentences telling steps of finding area.

Name _____

Trapezoids and Circles

Measure the trapezoid. Write the measurements and find the area.

Area = _____

Measure the radius and the diameter of each circle. Then find the circumference.

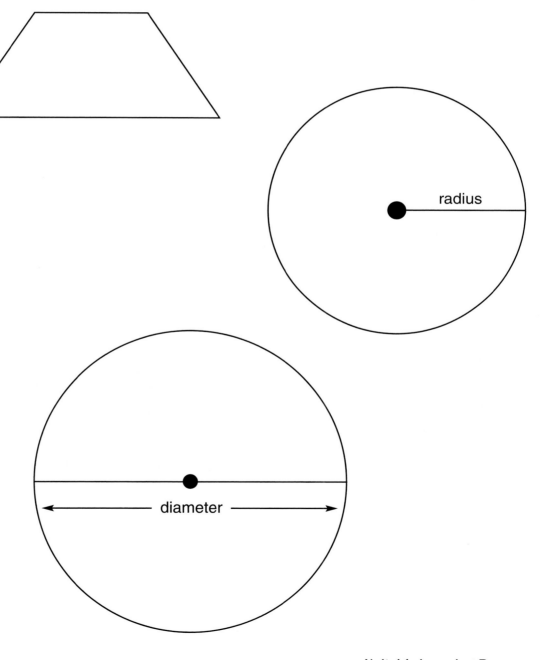

Problem Solving
Reading for Math

Read → Plan → Solve → Look Back

Remind students of
the basic steps
of problem solving.

SKILL: Distinguish Between Perimeter and Area
Model the skill using a word problem such as:

 Read

Martha wants to tile the floor of her patio. The patio is 8 feet long and 9 feet across. The tiles are 1 foot square. She bought 35 tiles. Did she guess correctly?

 Plan

I need to decide what to do to find the number of tiles. Then I can compare my answer to 35 tiles.

 Solve

Think: Martha wants to cover the surface of the patio. I need to find the area. I can find area by multiplying length times width. $9 \times 8 = 72$. Martha needs 72 tiles. She did not compute correctly.

 Look Back

Does my answer make sense? Yes. I can draw a diagram to check. What mistake did Martha make? $8 + 9 + 8 + 9 = 35$. Martha found the perimeter instead of the area.

Distribute **Math Center Card 11A** to students.

Math Center Card 11A

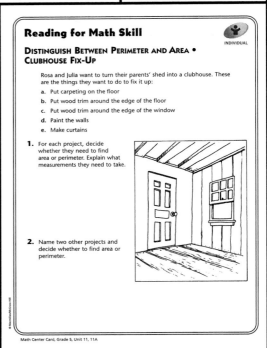

Reading for Math Skill

DISTINGUISH BETWEEN PERIMETER AND AREA • CLUBHOUSE FIX-UP

Rosa and Julia want to turn their parents' shed into a clubhouse. These are the things they want to do to fix it up:

a. Put carpeting on the floor
b. Put wood trim around the edge of the floor
c. Put wood trim around the edge of the window
d. Paint the walls
e. Make curtains

1. For each project, decide whether they need to find area or perimeter. Explain what measurements they need to take.

2. Name two other projects and decide whether to find area or perimeter.

Math Center Card, Grade 5, Unit 11, 11A

STRATEGY: Solve a Simpler Problem
Model the strategy using a word problem such as:

 Read

Chloe drew a rectangle that is 2 feet by 3 feet. Colin wants to draw a figure with a different shape but the same area. He makes the longer side of his figure 4 feet. What are the dimensions of his figure? What shape is it?

 Plan

I can convert all the measures to inches.

 Solve

I can find the area of Chloe's rectangle using inches. 24 inches $\times$ 36 inches = 864 inches Chloe's rectangle is 864 square inches.
Think: The longer side of Colin's figure is twice the size of 24 inches or 48 inches. $864 \div 48 = 18$. Colin's rectangle is 48 inches by 18 inches.

 Look Back

Does my answer make sense? Yes. I can covert the dimensions of Colins rectangle to feet. Colin's rectangle is 4 feet by $1\frac{1}{2}$ feet.

Distribute **Math Center Card 11B** to students.

Math Center Card 11B

Problem Solving: Strategy

SOLVE A SIMPLER PROBLEM • SUBTRACTING SHAPES

You need: construction paper, rulers, scissors, glue, compass (optional)

1. Draw a large shape on a piece of construction paper. Draw one of the shapes listed. Use a ruler to draw straight lines. Use a compass if you draw a circle. Cut out your shape.

square
rectangle
parallelogram
triangle
circle

2. Now draw a different shape *inside* your first shape. Again, draw one of the shapes listed. Cut it out, too.

3. Glue your shape to a different-colored piece of construction paper. Now find the area of your shape. You can find the area of the shape by doing simpler problems.

4. Measure each shape to the nearest centimeter.

5. First, find the area of the large shape. Write the area on the back.

6. Next, find the area of the small shape. Write the area on the back.

7. Finally, subtract the area of the small shape from the area of the large shape.

8. Share your paper with your partner. Find the area of your partner's shape. Compare results.

Math Center Card, Grade 5, Unit 11, 11B

Assessment Checklist

	STUDENT NAMES											
SCHOOL:												
TEACHER: **SCHOOL YEAR:**												
Mark: + = Mastery ✓ = Satisfactory – = Needs Improvement												
LEVEL OF LANGUAGE PROFICIENCY (1–5)												
MATH OBJECTIVES												
• Find perimeter of a rectangle.												
• Find perimeter of regular and irregular figures.												
• Find area of rectangles, triangles, and parallelograms.												
• Find circumference of circles.												
ESL/TESOL LISTENING/SPEAKING												
Analyze, synthesize, and infer from information.												
Connect new information to information previously learned.												
Participate in full-class, group, and pair discussion.												
Represent and interpret information visually.												
Request information and assistance.												
Select, connect, and explain information.												
ESL/TESOL READING												
Read about subject matter information.												
Apply basic reading comprehension skills.												
Follow written directions, implicit and explicit.												
ESL WRITING												
Write to demonstrate comprehension.												
Write using spelling patterns and targeted English vocabulary												

  **by Dinah Zike**

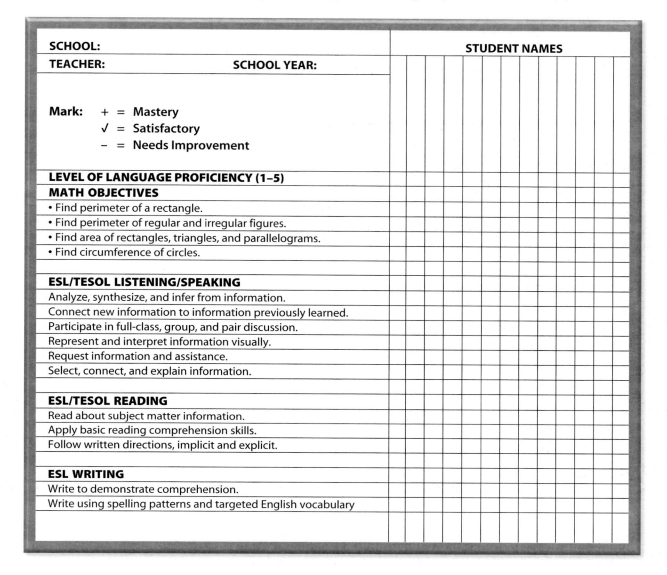

1 **Preproduction**
• Did students write the unit vocabulary?
• Did they copy the definitions?

2 **3** **Early Production and Speech Emergence**
• Did students label the tabs correctly?
• Did they write the vocabulary words?
• Did they copy the definitions?

4 **5** **Intermediate and Advanced Fluency**
• Did students write definitions for the unit vocabulary?
• Did they use correct spelling and grammar?

Circumference

Perimeter

Area

Perimeter | Both | Area

UNIT 12

Planner

Surface Area, Volume, and Symmetry

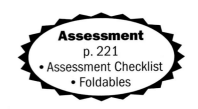

Assessment
p. 221
• Assessment Checklist
• Foldables

LOG ON Visit **www.mmhmath.com**

Unit Activities
- **Activity 1** (Readiness) Following Orders, p. 208
- **Activity 2** Measure by Measure, p. 208
- **Activity 3** Pattern Block Symmetry, p. 209
- **Activity 4** Symmetrical Polygons, p. 209

Lessons	Key Objectives	Vocabulary	Materials	Resources
READ TOGETHER "Surprising Symmetry," by Betsy Franco, pp. 206–207	**Math:** Find line and rotational symmetry. **ESL/TESOL:** Goal 1, Standard 3.	both, bugs, butterflies, explain, leaves, same, symmetry		
UNIT WARM-UP Understanding Three-Dimensional Figures p. 210	**Math:** Identify 3-dimensional figures. **ESL/TESOL:** Goal 1, Standard 3; Goal 2, Standard 2.	3-dimensional figure, cone, cube, cylinder, pyramid, rectangular prism, sphere	balls, blocks, boxes, cans, glue, magazines, poster board, scissors	
LESSON 1 Three-Dimensional Figures and Nets pp. 212–213	**Math:** Identify 3-dimensional figures and nets. **ESL/TESOL:** Goal 1, Standard 3; Goal 2, Standard 2.	base, cone, cube, cylinder, edge, face, net, prism, pyramid, sphere, vertices	compass, glue/ tape, ruler, scissors, 3-D figures	Learning Resource 45 Teacher Tools 4 and 9
LESSON 2 Surface Area and Volume pp. 214–215	**Math:** Find surface area of rectangular prisms; Find volume of rectangular prisms. **ESL/TESOL:** Goal 2, Standard 2.	surface area, volume	connecting cubes, glue/tape, pencils, ruler, scissors	Learning Resource 46
LESSON 3 Line and Rotational Symmetry pp. 216–217	**Math:** Find line symmetry. Find rotational symmetry. **ESL/TESOL:** Goal 2, Standard 2.	line of symmetry, point of rotation, rotational symmetry	pencils or pens, ruler, scissors	Learning Resource 47 Teacher Tool 9
LESSON 4 Tessellations pp. 218–219	**Math:** Identify tessellations. **ESL/TESOL:** Goal 2, Standard 2.	tessellate, tessellation	markers, pattern blocks, poster board, rulers, scissors	Learning Resource 48 **Teacher Tool 8**
PROBLEM SOLVING p. 220 • Skill: Follow Directions to Describe Figures • Strategy: Draw a Diagram	Use skills and strategies to solve problems.			**Math Center Cards 12A, 12B**

Math at Home

See **Math at Home Family Guide** for additional math vocabulary, activities, and games in English, Spanish, and Haitian Creole.

English Vocabulary

Dear Family: *Please help your child practice the key vocabulary words for this unit.*

cone a 3-dimensional figure that has a circular base and one curved surface from the base to a vertex

cube a rectangular prism in which every face is a square

cylinder a 3-dimensional figure having two parallel congruent circular bases and a curved surface connecting the two bases

edge a line segment where two faces of a 3-dimensional figure meet

face a flat side of a 3-dimensional figure

prism a 3-dimensional figure formed by flat surfaces that have the shape of polygons; two of the faces must be congruent and parallel, the rest of the faces must be rectangular

sphere a 3-dimensional figure that is the set of all points that are the same distance from a given point, called the center

surface area the total area of the surface of a 3-dimensional figure

Vocabulario en español

Estimados familiares: *Por favor ayuden a su hijo/a a practicar las palabras del vocabulario de esta unidad.*

cono figura tridimensional que tiene una base circular y una superficie curva desde la base a un vértice

cubo prisma rectangular en el cual cada cara es un cuadrado

cilindro figura tridimensional que tiene dos bases circulares, paralelas y congruentes, y una superficie curva que las conecta

arista segmento de recta donde se unen dos caras de una figura tridimensional

cara lado plano de una figura tridimensional

prisma figura tridimensional formada por superficies planas que tienen la forma de polígonos; dos de las caras deben ser congruentes y paralelas, las demás caras deben ser rectangulares

esfera figura tridimensional formada por un conjunto de puntos que están a la misma distancia de un punto determinado, llamado centro

área total medida total de la superficie de una figura tridimensional

Vokabilè an kreyòl

Chè paran: *Tanpri ede pitit la pratike mo vokabilè nan seksyon sa a.*

kone yon fòm twa dimansyon ki gen yon baz sikilè ak yon sifas koube depi baz la jiska tèt chapito a

kib yon "prism" rektang kote chak fas yo se yon kare

silenn yon fòm twa dimansyon ki gen de paralèl ki menm ak baz sikilè ak yon koub nan sifas la ki konekte de baz yo

kwen yon liy kote de fas yon fòm twa dimansyon rankontre

fas kote plat yon fòm ak twa dimansyon

prism yon fòm twa dimansyon ki fòme pa sifas plat ki gen fòm poligon; de nan sifas yo dwe parèy ak paralèl, rès sifas yo dwe gen fòm rektang

esfè yon fòm twa dimansyon ki se gwoup tout pwen yo ki menm distans yon pwen done ki rele sant

sipèfisi total yon sifas ki gen yon fòm twa dimansyon

Surprising Symmetry

by Betsy Franco

 25 minutes

Math Objective
- Find line and rotational symmetry.

ESL Objectives
- Listen to and imitate how others use English.
- Represent and interpret information presented visually.

Reading Skill
- Main Idea and Supporting Details.

Vocabulary
both, bugs, butterflies, explain, leaves, same, symmetry

Before Reading

Build Background/Oral Language
Read the title of the poem. Point to the illustrations to give meaning to the word *symmetry*. Ask students to listen for things in the poem that have symmetry.

Cultural Link Symmetrical figures play an important part in the design of many art and household objects throughout the world. Encourage students to bring in a sample of a design that uses symmetric figures from their native culture.

During Reading

Read the poem once. Say: *I will read the poem again. Try to fill in the missing words.* Read again, this time leaving out words and pausing for students to call out the words. On a third reading, see if students can say the poem along with you.

Phonological/Phonemic Awareness
Write *butterflies, sides,* and *why*. Say each word and have students repeat. Elicit that these words all have the long /i/ sound. Point out that long /i/ has different spellings: *ie, i,* and *y*. Make a 3-column chart on the board, label the columns with the three spellings, and brainstorm words.

After Reading

Ask students to identify the main idea (*symmetry*) and the examples provided by the poet.

Art Invite students to make symmetrical paintings. Fold paper in half. On one side, dribble and splotch finger paint. Fold the paper, press, then open. Have student label colors and shapes of their art.

Assessment

Observe fluency as students read the poem. See Assessment Checklist on page 221.

Multilevel Strategies

1 Preproduction
Say: *Point to a word with a long i sound.*

Writing Have students copy and illustrate the first three lines of the poem.

2 3 Early Production and Speech Emergence
Say: *Name a word with a long i sound.*

Writing Have students draw and label a symmetrical shape or object from the poem.

4 5 Intermediate and Advanced Fluency
Ask: *What are some words that have a long i sound?*

Writing Ask students to write and illustrate a sentence about symmetry using a long *i* word.

Surprising Symmetry

by Betsy Franco

On leaves,
On bugs,
On butterflies,
Both sides are
quite the same.
But if you ask
your mother why,
she really can't explain.

Activities

Activities

© Macmillan/McGraw-Hill

INDIVIDUAL

Readiness

ACTIVITY 1

Following Orders

Put the following boxes in order from smallest to largest.

The dimensions of each box are:

Green Box: 12 cm x 3cm x 2cm
Red Box: 7cm x 2cm x 4 cm
Blue Box: 4cm x 4cm x 2cm
Yellow Box: 10cm x 2cm x 2cm
Orange Box: 8cm x 2cm x 2cm
Purple Box: 3cm x 5cm x 2cm

Build the boxes with centimeter cubes.
Draw a picture that shows the correct order for the boxes.

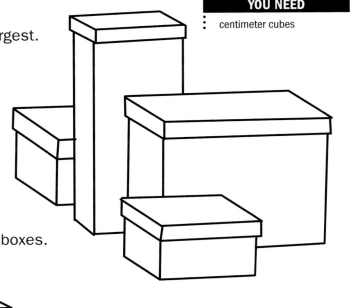

YOU NEED
centimeter cubes

See answers on p. 293.

Identify 3-Dimensional Figures

PARTNERS

ACTIVITY 2

Measure by Measure

Partner 1: Choose an object in the room that is a rectangular prism. For example, find a box, desk, or a book.

Partner 2: Choose another object with a different height, width, and length that you think has almost the same volume as the object of Partner 1.

- Each Partner: Use the tape measure to find the height, width, and length of the two objects. Using the formula $l \times w \times h = V$, find the volume of the two objects. Compare the volumes and see how close Partner 2's object was in volume to Partner 1's object. Switch roles, having Partner 2 choose the first object.

YOU NEED
metric measuring tape
centimeter cubes

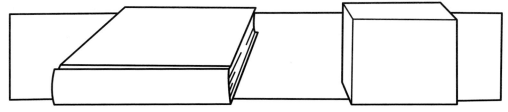

Volume of Rectangular Prisms

© Macmillan/McGraw-Hill

Game Zone
ACTIVITY 3

PARTNERS

Pattern Block Symmetry

- Put the pattern blocks in the paper bag.

- Take turns, pick up a pattern block out of the bag and say how many lines of symmetry you think it has. Your partner must check your guess by tracing the block and drawing the lines of symmetry with a ruler. You score a point for each correct guess. Your partner scores a point for each line of symmetry that you did not identify.

- After all six blocks have been picked, the student with the most points wins.

YOU NEED

six pattern blocks, one of each shape

ruler

paper bag

Line Symmetry

ACTIVITY 4

INDIVIDUAL

Symmetrical Polygons

YOU NEED

pattern blocks (optional)

dot, graph, or tracing paper

Draw or trace these regular polygons. Use pattern blocks when available. Drawing on dot or graph paper can help you make regular figures. Draw all possible lines of symmetry. Copy and complete the table. What pattern do you see?

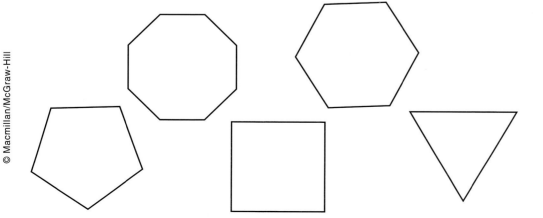

Polygon	Number of Lines of Symmetry
triangle	
square	
pentagon	
hexagon	
octagon	

See answers on p. 293.

Describe and Classify Geometric Figures

Understanding Three-Dimensional Figures

 **25 minutes**

▶ **Key Strategy**
Use manipulatives

▶ **Format**
Whole class
and small groups

▶ **Math Vocabulary**
3-dimensional figure, cone, cube, cylinder, pyramid, rectangular prism, sphere

▶ **Daily Vocabulary**
boxes, cans, containers, ice cream cone

▶ **Materials**
balls, blocks, boxes, cans, glue, magazines, poster board, scissors

Math Objective	**ESL/TESOL Descriptors**
▪ Identify 3-dimensional figures.	▪ Practice new language.
	▪ Select, connect, and explain information.

Activate Prior Knowledge Draw several 2-dimensional figures and ask students to name them. Then hold up some 3-dimensional figures, such as a box, a ball, or empty food containers of different sizes and shapes. Ask: **How are these shapes different from the ones on the board?** Elicit that we can hold them. They take up space.

Hands-on Lesson Discuss that the figures you drew on the board are 2-dimensional figures, which are drawn on a flat plane, whereas the containers, blocks, or balls are **3-dimensional.** Write a list of 3-dimensional figures on the board, such as **cube, sphere, cylinder, cone, rectangular prism, pyramid.**

- Draw an ice cream cone on the board. Elicit that the flat shape (in 2 dimensions) looks like a triangle. Ask: **How is a cone different from a triangle?** Elicit that a cone has three dimensions but a triangle has two dimensions. Hold up the containers or models of 3-D figures again and ask students what 2-D shapes they see in each one (a cube has squares, a pyramid has triangles, etc.).

- Draw 3-dimensional figures next to the words for each figure. Point out that these are 2-dimensional drawings of 3-dimensional figures. Each of the drawings is made up of one or more rectangles, triangles, squares, or circles.

- Divide students into small groups. Distribute materials. Have the groups look through magazines and cut out pictures of 3-dimensional figures (such as cans for cylinders, a TV that is a cube, etc.). Have the groups create collages to display.

Multilevel Strategies

1 Preproduction
Have students point to the different 3-dimensional figures as you name them.

2 3 Early Production and Speech Emergence
Have students name 3-dimensional figures in the collages.

4 5 Intermediate and Advanced Fluency
Have students name and describe a 3-dimensional figure.

 LOG ON Visit **www.mmhmath.com** to find printable **Vocabulary Cards** that help build academic language.

Procedure: Help students make these Foldables to write vocabulary words and definitions throughout the unit. Encourage students to use the Foldables as a study guide.

 **by Dinah Zike**

Web Book

1. Provide each student with a sheet of paper. Fold the paper in half like a hot dog, leaving a 1" tab uncovered along the top. Fold in half to form two tabs.

2. Help your students unfold the paper and cut along the center fold line on the short side.

3. Have your students label as illustrated.

4. As students work through the lessons, have them take notes and record main ideas under the tabs of their Web Books. Students can use main idea phrases, vocabulary words, lists, and examples.

Labels may include:

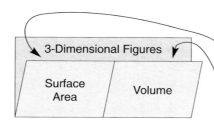

3-Dimensional Figures

Surface Area | Volume

Surface area is the total area of the surface of a 3-D figure, such as a rectangular prism.

Volume is the amount of space a 3-D figure encloses. Volume is measured in cubic units, such as cubic centimeters (cm³).

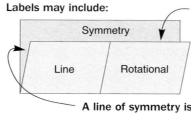

Labels may include:

Symmetry

Line | Rotational

by Dinah Zike

Web Book

1. Provide each student with a sheet of paper. Fold the paper in half like a hot dog, leaving a 1" tab uncovered along the top. Fold in half to form two tabs.

2. Help your students unfold the paper and cut along the center fold line on the short side.

3. Have your students label as illustrated.

4. As students work through the lessons, have them take notes and record main ideas under the tabs of their Web Books. Students can use main idea phrases, vocabulary words, lists, and examples.

A figure has rotational symmetry if it can be rotated less than 360° around a point of rotation and still match the original figure.

A line of symmetry is a line that divides a figure into two congruent halves. They match exactly when the figure is folded on that line.

 45 minutes

▶ **Key Strategy**
Use manipulatives

▶ **Format**
Whole class and
small groups

▶ **Math Vocabulary**
base, cone, cube, cylinder,
edge, face, net, prism,
pyramid, sphere, vertices

▶ **Daily Vocabulary**
length, point, width

▶ **Resources**
Learning Resource 45
Teacher Tools 4 and 9

Materials
- compass
- glue/tape
- paper
- pencils
- ruler
- scissors
- 3-D figures

Assessment

Check students' understanding
of three-dimensional figures as
they complete the lesson. See
Assessment Checklist on
page 221. Remind students to
work on their Foldables.

Home Connection

Have students work with family
members to list items that are
3-dimensional figures.

Three-Dimensional Figures and Nets

Math Objective	**ESL/TESOL Descriptors**
■ Identify 3-dimensional figures and nets.	■ Analyze, synthesize, and infer from information.
	■ Interpret information presented visually.

Activate Prior Knowledge Hold up 3-dimensional figures and ask students
to name them. Then ask them to tell you what 2-dimensional shapes they see on
the surfaces. Have them count surfaces, for example, six squares on a **cube.**

Hands-on Lesson With students' help, make a list of the number of **faces** (flat
surfaces) each figure has, **edges** (lines where two faces meet), and **vertices**
(points where edges meet). Discuss whether the faces are congruent figures
(same size and shape), and whether edges are parallel or intersecting.

● Distribute Teacher Tool 4: Number Cube, scissors, and tape. Explain that this is
called a **net,** a pattern to make a cube. It is a 2-dimensional figure that can be
folded into a 3-dimensional figure. Have them assemble the cube. Ask: *How
many faces (edges, vertices) does it have?*

● Distribute Learning Resource 45 and two sheets of Teacher Tool 9: Graph Paper.
Ask students to look at the net of the rectangular **prism.** It has this name
because its **base** is a rectangle. Then have them look at the other nets. For each,
have them identify the shapes of the faces and count the faces, vertices, and
edges.

● Divide students into small groups. Have each group choose a net, draw a larger
version of it on graph paper, then cut and assemble it.

Challenge Have students design a net for a longer rectangular prism or a taller
pyramid.

Multilevel Strategies

❶ Preproduction
Say: *Show me the net for
the (cylinder).*

Writing Ask students to
write the names of the
figures they made.

**❷ ❸ Early Production
and Speech Emergence**
Have students say the
names of the shapes each
net will make.

Writing Encourage
students to draw and label
the parts of each figure.

**❹ ❺ Intermediate
and Advanced Fluency**
Have students compare
net prisms or triangles.

Writing Ask students to
write a list of figures and
their parts.

Name _____

Nets

Copy a net on graph paper. Cut your net and make a
3-dimensional figure.

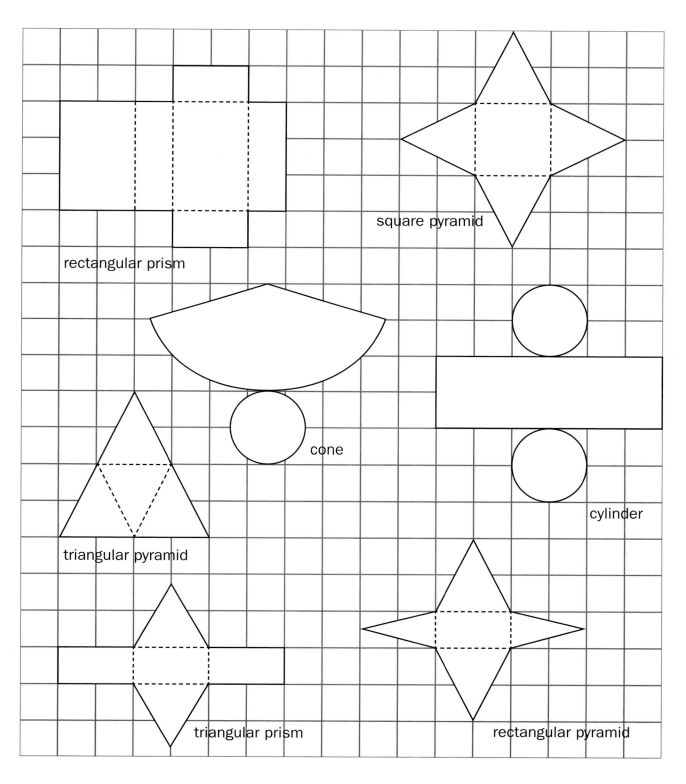

rectangular prism

square pyramid

cone

cylinder

triangular pyramid

triangular prism

rectangular pyramid

⏱ **45 minutes**

▶ **Key Strategy**
Use manipulatives

▶ **Format**
Whole class and
student pairs

▶ **Math Vocabulary**
surface area, volume

▶ **Daily Vocabulary**
measurements

▶ **Resource**
Learning Resource 46

Materials
- connecting cubes
- glue/tape
- pencils
- ruler
- scissors

Assessment

Observe students' mastery of
finding surface area and volume
as they complete the lesson.
See Assessment Checklist on
page 221. Remind students to
work on their Foldables.

Home Connection

Have students work with a family
member to find the volume and
surface area of an object at
home. Have them share results
with the class.

Surface Area and Volume

Math Objectives
- Find surface area of rectangular prisms.
- Find volume of rectangular prisms.

ESL/TESOL Descriptors
- Interpret information presented visually.
- Demonstrate knowledge through application in a variety of contexts.

Activate Prior Knowledge Draw a rectangle and ask: *Who remembers how to find the area of a rectangle?* Review the formula: $Area = l \times w$. Hold up a rectangular prism. Ask: *How can we find the area of all of the faces?*

Hands-on Lesson Elicit that if we know how to find the area of one face, we can find the **surface area** of the figure, the total area of all its surfaces.

- Divide students into pairs and distribute Learning Resource 46. Ask students to look at the net on the page. Ask: *How many faces does a rectangular prism have?* (6) *How many pairs of congruent faces?* (3) Have them use three colors to color the three sets of congruent rectangles in the net. Then read the formula for surface area: $SA = 2lw + 2lh + 2wh$. There are 3 pairs of equal faces, so there are three measurements, each multiplied by two, as shown in the formula.

- Ask students to find the surface area of the large prism on the page. First they count the boxes to get the three measurements (length, height, width) and then they use the formula.

- Distribute connecting cubes and have students construct a rectangular prism with the same number of cubes as the prism on the page. Ask a student to read the formula for **volume.** Have students find the volume, and count the cubes in the prism they have made to check the answer.

Challenge Have students compare the changes in the volume of a rectangular prism when all of its dimensions are doubled.

Multilevel Strategies

❶ Preproduction
Have students point to the letters in formulas as you name them.

Writing Ask them to copy the formulas.

❷❸ Early Production and Speech Emergence
Ask: *What is the formula for (surface area) of a rectangular prism?*

Writing Ask them to write the formulas for volume and area with letters (*l, w, h*) and words (*length, width, height*).

❹❺ Intermediate and Advanced Fluency
Ask: *How did you find the (surface area)?*

Writing Ask students to write the steps for finding the surface area or volume.

Name _____

Surface Area and Volume

Measure the length and width of the faces of the diagram of the rectangular prism. Then use the measurements to find the surface area and volume.

Formula for surface area	Formula for volume
Surface area = $(2 \times l \times w) + (2 \times l \times h) + (2 \times w \times h)$	Volume = $l \times w \times h$

Rectangular Prism

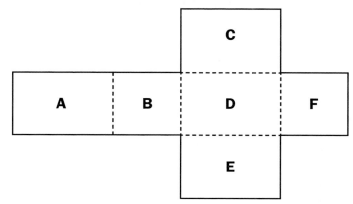

Surface area _____

Volume _____

Find the surface area and volume of this rectangular prism.

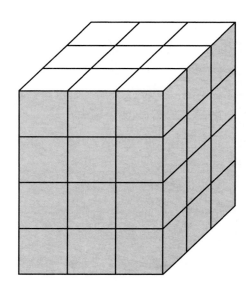

Surface area _____

Volume _____

Lesson 3

 45 minutes

▶ **Key Strategy**
Use manipulatives

▶ **Format**
Whole class and individual

▶ **Math Vocabulary**
line of symmetry, point of rotation, rotational symmetry

▶ **Daily Vocabulary**
fold, spin, toothpicks, turn

▶ **Resources**
Learning Resource 47
Teacher Tool 9

Materials
- pencils or pens
- ruler
- scissors

Assessment

Check students' mastery of line and rotational symmetry as they complete the lesson. See Assessment Checklist on page 221. Remind students to work on their Foldables.

Home Connection

Have students test shapes for line symmetry with family members by placing a mirror on the center line to see if the other half appears and matches it exactly. Have them report results to the class.

Line and Rotational Symmetry

Math Objectives	**ESL/TESOL Descriptors**
▪ Find line symmetry.	▪ Understand technical vocabulary according to content area.
▪ Find rotational symmetry.	▪ Demonstrate knowledge through application in a variety of contexts.

Activate Prior Knowledge Draw a heart with a line down the middle. Say: *Look at the two sides. Are they the same?* (*Yes.*) Draw another one and draw a line across it. Elicit that the top and bottom halves are different.

Hands-on Lesson Point to the **line of symmetry** that divided the heart into two congruent halves. Ask: *Does every figure have a line of symmetry?* Ask students to draw imaginary lines through the middle of various classroom objects or figures and say which they think have line symmetry.

- Have students cut out a square from Teacher Tool 9: Inch Graph Paper, fold it in half multiple times, and open it. Elicit that some shapes can have more than one line of symmetry. Show the three lines of symmetry on a triangle.

- Distribute Learning Resource 47: Symmetry. Have students draw a line through the center (down or across) if the shape has line symmetry. (*All do except the Z and the scalene triangle.*)

- Now have students cut out the shapes on the Learning Resource to test for **rotational symmetry.** Ask them to place the square on the desk and place pencil points on the middle dot, the **point of rotation.** Holding the pencil in place, have them rotate the square a quarter turn. It has rotational symmetry because the shape looks the same. Have students spin the letter *B.* It does not have rotational symmetry because it has to spin all the way around (360°) to look the same. Have students spin each figure to determine which have rotational symmetry.

Challenge Have students figure out how many lines of symmetry a figure has.

Multilevel Strategies

1 Preproduction
Ask: *Does this shape have line symmetry?*

Writing Invite students to draw a symmetrical and a nonsymmetrical figure.

2 3 Early Production and Speech Emergence
Have students say which figures have line symmetry.

Writing Encourage students to list the symmetrical figures.

4 5 Intermediate and Advanced Fluency
Ask: *How do you know if a figure has line symmetry?*

Writing Have students write a sentence about rotational symmetry.

Name _____

Symmetry

Draw a line down the center of the figures that have line symmetry. Cut out the shapes. Spin the shapes to find out if they have rotational symmetry.

© Macmillan/McGraw-Hill

Lesson 4

 45 minutes

▶ **Key Strategy**
Use visuals

▶ **Format**
Whole class and individual activity

▶ **Math Vocabulary**
tessellate, tessellation

▶ **Daily Vocabulary**
flip, rotate, turn

▶ **Resources**
Learning Resource 48
Teacher Tool 8

Materials
• markers
• pattern blocks
• poster board
• rulers
• scissors

Assessment

Check students' understanding of tessellations as they complete the lesson. See page 221 for Assessment Checklist. Remind students to work on their Foldables.

Home Connection

Have students find examples of tessellations at home with family members and share them in class.

Tessellations

Math Objective	**ESL/TESOL Descriptors**
■ Identify tessellations.	■ Interpret information presented visually.
	■ Demonstrate knowledge through application in a variety of contexts.

Activate Prior Knowledge Hold up two identical paper triangles. Remind students of the three ways they learned (in Unit 10) to transform figures, by flipping, turning, or sliding (to create reflections, rotations, or translations). Put the shapes side by side on a desk and have a volunteer rotate or reflect one of them to make the sides of the two shapes touch.

Hands-on Lesson Show the **tessellation** on the top of Learning Resource 48 (or show patterns in pictures of quilts, or from the Internet. M.C. Escher's art has good examples of tessellations). Explain that shapes **tessellate** when they can fit together without spaces between them. Draw circles touching each other and point out the gaps beween them to show that not all geometric figures can tessellate. Ask: *What shapes do you think can tessellate?*

● Point out that some tessellations, like the one on the top of the Learning Resource, use two or more shapes that fit together.

● Have students complete the bottom of the Learning Resource 48 and share their answers. Distribute scissors, poster board, and markers. Have students design their own tessellations, using one or two figures. Have them draw the shapes on Teacher Tool 8: Graph Paper, using pattern blocks. Have students cut them out, and trace one against another on poster board. Have them color their tessellations in interesting patterns. Have students describe each other's tessellations. Display their artwork.

Challenge Have students describe the transformations or reflections used in their tessellations.

Multilevel Strategies

1 **Preproduction**
Have students show you tessellating shapes.

Writing Ask them to draw two figures to show tessellation.

2 3 **Early Production and Speech Emergence**
Ask: *Which of these figures can tessellate?*

Writing Ask students to list some shapes that can or can't tessellate.

4 5 **Intermediate and Advanced Fluency**
Have students describe a tessellation.

Writing Ask students to write a sentence about how they made their tessellations.

Name _____

Terrific Tessellations

Look at the tessellations.

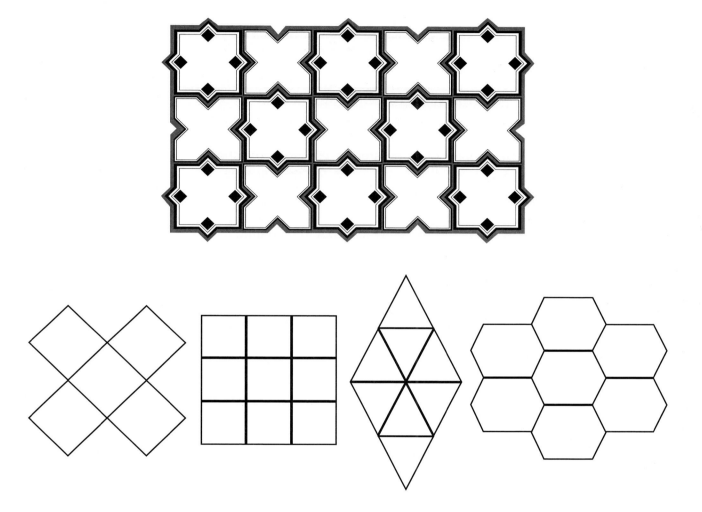

Look at the shapes below and decide if they can tessellate.

Write *yes* or *no* in the blanks.

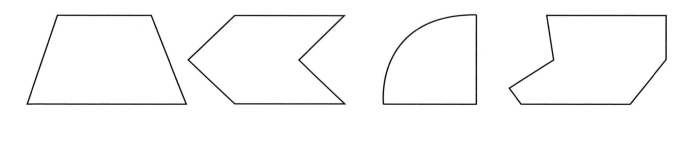

_____   _____   _____   _____

Problem Solving
Reading for Math

Read → Plan → Solve → Look Back

Remind students of
the basic steps
of problem solving.

SKILL: Follow Directions to Describe Figures
Model the skill using a word problem such as the
following:

Deana has two large pieces of tag board. She
wants to make a large poster. One piece is 37
inches across and 26 inches high. The other is 18
inches across and 42 inches high. Which piece of
tag board is bigger?

I can find the area of both pieces of tag board and
compare.

Tag board 1: 37 × 26 = 962
Tag board 1 has an area of 962 square inches
Tag board 2: 18 × 42 = 756
Tag board 2 has an area of 756 square inches
962 > 756. Tag board 1 has the greater area.

Does my answer make sense? Yes.

Distribute **Math Center Card 12A** to students.

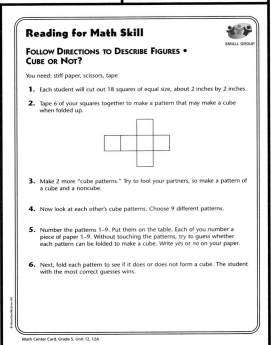

Math Center Card 12A

Reading for Math Skill
SMALL GROUP

FOLLOW DIRECTIONS TO DESCRIBE FIGURES •
CUBE OR NOT?

You need: stiff paper, scissors, tape

1. Each student will cut out 18 squares of equal size, about 2 inches by 2 inches.

2. Tape 6 of your squares together to make a pattern that may make a cube
   when folded up.

3. Make 2 more "cube patterns." Try to fool your partners, so make a pattern of
   a cube and a noncube.

4. Now look at each other's cube patterns. Choose 9 different patterns.

5. Number the patterns 1–9. Put them on the table. Each of you number a
   piece of paper 1–9. Without touching the patterns, try to guess whether
   each pattern can be folded to make a cube. Write *yes* or *no* on your paper.

6. Next, fold each pattern to see if it does or does not form a cube. The student
   with the most correct guesses wins.

Math Center Card, Grade 5, Unit 12, 12A

STRATEGY: Draw a Diagram
Model the strategy using a word problem such as
the following:

Carol has tulip and daffodil bulbs. She wants to
plant them in an alternating pattern, tulip, then daffodil, then tulip, and so on. Each row has room for
5 plants. If she has 15 of each plant how many
rows can she plant?

I can draw a diagram.

I will use a different symbol for each kind of plant.
Tulip = ○
Daffodil = □

She can plant 6 rows.

Does my diagram show all 30 plants? Yes.

Distribute **Math Center Card 12B** to students.

Math Center Card 12B

Problem Solving: Strategy
INDIVIDUAL

DRAW A DIAGRAM • ART CENTER

Your school is building an Art Center.
- There are 6 tables. At least 11 students need to sit at the tables.
- All the tables must touch at least one other table.
- One person can sit on each side of the table.
- You need 2 tables for art supplies. Only one person can sit at a table with the
  art supplies.

Draw a diagram to show where the tables, chairs, and art supplies go. Look at this
diagram as an example—there are 12 seats for students. The diagram uses squares
for tables and circles for chairs.

Now draw your own diagram using the same information.

Math Center Card, Grade 5, Unit 12, 12B

Assessment Checklist

	STUDENT NAMES									
SCHOOL:										
TEACHER: **SCHOOL YEAR:**										
Mark: + = Mastery √ = Satisfactory – = Needs Improvement										
LEVEL OF LANGUAGE PROFICIENCY (1–5)										
MATH OBJECTIVES										
• Find line and rotational symmetry.										
• Identify 3-dimensional figures and nets.										
• Find volume of rectangular prisms.										
• Find surface area of rectangular prisms.										
• Identify tessellations.										
ESL/TESOL LISTENING/SPEAKING										
Analyze, synthesize, and infer from information.										
Demonstrate knowledge through application in a variety of contexts.										
Listen to and imitate how others use English.										
Practice new language.										
Represent and interpret information presented visually.										
Select, connect, and explain information.										
Understand technical vocabulary according to content area.										
ESL/TESOL READING										
Read about subject matter information.										
Apply basic reading comprehension skills.										
Follow written directions, implicit and explicit.										
ESL WRITING										
Write to demonstrate comprehension.										
Write using spelling patterns and targeted English vocabulary.										

 **Foldables**   **by Dinah Zike**

1 **Preproduction**
- Did students write the unit vocabulary?
- Did they copy the definitions?

2 **3** **Early Production and Speech Emergence**
- Did students label the tabs correctly?
- Did they write the vocabulary words?
- Did they copy the definitions?

4 **5** **Intermediate and Advanced Fluency**
- Did students write definitions for the unit vocabulary?
- Did they use correct spelling and grammar?

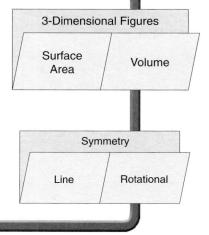

Planner
Ratio and Probability

Assessment
p. 241
• Assessment Checklist
• Foldables

LOG ON Visit **www.mmhmath.com**

Unit Activities	• **Activity 1** Readiness Fishing for Ratios, p. 226	• **Activity 3** Ratio Roll, p. 227
	• **Activity 2** Carnival Spins, p. 226	• **Activity 4** Pizza Chef, p. 227

Lessons	Key Objectives	Vocabulary	Materials	Resources
READ TOGETHER "The Apache Stick Game," pp. 224–225	**Math:** Understand probability. Find the probability of a simple event. **ESL/TESOL:** Goal 2, Standard 3.	ancestral, Apache, charcoal, determined, game, lumber, ranches, settled, sticks, stone		Graphic Organizer 4
UNIT WARM-UP Understanding Probability p. 228	**Math:** Make predictions. **ESL/TESOL:** Goal 2, Standard 2.	certain, equally likely, impossible, less likely, likely, more likely, unlikely	chart paper	
LESSON 1 Ratios pp. 230–231	**Math:** Understand ratio. Find equivalent ratios. **ESL/TESOL:** Goal 2, Standard 2.	cross product, equivalent ratios, proportion, ratio, terms	counters	Learning Resource 49
LESSON 2 Rates and Unit Prices pp. 232–233	**Math:** Determine and apply rates and unit prices. **ESL/TESOL:** Goal 2, Standards 1, 2.	rate, unit price, unit rate	supermarket flyers	Learning Resource 50
LESSON 3 Scale Drawings pp. 234–235	**Math:** Use scale drawings and maps. **ESL/TESOL:** Goal 2, Standard 2.	scale, scale drawing	centimeter rulers, connecting cubes, meter stick	Learning Resource 51
LESSON 4 Probability pp. 236–237	**Math:** Understand probability. Use skills and strategies to solve problems. **ESL/TESOL:** Goal 2, Standard 2.	equally likely, event, outcome, probability	number cube, spinner	Learning Resource 52 Teacher Tool 4
LESSON 5 Compound Events pp. 238–239	**Math:** Make predictions. Find the probability of a compound event. **ESL/TESOL:** Goal 2, Standard 2.	compound events, counting principle, theoretical probability, tree diagram, trial	crayons, spinners	Learning Resource 53 Teacher Tool 11
PROBLEM SOLVING p. 240 • Skill: Check the Reasonableness of an Answer • Strategy: Do an Experiment	Use skills and strategies to solve problems.			**Math Center Cards 13A, 13B**

See **Math at Home Family Guide** for additional math vocabulary, activities, and games in English, Spanish, and Haitian Creole.

English Vocabulary

Dear Family: Please help your child practice the key vocabulary words for this unit.

certain an outcome or event is certain if it has a probability of 1

equivalent ratios ratios that can be represented by equivalent fractions

event a set of one or more outcomes in a probability experiment

impossible an outcome or event is impossible if it has a probability of 0

likely an outcome is likely if it probably will happen

outcome a possible result in a probability experiment

ratio a comparison of two quantities

scale the ratio of the lengths on a map or scale drawing with the actual lengths

unlikely an outcome is unlikely if it probably will not happen

Vocabulario en español

Estimados familiares: Por favor ayuden a su hijo/a a practicar las palabras del vocabulario de esta unidad.

seguro un resultado o suceso es seguro si tiene una probabilidad de 1

razones equivalentes razones representadas por fracciones equivalentes

suceso conjunto formado por uno o más resultados posibles en un experimento de probabilidad

imposible un resultado o suceso es imposible si tiene una probabilidad de 0

probable un resultado es probable si es posible que ocurra

resultado lo que puede ocurrir en un experimento de probabilidad

razón comparación de dos cantidades

escala la razón que compara las distancias en un mapa o dibujo a escala con las distancias reales

improbable suceso que no tiene la probabilidad de ocurrir

Vokabilè an kreyòl

Chè paran: Tanpri ede pitit la pratike mo vokabilè nan seksyon sa a.

sèten yon rezilta osnon evenman sèten si li genyen yon pwobabilite 1

rapò a menm valè rapò ki ka reprezante pa fraksyon ekivalan

evenman yon gwoup youn osnon plizye rezilta nan yon eksperyans pwobabilite

enposib yon rezilta osnon yon evenman enposib si-l gen yon pwobalite 0

posib yon evenman posib si-l ka rive

konsekans rezilta yon eksperyans pwobabilite

rapò konparezon de kantite

a léchèl rapò longè ki sou yon kat jeografik, osnon yon desen a léchèl, ak vrè longè-a

pa posib yon rezilta pa posib si li sanble li pa ka rive

© Macmillan/McGraw-Hill

Read Together

The Apache Stick Game

 25 minutes

Math Objectives
- Understand probability.
- Find the probability of a simple event.

ESL/TESOL Descriptors
- Listen to, speak, read, and write about subject matter information.
- Learn and use language "chunks."

Reading Skill
- Recognize Main Idea and Supporting Details.

Vocabulary
ancestral, Apache, charcoal, determined, game, lumber, ranches, settled, sticks, stone

---

Before Reading

Build Background/Oral Language
Read the title. Discuss the illustrations to predict the main idea or topic. Find Arizona on a map. Show pictures of native Americans as they lived many years ago. Have students identify words they know in the text.

During Reading

- Read text through slowly once without stopping as students track it.
- Reread text, pausing often to encourage students to ask about new or difficult words. Clarify meaning by drawing pictures of the sticks and pantomiming the game.
- Invite volunteers to read sentences from the story.

Phonological/Phonemic Awareness
Write *play, playing, played,* and *player* on the board. Elicit meanings from students. Explain the regular verb tenses of *play, playing,* and *played.* Explain that *-er* added to the end of a verb often indicates someone who does the action of the verb. In the story it is someone who plays. Brainstorm other words that have these regular forms, such as *listen, talk, walk,* and *work.*

After Reading

Distribute Graphic Organizer 4: Main Idea and Supporting Details. Identify the main topic or idea of the story *(the game)* and the details, which describe it *(who plays and how the game is played).* Have students complete the chart.

Drama Divide the class into groups. Have them devise a game that uses simple materials, such as sticks and stones. Have them act out their game idea for the class.

Assessment

Observe fluency as students work together in groups. See Assessment Checklist on page 241.

Multilevel Strategies

1 Preproduction
Say: *Point to these words: play, played, playing, and player.*

Writing Invite students to copy or write the words, underlining the base word *play.*

2 3 Early Production and Speech Emergence
Say: *Finish this sentence: A person who plays a game is a_.*

Writing Encourage students to copy or write the completed sentence.

4 5 Intermediate and Advanced Fluency
Say: *Use play, played, playing and player in sentences.*

Writing Challenge students to write their sentences.

The Apache Stick Game

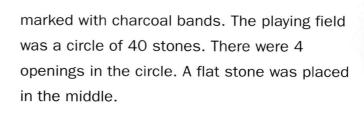

Over 400 years ago the Apache of eastern Arizona played this circle tossing game.

The White Mountain Apache live in their ancestral homeland in the mountains and tall pine forests of eastern Arizona. Apache have lived in this area for over 400 years. In the past, family groups moved often to hunt and gather food. Today, the White Mountain Apache live in settled communities and manage large cattle ranches and lumber industries.

Throughout their history, the White Mountain Apache have enjoyed a variety of sports and games. A popular game among adults was a game played with foot-long green sticks that were split in half. The bark was left on the round side of each stick, and the flat side was marked with charcoal bands. The playing field was a circle of 40 stones. There were 4 openings in the circle. A flat stone was placed in the middle.

A player threw 3 playing sticks against the center stone. The number of spaces, or stones, a player could move was determined by how the sticks fell. The most points were awarded if all the sticks landed with their rounded sides up. The player could toss again. The first player to move her marker or counting stick around the circle three times was the winner.

Activities

Activities

Readiness

ACTIVITY 1

INDIVIDUAL

Fishing for Ratios

- The park ranger stocks the fishing pond with a ratio of 3 halibut to 4 perch to 2 trout. If there are a total of 306 fish, how many of each type are in the pond?

- What are two other possible totals the park ranger could have if she stocks two other ponds with the same ratio, and stays within a range of 300 to 350 fish for each? Be sure you choose totals that will result in whole numbers of each type of fish. What are the totals for each type of fish?

Copy and complete this table.

Halibut	Perch	Trout	Total
3	4	2	

See answers on p. 293.

Explore Ratio

ACTIVITY 2

PARTNERS

Carnival Spins

Find the probability of spinning each event. Check your answers by copying the spinner. Instead of spinning, drop a penny on it 50 times. Record each result. Compare your answers with a partner.

YOU NEED
penny
scissors
compass
cutout of large circle folded in half three times to make 8 sections

1. the number 13
2. an odd number
3. an even number
4. numbers 2 or 3
5. a multiple of 3
6. a factor of 60
7. a prime number
8. a number divisible by 3 or 7
9. a number less than 100
10. a number less than 14
11. a number whose spelling ends in the letter *n*.
12. digits having a sum of 5

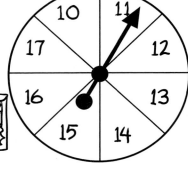

Explore Probability

Game Zone

ACTIVITY 3

PARTNERS

Ratio Roll

© Macmillan/McGraw-Hill

- **Player 1:** Roll two number cubes to tell how many connecting cubes of each color to put into the paper bag.

- **Player 2:** Use the ratio formula for finding probability to compute the probability of picking each color.

- (HINT: Be sure to use the total number of cubes as the number for possible outcomes.)

- **Each Player:** Choose the color you think you will most likely pick based on the ratio. Pick from the bag. If you picked the correct color, you get a point.

- Play 10 rounds. In each case, start over by rolling new numbers and setting up a new experiment. The player with more points wins.

YOU NEED
connecting cubes (two colors)
number cubes
paper bag

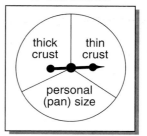

Ratio

ACTIVITY 4

PARTNERS

Pizza Chef

The pizza chef makes three varieties of pizzas with four possible toppings but she uses only one topping per pizza. Each partner chooses their pizza by spinning the two spinners. Then find the probability for getting each one of the pizzas below.

1. thin with mushrooms

2. thick with broccoli

3. personal with any topping

4. thin or thick with onions

5. thin with broccoli or mixed vegetables

6. any varieties with mixed vegetables

Make your own pizza-toppings and spinners and trade with your partner. Use your spinners and list to find the probabilities for getting each pizza variety.

© Macmillan/McGraw-Hill

3 varieties

thick crust / thin crust / personal (pan) size

4 toppings

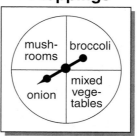

mushrooms / broccoli / onion / mixed vegetables

Probability

Understanding Probability

 40 minutes

▶ **Key Strategy**
Use charts and graphs

▶ **Format**
Whole class and small groups

▶ **Math Vocabulary**
certain, equally likely, impossible, less likely, likely, more likely, unlikely

▶ **Daily Vocabulary**
conditions, fall, predictions, rainy, snowy, spring, summer, weather, windy, winter

▶ **Materials**
chart paper

Math Objective	ESL/TESOL Descriptors
▪ Make predictions.	▪ Represent information visually. ▪ Hypothesize and predict.

Activate Prior Knowledge Say: *It's sunny today. True or false?* Ask a student to describe the day's weather conditions. Discuss weather conditions in different seasons. If necessary, review words for talking about the weather *(rainy, windy, snowy, etc.)*.

Hands-on Lesson Form small groups of fluent and nonfluent students. Explain that they will predict what the weather will be like for the next four days.

● Write a long line on the board. Put **impossible** on the left and **certain** on the right. Put **equally likely** in the middle. Show which side of equally likely to put the words **unlikely, less likely,** and **more likely.** Have groups copy chart.

● Explain that groups will monitor the weather for the next four days. Encourage them to make their own weather predictions, based on what they know about the current conditions. Have them make a chart to show the predictions and results. Ask them to listen to and watch weather reports at home, adding any new information to their charts. Then ask them to illustrate and list the real weather conditions.

● Have groups compare their predictions and actual weather conditions. Ask: *How many days out of the four was it sunny? windy?*

Multilevel Strategies

1 Preproduction
Ask students to point to opposite of *certain.*

2 3 Early Production and Speech Emergence
Have students say vocabulary words as you point to them.

4 5 Intermediate and Advanced Fluency
Invite students to use vocabulary words in original sentences.

 LOG ON Visit **www.mmhmath.com** to find printable **Vocabulary Cards** that help build academic language.

Procedure: Help students make these Foldables to write vocabulary words and definitions throughout the unit. Encourage students to use the Foldables as a study guide.

 **by Dinah Zike**

Shutter Fold

1. Provide each student with a large sheet of paper. Have students estimate and mark the mid-point of the long side of the sheet of paper. Then, fold outer edges in to the middle. Label the outside of the Shutter Fold RATIOS.

2. Have students staple five sheets of notebook paper inside the Shutter Fold.

3. Students can label each of the sheets with the title from each lesson.

4. As students progress, have them take notes and record main ideas on the paper inside their Shutter Fold, while noting vocabulary words and definitions on the inside of the tabs.

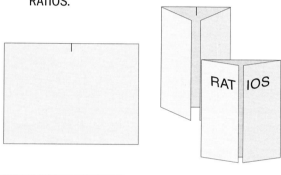

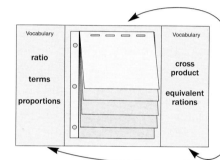

Lesson titles such as:

1 Ratios
2 Rates and Unit Prices
3 Scale Drawings, etc. . .

Vocabulary such as

 **by Dinah Zike**

Shutter Fold

1. Provide each student with a large sheet of paper. Have students estimate and mark the mid-point of the long side of the sheet of paper. Then, fold outer edges into the middle. Label the outside of the Shutter Fold PROBABILITY.

2. Have students staple five sheets of notebook paper inside the Shutter Fold.

3. Students can label each of the sheets with the title from each lesson.

4. As students progress, have them take notes and record main ideas on the paper inside their Shutter Fold, while noting vocabulary words and definitions on the inside of the tabs.

Lesson titles such as:

4 Probability
5 Compound Events

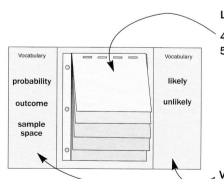

Vocabulary such as

 45 minutes

▶ **Key Strategy**
Use charts and graphs

▶ **Format**
Whole class and student pairs

▶ **Math Vocabulary**
cross product, equivalent ratios, proportion, ratio, terms

▶ **Daily Vocabulary**
denominator, fractions, numerator, percent

▶ **Resource**
Learning Resource 49

Materials
• counters

Assessment

Check students' understanding of ratios as they complete the lesson. See Assessment Checklist on page 241.
Remind students to work on their Foldables.

Home Connection

Have students find ratios of household items, such as the number of cups to the total number of dishware items, with family members. Invite them to share their ratios with the class.

Ratios

Math Objectives	**ESL/TESOL Descriptors**
▪ Understand ratio. ▪ Find equivalent ratios.	▪ Select, connect, and explain information. ▪ Analyze, synthesize, and infer from information.

Activate Prior Knowledge Write: $\frac{2}{4}$, $\frac{3}{6}$, $\frac{2}{6}$, $\frac{11}{99}$, $\frac{27}{3}$. Invite volunteers to name the fractions. Assist the class in finding the simplest form of each one.

Hands-on Lesson Model a ratio game. Ask students to write their names on pieces of paper and count the letters in each name. Give an example: *Rosa Mendes.* Invite a volunteer to count the letters in the first name (4) and in the last name (6). Explain that 4 to 6 is a **ratio,** or a comparison of the numbers. The **terms** of the ratio are 4 and 6. Another way to write this ratio is *4:6.*

• Ask students to find the ratio between a specific letter in the whole name and the whole name itself. Ask a volunteer to count the number of times the letter *s* appears in *Rosa Mendes.* Ask a volunteer to write the ratio. *(2 to 10 or 2:10)*

• Show that ratios can also be written as fractions. $\left(\frac{2}{10}\right)$ Ask students to write this fraction in its simplest form. $\left(\frac{1}{5}\right)$ They can check whether $\frac{2}{10}$ and $\frac{1}{5}$ are equivalent ratios by using **cross products.** Multiply the numerator of one fraction, 2, and the denominator of the other, 5. Do the same for the remaining numerator and denominator (1×10). If the products are equal, 2:10 and 1:5 are **equivalent ratios** and therefore are in **proportion.**

• Divide students into groups and distribute Learning Resource 49: Name Ratios. Have students find the ratio of a particular letter to the total letters in their name.

Challenge Invite the class to find the percents of their letter ratios.

Multilevel Strategies

1 Preproduction
Have students arrange the counters for the pair.

Writing Invite students to write a ratio.

2 3 Early Production and Speech Emergence
Have students name the equal ratios they find.

Writing Encourage students to write a phrase using a ratio.

4 5 Intermediate and Advanced Fluency
Have students explain how they found equal ratios.

Writing Challenge students to write their explanation.

Name _____

Name Ratios

Write names and ratios. Use colored counters to help you.

NAME	PICK A LETTER IN THE NAME	NUMBER OF TIMES LETTER APPEARS	TOTAL NUMBER OF LETTERS	WRITE RATIO 3 WAYS	FRACTION IN SIMPLEST FORM
Rosa Mendes	S	2	10	$\frac{2}{10}$ 2 to 10 2:10	$\frac{1}{5}$

▶ **Key Strategy**
Use visuals

▶ **Format**
Whole class and pairs

▶ **Math Vocabulary**
rate, unit price, unit rate

▶ **Daily Vocabulary**
better buy, better value, supermarket items

▶ **Resource**
Learning Resource 50

Materials
• supermarket flyers (one per group)

Assessment

Check students' mastery of unit pricing as they complete the lesson. See Assessment Checklist on page 241. Remind students to work on their Foldables.

Home Connection

Have students find the unit price of an item at home and compare it to another brand or size in the grocery store when they shop with family members. Have them share their information with the class.

Rates and Unit Prices

Math Objective	**ESL/TESOL Descriptors**
■ Determine and apply rates and unit prices.	■ Negotiate and manage interaction to accomplish tasks. ■ Interpret information presented visually.

Activate Prior Knowledge Draw a car on the board. Ask: *How fast can a car go?* Students may be familiar with the words *miles per hour* or *kilometers per hour.* Say: *This car went 300 miles in three hours! How many miles can it go per hour?*

Hands-on Lesson Point out that we just used ratios to talk about the car's speed, the ratio of miles to hours. We knew its **rate** (300 miles in 3 hours) and we wanted to know its rate per hour. This is a **unit rate,** which we can use to compare its speed to that of other cars.

• Say: *We can also use ratios to compare amounts and prices.* Hold up or draw two food containers of different sizes, such as two cereal boxes. Ask: *Is it better to buy a small package or a large one? How can we find out?* Elicit that to find the better buy we need to find the **unit price,** the price per unit.

• Point out that a unit can be a piece, an ounce, a pound, etc., as long as we compare with equivalent units. Review the units in which some products are sold. For example, candy bars can be sold by the piece and juice can be sold by the gallon. Explain that we find the unit price by dividing the total price by the number of units in the package. Review the fact that we use pounds and ounces whereas ESL students may use kilos and liters.

• Divide students into groups and distribute supermarket flyers. Ask students to look at various sale items and find their unit prices. Then distribute Learning Resource 50: Best Buy! and have students work together to figure out the best buy for each of the pairs of products on the page.

Challenge Have students make up their own supermarket flyers with favorite items. Have them write prices and cost per unit.

Multilevel Strategies

① Preproduction
Have students point to a price and show you the unit price.

Writing Encourage students to write a unit price in words and numerals.

② ③ Early Production and Speech Emergence
Ask: *What are the unit prices of these two foods containers?*

Writing Have students write the foods that are a better buy.

④ ⑤ Intermediate and Advanced Fluency
Have students explain how to figure out unit price.

Writing Invite students to write the steps of finding a unit price.

Name _____

Best Buy!

Write the unit price under each item. Circle the best buy.

Lesson 3

50 minutes

▶ **Key Strategy**
Use manipulatives

▶ **Format**
Whole class and student pairs

▶ **Math Vocabulary**
scale, scale drawing

▶ **Daily Vocabulary**
centimeter, length, measure, meter, width

▶ **Resource**
Learning Resource 51

Materials
- centimeter rulers
- connecting cubes
- meter stick

Assessment

Observe students' understanding of scale drawings as they complete the lesson. See Assessment Checklist on page 241.
Remind students to work on their Foldables.

Home Connection

Have students work with family members to create a scale drawing of a room in their home. Invite students to share their drawings with the class.

Scale Drawings

Math Objective	**ESL/TESOL Descriptors**
▪ Use scale drawings and maps.	▪ Interpret information presented visually.
	▪ Compare and contrast information.

Activate Prior Knowledge Ask students wearing red shirts to raise their hands. Use this number in relation to the total number of students to create a ratio. Ask volunteers to write the ratio as a fraction and then to reduce the fraction to its simplest form.

Hands-on Lesson Point to the picture on Learning Resource 51: Scale Model and ask: *Are the rooms in your homes bigger or smaller than this one?* Explain that this is a **scale drawing** of a real room. Tell students that they are going to make a scale drawing of their classroom.

- Pair students. Distribute connecting cubes. Tell the class that each cube measures one centimeter. Allow volunteers to use a meter stick to measure the length and width of the classroom. For each meter measured, ask pairs to add another cube to their models. Guide pairs to complete these models.

- Write: 1 cm = 1 m. Explain that this represents the **scale** of the students' models. Rewrite this relationship as a ratio. *(1:1)* Distribute Learning Resource 51, and encourage students to draw their scale models on it.

- Distribute centimeter rulers. Point to the drawing and ask volunteers to name each room and identify the scale. Write this ratio as a fraction: $\frac{1}{1}$. Read the questions together. Help students use the scale to determine the size of model and the rooms.

Challenge Encourage students to label their classroom drawings (for example: *classroom library, listening center, science center*).

Multilevel Strategies

1 Preproduction
Have students connect the cubes during the measurement.

Writing Invite students to write the scale.

2 3 Early Production and Speech Emergence
Have students read the scale as you point to it.

Writing Ask students to write the scale and measurement in words.

4 5 Intermediate and Advanced Fluency
Ask students to explain how they determined their measurements.

Writing Have students write sentences describing how they made their scale models.

Name _____

Scale Model

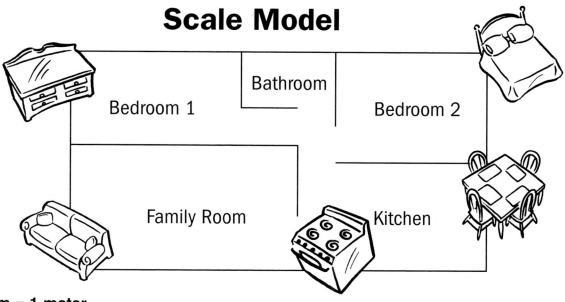

Bedroom 1   Bathroom   Bedroom 2

Family Room   Kitchen

Key: 1cm = 1 meter

Measure the scale model and answer the questions.

1. What is the size of the real house? _____

2. How big is the real kitchen? _____

3. How big is the real bedroom? _____

Now make a scale model of your classroom on the centimeter graph. Write the ratio as part of the key.

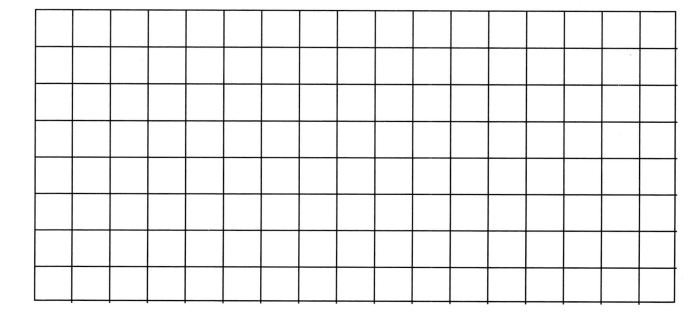

⏱ **45 minutes**

▶ **Key Strategy**
Use manipulatives

▶ **Format**
Whole class and student pairs

▶ **Math Vocabulary**
equally likely, event, outcome, probability

▶ **Daily Vocabulary**
often, results

▶ **Resources**
Learning Resource 52
Teacher Tool 4

Materials
- number cube
- spinner

Assessment

Check students' mastery of probability as they complete the lesson. See page 241 for Assessment Checklist. Remind students to work on their Foldables.

Home Connection

Have students and a family member predict probability for pulling a certain coin out of a bag. Have them share the results with the class.

Probability

> **Math Objectives**
> - Understand probability.
> - Use skills and strategies to solve problems.
>
> **ESL/TESOL Descriptors**
> - Represent and interpret information visually.
> - Demonstrate knowledge through application in a variety of contexts.

Activate Prior Knowledge Review with students the chart they kept on the weather earlier in the week. Elicit the weather conditions that were more likely, less likely, certain, or impossible.

Hands-on Lesson Tell students they are going to do a number cube experiment to learn more about **probability.** Explain that probability is the measure of how likely it is that a given **event** will occur.

- Divide the class into groups of four. Distribute Teacher Tool 4: Number Cube Patterns and Learning Resource 52: How Often? Ask groups to look at their number cubes and predict the probability of rolling a specific number, for example 4. Elicit that the event of any one number coming up is **equally likely** because there is only one of each number. Have them write the probability for a specific number: (1 to 6 or 1:6). Ask them to list the 6 numbers on their chart and write the probability of rolling each one.

- Have students take turns rolling the number cube twelve times, tallying the **outcome,** or result, of each roll. When they are finished, ask groups to compare the predictions with the outcomes of their experiment.

- Discuss the probability of rolling an odd number or an even number. Lead students to see that the number cube has three odd numbers out of six numbers. Have them write this as a ratio (3 to 6 or 3:6) and write it in their tables.

Challenge Have students create a probability experiment using spinners or hand-drawn number cards. Ask them to demonstrate their experiment.

Multilevel Strategies

1 Preproduction
Ask students to count the faces of the number cube and the odd numbers.

Writing Encourage students to record the results for their group.

2 3 Early Production and Speech Emergence
Have students read aloud the results they recorded.

Writing Invite students to write the results in single words or phrases.

4 5 Intermediate and Advanced Fluency
Ask: *How did you figure out the probability of getting an odd number?*

Writing Ask students to write the steps for determining probability.

Name _____

How Often?

Write your prediction and write your outcomes in the table.

PREDICTION		OUTCOME	
Number	Probability	Tally	Ratio

Lesson 5

45 minutes

▶ **Key Strategy**
Use manipulatives

▶ **Format**
Whole class and pairs

▶ **Math Vocabulary**
compound events, counting principle, experimental probability, theoretical probability, tree diagram, trial

▶ **Daily Vocabulary**
combination, spinners

▶ **Resources**
Learning Resource 53, Teacher Tool 11

Materials
- crayons
- spinners

Assessment

Observe students' understanding of the math concept as they engage in classroom activities. See page 241 for Assessment Checklist. Remind students to work on their Foldables.

Home Connection

Have students create a compound event with a family member by picking two items from a paper bag. Have students share the results with the class.

Compound Events

Math Objectives	**ESL/TESOL Descriptors**
■ Make predictions.	■ Hypothesize and Predict.
■ Find the probability of a compound event.	■ Compare and contrast information.

Activate Prior Knowledge Invite a student to spin a spinner colored half red and half green. Ask: *What are the chances of spinning red? (1 to 2)* Explain that now students will learn how to find all the results for spinning two spinners.

Hands-on Lesson Explain that spinning two spinners is a **compound event.** Divide students into pairs and distribute Learning Resource 53: What Are the Chances? and Teacher Tool 11: Spinners. Ask one student to color a spinner half red, half blue, and the partner to color one half green, half yellow.

- Explain how to fill in the **tree diagram.** On the lines on the left, they will write possible outcomes of one spinner, using the first letter of each color. *(R, B)* On the lines on the right, they will write the combinations of those colors with the colors on the other spinner. *(RG, RY, BG, BY).*

- Ask: *What is the probability of getting blue on one spinner and green on the other?* $(\frac{1}{4}$ *because there are 4 possible outcomes).* Explain that this number is the **theoretical probability.** Now students will spin the spinners together 20 times (20 **trials**) and record results to find the **experimental probability.** This will be a ratio of the number of times they get *BG* to the number of trials.

- Point out that another way to find the number of outcomes is to use the **counting principle.** Multiply the number of outcomes of each spinner. *(2 colors on one × 2 colors on the other = 4 outcomes)*

Challenge Ask students to find the number of possible outcomes of spinning two counters with 10 colors each. *(100)*

Multilevel Strategies

1 Preproduction
Ask students to show you the four outcomes on the tree diagram.

Writing Invite students to write the outcomes in numerals and words.

2 3 Early Production and Speech Emergence
Ask students to read the results of their experiment aloud.

Writing Have students list the outcomes in both abbreviations and words.

4 5 Intermediate and Advanced Fluency
Ask students to explain the results of their experiment.

Writing Encourage students to write sentences describing the outcomes.

Name _____

What Are the Chances?

Fill in the tree diagram. Use the first letter of each color.

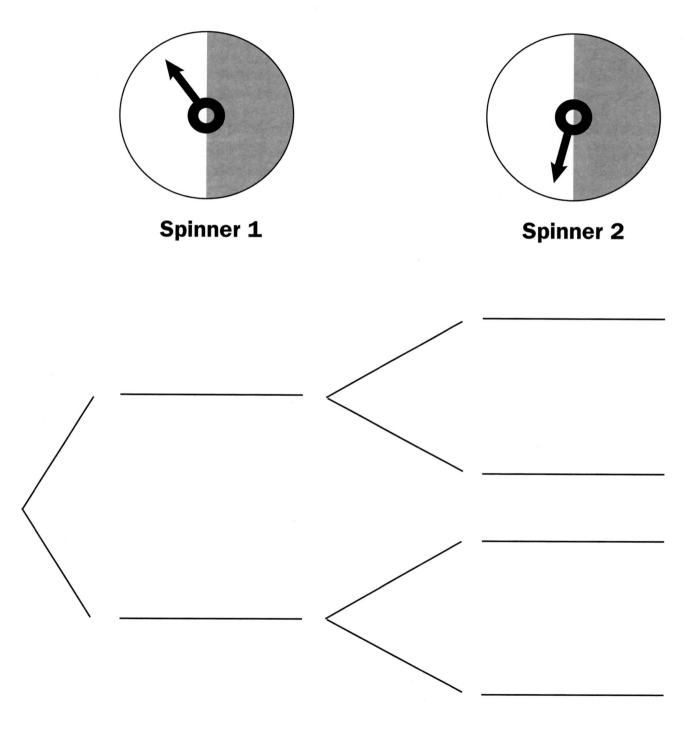

Spinner 1   Spinner 2

Problem Solving
Reading for Math

SKILL: Check the Reasonableness of an Answer
Model the skill using a word problem such as:

 Read
Jason rode his bike every day during July. He rode 6 miles from his house to the beach and 6 miles back. He told his friends he rode about 200 miles in July. Is his estimate reasonable?

 Plan
I can multiply to find the exact number of miles.

 Solve
$6 \times 2 = 12$
Jason rode 12 miles each day.
Think: There are 31 days in July.
$12 \times 31 = 372$
Jason rode 372 miles in July.
His estimate is too low.

 Look Back
What mistake did Jason make? He didn't double the miles to account for riding both ways.

Distribute **Math Center Card 13A** to students.

Math Center Card 13A

Reading for Math Skill
INDIVIDUAL

CHECK THE REASONABLENESS OF AN ANSWER • DOES IT MAKE SENSE?

During the summer, Tim makes blueberry muffins for his aunt's restaurant. His aunt pays him $5 for each batch of muffins. This is the recipe he uses.

> Blueberry Muffins - makes 12 large muffins
> 4 cups flour
> 1 tsp salt
> 4 tsp sugar
> 2 tsp baking powder
> 2 eggs
> 2 tbsp butter
> 4 cups milk
> 1 cup blueberries

1. Tim worked 5 days one week. He made 3 batches of muffins each day. He calculated that he would earn about $15 that week. Is this estimate reasonable? Explain your answer.

2. Tim tells his aunt how much of each ingredient he needs each day. One day, he planned to make 4 batches of muffins. He told her that he needed about 8 cups of flour, 1 cup of sugar, and 4 eggs. Will this be enough of each ingredient? Explain.

3. Tim wants to earn $100 dollars in a week. He calculates that he has to make 20 batches of muffins. Is this answer reasonable? Explain your answer.

4. Tim knows he will need 45 blueberry muffins for Sunday morning. He estimates that he will have to make 6 batches of muffins. Is his estimate reasonable? Explain.

Math Center Card, Grade 5, Unit 13, 13A

STRATEGY: Do an Experiment
Model the strategy using a word problem such as:

 Read
How long do you think you can stand on one foot? How can you find out?

 Plan
I can do an experiment.
I will predict the time first, then I will time myself.

 Solve
Think: I will need a clock with a second hand or a stopwatch.
I will time myself 10 times and record the amount of time.

 Look Back
Why do I time myself more than once?
I want to predict a general amount of time. I can use the data to make the prediction.

Distribute **Math Center Card 13B** to students.

Math Center Card 13B

Problem Solving: Strategy
PARTNERS

DO AN EXPERIMENT • DROP AND PREDICT

You need: a thumbtack, flat-bottomed paper cup, cone-shaped cup

For coins or number cubes, it is easy to predict the results of 1,000 tosses. For other objects, it is more difficult.

1. Design your own experiment. Find an object that will land in more than one way if you drop it. Try a thumbtack, a flat-bottomed paper cup, a cone-shaped cup, or another object.

2. Predict what would happen if you dropped the object 1,000 times. But you don't want to drop it more than 50 times. Decide how many times you will drop the object.

3. Start your experiment. Write down your results as you go.

4. Use your data to predict the results of 1,000 drops.

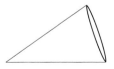

Math Center Card, Grade 5, Unit 13, 13B

Assessment Checklist

	STUDENT NAMES									
SCHOOL:										
TEACHER: **SCHOOL YEAR:**										
Mark: + = Mastery √ = Satisfactory – = Needs Improvement										
LEVEL OF LANGUAGE PROFICIENCY (1–5)										
MATH OBJECTIVES										
• Understand ratio and probability.										
• Find equivalent ratios.										
• Determine and apply rates and unit prices.										
• Use scale drawings and maps.										
• Make predictions.										
• Find the probability of a simple and compound event.										
ESL/TESOL LISTENING/SPEAKING										
Analyze, synthesize, and infer from information.										
Compare and contrast information.										
Demonstrate knowledge through application in a variety of contexts.										
Hypothesize and predict.										
Learn and use language "chunks."										
Represent and interpret information visually.										
ESL/TESOL READING										
Read about subject matter information.										
Apply basic reading comprehension skills.										
Follow written directions, implicit and explicit.										
ESL WRITING										
Write to demonstrate comprehension.										
Write using spelling patterns and targeted English vocabulary.										

Foldables   by Dinah Zike

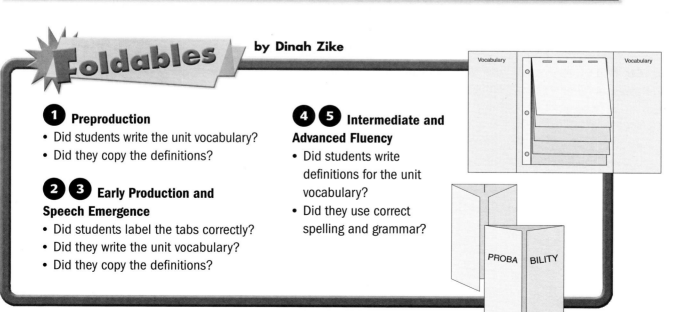

1 Preproduction
• Did students write the unit vocabulary?
• Did they copy the definitions?

2 3 Early Production and Speech Emergence
• Did students label the tabs correctly?
• Did they write the unit vocabulary?
• Did they copy the definitions?

4 5 Intermediate and Advanced Fluency
• Did students write definitions for the unit vocabulary?
• Did they use correct spelling and grammar?

UNIT 14

Planner

Percents

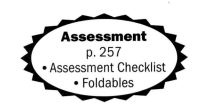

Assessment
p. 257
• Assessment Checklist
• Foldables

Visit **www.mmhmath.com**

Unit Activities	
• **Activity 1** Readiness All or Nothing, p. 246	• **Activity 3** Write a Book! p. 247
• **Activity 2** Dining Out, p. 246	• **Activity 4** Tell It to the Teacher, p. 247

Lessons	Key Objectives	Vocabulary	Materials	Resources
READ TOGETHER "Too Clever by Half" by Michael Garin, pp. 244–245	**Math:** Find what percent one number is of another. **ESL/TESOL:** Goal 2, Standards 2, 3.	clever, cried, earlier, fuss, halfway, homework, outside, play, quarter		Graphic Organizer 4
UNIT WARM-UP Understanding Percent p. 248	**Math:** Understand the meaning of percents. Change numbers between percents, decimals, and fractions. **ESL/TESOL:** Goal 1, Standard 2.	percent, repeating decimal	newspapers, paper bags, scissors	Teacher Tools 1, 2, and 3
LESSON 1 Percents, Decimals, and Fractions pp. 250–251	**Math:** Understand and interpret percent. Change numbers between percents, decimals, and fractions. **ESL/TESOL:** Goal 2, Standards 2, 2.	percent	pencils	Learning Resource 54 **Overhead Manipulatives**
LESSON 2 Percent of a Number pp. 252–253	**Math:** Find percent of a number. Find what percent one number is of another. **ESL/TESOL:** Goal 2, Standards 2, 1.	percent	crayons, glue, scissors, shirt	Learning Resource 55
LESSON 3 Circle Graphs pp. 254–255	**Math:** Find what percent one number is of another. Interpret and make circle graphs. **ESL/TESOL:** Goal 2, Standards 2, 2.	circle graph	crayons or markers, pencil, scissors	Learning Resource 56 Teacher Tool 13
PROBLEM SOLVING p. 256 • Skill: Represent Numbers • Strategy: Use Logical Reasoning	Use skills and strategies to solve problems.			**Math Center Cards 14A, 14B**

See **Math at Home Family Guide** for additional math vocabulary, activities, and games in English, Spanish, and Haitian Creole.

English Vocabulary

Dear Family: *Please help your child practice the key vocabulary words for this unit.*

circle graph a graph in which data are represented by parts of a circle; also known as a pie graph or pie chart

percent per hundred, or part of a hundred

repeating decimal sometimes in division, the quotient does not end; this is called a repeating decimal

---

Vocabulario en español

Estimados familiares: *Por favor ayuden a su hijo/a a practicar las palabras del vocabulario de esta unidad.*

gráfica circular gráfica en la cual los datos están representados como partes en un círculo

porcentaje por ciento, o parte de un ciento

decimal periódico algunas veces en la división, el cociente no termina; a éste se le llama decimal periódico

---

Vokabilè an kreyòl

Chè paran: *Tanpri ede pitit la pratike mo vokabilè nan seksyon sa a.*

tablo an sèk yon desen kote done yo reprezante pa moso yon sèk, yo rele-l tou desen an tranch pitza osnon "tat"

pousantaj moso sou san

desimal repete pafwa nan divizyon, kosyan an pa fini; yo rele sa yon desimal repete

Too Clever by Half

by Michael Garin

 25 minutes

Math Objective
- Find what percent one number is of another.

ESL/TESOL Descriptors
- Focus attention selectively.
- Connect new information to information previously learned.

Reading Skill
- Recognize main idea and supporting details.

Vocabulary
clever, cried, earlier, fuss, halfway, homework, outside, play, quarter

Before Reading

Build Background/Oral Language
Read aloud the title of the story. Explain that *clever* means smart.

Have students find words in the text that they know. Discuss when students do homework and how they feel about it.

During Reading

- Read the poem through without stopping as students track text.
- Reread and have students repeat each line. Encourage them to ask about new or difficult words. Then divide the class into two groups and have them read alternate verses in unison.

Phonological/Phonemic Awareness
Write *outside, homework,* and *understand* on the board. Show students how these words are made up of two words. Explain that each word alone has its own meaning but together they form a new word, such as the word *homework.* Brainstorm other common compound words such as *inside, overhear, airplane,* and *schoolbook.*

After Reading

Have volunteers write a numerical representation of some of the text; for example, *quarter to 3, halfway done, divide homework between the two of us,* and so on.

Pair nonfluent and fluent students. Ask students to write the main idea and details from the poem. Use Graphic Organizer 4. Explain that a quarter is a coin, $\frac{1}{4}$ of something, or quarter to/after the hour.

Drama Invite students to role-play Indris and Shakira. Add characters, such as friends. Have students make up additional dialogue.

Assessment

Observe fluency as students read the poem aloud

Multilevel Strategies

1 **Preproduction**
Say: *Point to the words in the poem that name fractions.*

Writing Have students write or copy and illustrate the words *quarter* and *half.*

2 3 **Early Production and Speech Emergence**
Ask: *What words in the poem name fractions?*

Writing Invite students to write the words and the fractions for each.

4 5 **Intermediate and Advanced Fluency**
Ask: *Do Shakira and Indris know anything about fractions? Explain.*

Writing Ask students to write about the fractions in the poem that are not part of the homework.

Too Clever by Half

by Michael Garin

*In this poem two children try
to use fractions to get their homework done
faster. They don't understand fractions. Do you?*

Indris and Shakira
Were brother and sister
And wanted to play outside.

But they had to do
Math homework
And so they almost cried.

It's a quarter to 3
We're halfway done
What are we to do?

I don't understand fractions.
Do you?

If we divide the homework
Between the two of us.

We'll get it done in half the time
It shouldn't be a fuss.

If each of us did a quarter
That adds up to a half
We'll go outside and run and play
Jump around and laugh.

We should have done it earlier
At a quarter after two.

I don't understand fractions.
Do you?

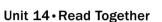

Activities

ACTIVITY 1

INDIVIDUAL

All or Nothing

- Draw a 10-by-10 grid to show these percents. Find the missing percents.

YOU NEED
graph paper
crayons or markers
2 number cubes

1. Books in the Library

Fables	7 %
Mystery	16 %
Adventure	38 %
Nonfiction	x

2. Daily Calories

Breakfast	21%
Lunch	29 %
Dinner	x
Snack	12 %

- Roll two number cubes three times to form three–digit numbers. Create a problem like the ones above. Look for a fourth number–the missing percent. (You may need to roll more than three times to get numbers you can use for your problem.)

- Find the missing percentage.

3. Weekly Budget

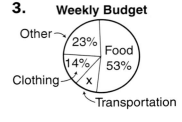

4. Band Members

Violinists, x, 43%, 12%, Others, 23%, Drummers, Trumpeters

See answers on p. 293.

Explore the Meaning of Percent

PARTNERS

ACTIVITY 2

Dining Out

- Solve with a partner.

When the waiter presented the bill, Mark paid $\frac{1}{5}$, Sam paid **18%**, Teresa paid **0.23**, and Debra paid $\frac{1}{4}$ of the bill. Juan paid the remaining amount. What percent of the bill did he pay? If the bill was exactly $100 what amount did he pay?

- Now you and your partner should each rewrite the problem by changing 2 of the numbers in the boxes. Exchange the problems. With the new numbers, determine if the problem can still be solved and can still make sense.

- Try rewriting and exchanging two more times.

MO SERVES THE *BEST* FOOD IN TOWN!

See answers on p. 293.

Percents, Fractions, and Decimals

Game Zone

ACTIVITY 3

PARTNERS

Write a Book!

Play this game with a partner. Take turns. You are each writing a book.

YOU NEED

2 number cubes

- Toss both number cubes.

- Find the product. This represents the percent of the book you have written.

- Record this percent with its equivalent fraction and decimal.

- Repeat. Keep a running total of your percents, fractions, and decimals.

- The first player to reach 100 percent has completed the book and wins the game.

More About Percent

ACTIVITY 4

PARTNERS

Tell It To the Teacher

- **Step 1.** You are both 5th grade teachers. Use the information on the circle graph to make up 10 questions about the survey it represents. Write an answer key on a separate sheet of paper.

- **Step 2.** Change roles. Now you are both students. Exchange questions and answer again.

- **Step 3.** Change roles again. Now you are both teachers. Collect the answers to the questions you made up. Check them with your answer key. Give 10 points for each correct answer. Grade the paper.

- When finished, check each other's answers to be sure they are correct. Compare to see who scored higher on the test.

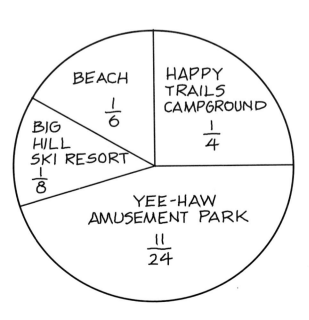

Circle Graphs

© Macmillan/McGraw-Hill

Understanding Percent

 25 minutes

▶ **Key Strategy**
Use manipulatives

▶ **Format**
Whole class and student pairs

▶ **Math Vocabulary**
percent

▶ **Daily Vocabulary**
coins, U.S. currency

▶ **Resources**
Teacher Tools 1, 2, and 3

▶ **Materials**
newspapers, paper bags, scissors

Math Objectives	**ESL/TESOL Descriptors**
▪ Understand the meaning of percent.	▪ Explore alternative ways of saying things.
▪ Change numbers between percents, decimals, and fractions.	▪ Use context to construct meaning.

Activate Prior Knowledge Hold up a penny, nickel, dime, quarter, and half dollar, and ask students to name the coins. Have volunteers write the value of a each coin on the board in cents: *1¢, 5¢, 10¢, 25¢,* and *50¢.* Read the values.

Hands-on Lesson Point out that all the coin values students named are part of one dollar, or 100 cents. Rewrite 1¢ as *$0.01,* and invite volunteers to rewrite the other values as *$0.05, $0.10, $0.25,* and *$0.50.* Remind students that these decimals are written to the hundredth place, so they show part of one hundred.

- Write the word **percent** and the symbol **%** and explain that it means part of one hundred. Elicit other words that have *cent* in them such as *centimeter.* Point out that *cent* means hundred. Write and say: **50%.** Explain that 50% means 50 parts of one hundred, just like $0.50 means 50 parts of one dollar.

- Pair students and distribute Teacher Tools 1, 2, and 3; Coins, Bills, and Place-Value Charts. Review place value by reading the column headings: *ones, decimal point, tenths, hundredths.* Draw the chart and model how to show coin values. For example, hold up a dime and write *1* and *0* under the tenth and hundredths columns. Ask students to write amounts such as *3¢,* or *15¢,* or *79¢.* For numbers under 10¢, remind them that the tenths place will have a zero.

- Write 99¢ on the chart. Then ask: **What happens when I add 1¢ to 99¢?** Elicit that the amount becomes 100¢, which becomes $1.00.

- Ask pairs to put their coins in a paper bag and take turns picking two or three coins, adding them, and writing them on Teacher Tool 2. Then have them write the amounts as percents.

Cultural Link Decimals are indicated by a period in English and a comma in many other languages.

Multilevel Strategies

❶ Preproduction
Have students point to amounts on the chart as you say them.

❷❸ Early Production and Speech Emergence
Have students say amounts on the chart as percents.

❹❺ Intermediate and Advanced Fluency
Have students explain what amounts go to the right of the decimal point.

LOG ON Visit **www.mmhmath.com** to find printable **Vocabulary Cards** that help build academic language.

Procedure: Help students make these Foldables to write vocabulary words and definitions throughout the unit. Encourage students to use the Foldables as a study guide.

 **by Dinah Zike**

Accordion Book

1. Provide each student with two sheets of paper. Have students fold the two sheets in half like hamburgers. Help your students tape the ends of the sheets together to make an Accordion Book.

2. Students can label lesson titles on one side and draw a number line on the other. As they work through the unit, have them take notes and record main ideas on one side of their Accordion Books using complete sentences, main idea phrases, vocabulary words, lists, and examples.

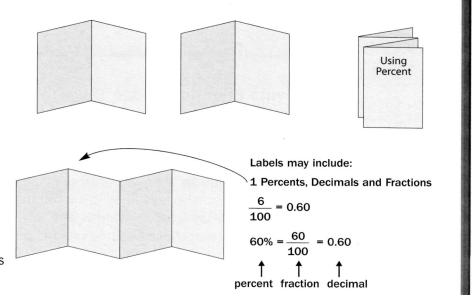

Labels may include:

1 Percents, Decimals and Fractions

$$\frac{6}{100} = 0.60$$

$$60\% = \frac{60}{100} = 0.60$$

percent   fraction   decimal

 **by Dinah Zike**

Accordion Book

1. Provide each student with two sheets of paper. Have students fold the two sheets in half like hamburgers. Help your students tape the ends of the sheets together to make an Accordion Book.

2. Students can label lesson titles on one side and draw a number line on the other. As they work through the unit, have them take notes and record main ideas on one side of their Accordion Books using complete sentences, main idea phrases, vocabulary words, lists, and examples.

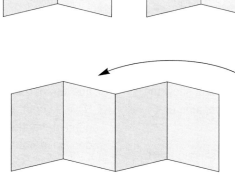

Labels may include:

3 Percent of a Number

3 is what percent of 12?

$$\frac{3}{12} \begin{array}{l} \leftarrow \text{part} \\ \leftarrow \text{whole} \end{array}$$

$$12\overline{)3.00}^{\,0.25}$$

$0.25 = 25\%$

Check: $12 \times .25 = \frac{1}{4} \times 12 = 3$

⏱ **45 minutes**

▶ **Key Strategy**
Use visuals

▶ **Format**
Whole class and pairs

▶ **Math Vocabulary**
percent, repeating decimal

▶ **Daily Vocabulary**
decimal, hundreds,
hundredths, place value

▶ **Resources**
Overhead Manipulatives:
Fraction Strips
Learning Resource 54
Teacher Tools 7 and 10

Materials
• pencils

Assessment

Check students' mastery of
percent as they complete the
lesson. See Assessment
Checklist on page 257. Remind
students to work on their
Foldables.

Home Connection

Send home grid paper and ask
students to work with family
members to make colorful
percent models. Assign different
percent amounts to each
student. Have students share
their models with the class.

Percents, Decimals, and Fractions

Math Objectives	**ESL/TESOL Descriptors**
▪ Understand and interpret percents.	▪ Select, connect, and explain information.
▪ Change numbers between percents, decimals, and fractions.	▪ Analyze, synthesize, and infer from information.

Activate Prior Knowledge Review the meaning of the word **percent,** which is part of a hundred. Show a grid of 100 squares with 30 shaded. Say: **There are 100 squares. Thirty are shaded. What percent is shaded?** Ask a volunteer to write the answer with the word and symbol. *(30%, 30 percent)*

Hands-on Lesson Remind students of the money amounts and place-value charts in the Warm-Up lesson. Write *.40* on the board. Ask a volunteer to write the amount as a percent, *(40%)*. Write *.4* and *.400* and ask: **How can we change these numbers to percents?** Elicit that we use the tenths and hundredths places and round to hundredths or add zeros if needed. *(They both show 40%.)*

● Say: **How else can we show part of 100?** *(with fractions)* **How can we write .40, or 40%, as a fraction?** Show that because it is part of 100, we can turn it into a fraction with 100 as the denominator, $\frac{40}{100}$, simplified to $\frac{2}{5}$.

● Review that to turn a fraction into a decimal, we divide the numerator by the denominator. We can then change the decimal to a percent.

● Distribute Teacher Tool 10: Fraction Strips and Teacher Tool 7: 10 x 10 Grid. Ask students to shade 50 squares out of 100 on a grid and write the percent, fraction, and decimal amount. *(50%, $\frac{50}{100}$ or $\frac{1}{2}$, .50)* Then ask each student in a group to show one of the fractions on the strips as a part of 100 on grid paper, and write amounts as decimals and percents. Distribute Learning Resource 54: Percent and have students complete the page. Point out that the fraction $\frac{1}{3}$ becomes a **repeating decimal** (.33333...).

● Use Fraction Strips from **Overhead Manipulatives** to reinforce the lesson concept.

Multilevel Strategies

❶ Preproduction
Have students show the decimal, percent, or fraction.

Writing Ask students to write a percent as a fraction.

❷❸ Early Production and Speech Emergence
Have students name the percent, fraction, and decimal amounts.

Writing Invite students to write the percents in numbers and symbols and in words.

❹❺ Intermediate and Advanced Fluency
Have students explain what *percent* means.

Writing Encourage students to write how they changed a fraction to a percent.

Name _____

Percent

Complete the chart.

PERCENT	FRACTION*	DECIMAL
		.89
		.06
82%		
1%		
	$\frac{1}{3}$	
	$\frac{21}{100}$	$\frac{1}{3}$
25%		
	$\frac{40}{100}$	
		.72

*Find the simplest form.

45 minutes

▶ **Key Strategy**
Use realia

▶ **Format**
Whole class, small groups, and pairs

▶ **Math Vocabulary**
percent

▶ **Daily Vocabulary**
clothing items

▶ **Resource**
Learning Resource 55

Materials
- crayons
- glue
- scissors
- shirt

Assessment

Check students' mastery of percent as they complete the lesson. See Assessment Checklist on page 257. Remind students to work on their Foldables.

Home Connection

Ask students to look for sale ads in magazines or supermarket flyers with family members and figure out what percent of the original price the sale price is. Have them share the prices with the class.

Percent of a Number

Math Objectives	**ESL/TESOL Descriptors**
▪ Find percent of a number.	▪ Select, connect, and explain information.
▪ Find what percent one number is of another.	▪ Negotiate and manage interaction to accomplish tasks.

Activate Prior Knowledge Hold up a shirt. Say: *This shirt is on sale. It was $30.00. The store is having a half-price sale. Everything is $\frac{1}{2}$ price.* Ask students to tell you the new price. *($15.00)* Then ask them what percent of the original price the shirt is now. *(50%)*

Hands-on Lesson Ask students how they figured out the price of the shirt and the percent. Point out that it is easier to figure out a percent if it equals a fraction, such as $\frac{1}{2}$. But how can they find any percent of a number?

- Write *45% of $60.00.* Ask a volunteer to turn 45% into a decimal. Then ask students to multiply $.45 \times 60$ to figure out 45% of 60. *(27)*

- Distribute Learning Resource 55: How Much Is It? and ask students to look at the sale sign. Have a volunteer read the sign aloud. Then have pairs work together to find the new sales prices, using the percentages on the sign. Have them practice finding percents of the amounts listed on the page.

- Divide the class into small groups and distribute crayons and paper. Have each group make different items of clothing, such as pants, shirts, socks, or shoes. Have them cut out the items and display them on a table to make a class clothing store. Ask them to assign prices to the items. Then have groups make signs telling the new sale price of each item as percents of original prices. Have groups write a list of the new prices of each item by finding the percents.

Cultural Link Ask students to tell about shopping in their native countries. For example, there may not be shopping malls but outdoor markets. Mention that the currency and prices may differ.

Multilevel Strategies

1 **Preproduction**
Have students hold up items of clothing and show you the original and sale prices.

Writing Invite students to write the numeral and name of one item and its sale price.

2 3 **Early Production and Speech Emergence**
Ask: *What is the sale price of this shirt?*

Writing Have students list store items, prices, and sale prices.

4 5 **Intermediate and Advanced Fluency**
Say: *Tell me about this sale. What can I buy? What are the prices?*

Writing Encourage students to write a description of the sale at the store.

Name _____

How Much Is It?

1. Look at the sign. Write the new sale price.

shirt _____

pants _____

shorts _____

shoes _____

Clothing Sale!

$40.00 $60.00

$30.00 $85.00

Shirts, pants
and shorts...75% of original price.

Shoes...60% of original price.

2. Find the following percents.

Find 30% of 18   Find 5% of 64   Find 18% of $56.00

_____   _____   _____

Find 145% of 25.4   Find 60% of 200   Find 95% of $621.00

_____   _____   _____

45 minutes

▶ **Key Strategy**
Use charts and graphs

▶ **Format**
Whole class and small groups

▶ **Math Vocabulary**
circle graph

▶ **Daily Vocabulary**
bicycle, city bus, school bus, transportation

▶ **Resources**
Learning Resource 56
Teacher Tool 13

Materials
- crayons or markers
- pencil
- scissors

Assessment

Check students' mastery of making circle graphs as they complete the lesson. See Assessment Checklist on page 257. Remind students to work on their Foldables.

Home Connection

Have students find circle graphs in magazines with family members and bring them in to share with the class.

Circle Graphs

Math Objectives	**ESL/TESOL Descriptors**
■ Find what percent one number is of another. ■ Interpret and make circle graphs.	■ Interpret information presented visually. ■ Demonstrate knowledge through application in a variety of contexts.

Activate Prior Knowledge Draw circles on the board and write the fractions $\frac{1}{2}, \frac{1}{4}, \frac{1}{3}, \frac{3}{4}$. Have volunteers divide and shade the circles to show each fraction. Then ask them to change the fractions to percents.

Hands-on Lesson Distribute Learning Resource 56: Make a Circle Graph, and look at the **circle graph** together. Explain that it shows how 120 students traveled to school. Ask them to find each percent of 120 to discover how many traveled by car, school bus, city bus, on foot, and bike. Write the five ways of getting to school on the board and take a show of hands for your own class of how many go to school each way. Have a student record the information.

- Divide students into groups. Have students show each number as a fraction, putting the total students in the class as the denominator each time. Then have students work together to turn the fractions into decimals, by dividing numerators by denominators, and write the decimals as percents.

- Distribute Teacher Tool 13: Ruler/Protractor. Explain how to make a circle graph. Ask students to look again at the circle graph on their page. Remind them that a circle has 360°, so the angles formed at the center add up to 360°. Point out the angle in the 40% section. Explain that it is 40% of 360. Have students find 40% of 360° (144°) and measure the angle.

- Have groups make circle graphs about the class survey using their protractors to make angles representing each percentage. Ask them to color the sections and draw a bus, bike, car, or student walking to show what each section represents.

Challenge Invite students to create a survey for another class and make a circle graph to show results.

Multilevel Strategies

1 **Preproduction**
Ask: *Which section of the circle shows 40%?*

Writing Invite students to list the angles and percents.

2 **3** **Early Production and Speech Emergence**
Have students tell you the angles and percents.

Writing Encourage students to list in phrases the information shown on the graph.

4 **5** **Intermediate and Advanced Fluency**
Ask: *How did you make the circle graph?*

Writing Have students list the steps needed to make a circle graph.

Name _____

Make a Circle Graph

This circle graph shows how 120 students travel to school. Read the graph. Find out how many students travel each way.

by car _____

by city bus _____

by school bus _____

by bike _____

on foot _____

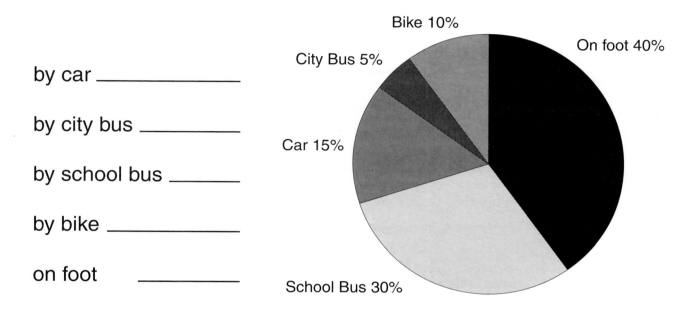

Now make a circle graph to show how students in your class travel to school.

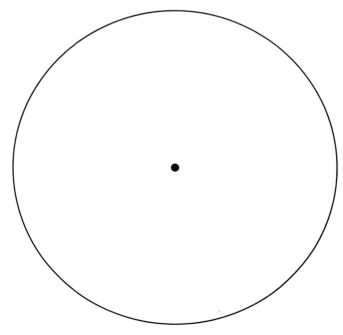

© Macmillan/McGraw-Hill

Problem Solving

Problem Solving

Problem Solving
Reading for Math

Read → Plan → Solve → Look Back

Remind students of
the basic steps
of problem solving.

SKILL: Represent Numbers
Model the skill using a word problem such as:

 Read

Gerry came home hungry for pizza. His sister Rachael said she only ate $\frac{2}{8}$ of the pizza. His brother Mike said he ate 50% of the pizza. His dad said he only had 0.25 of the pizza. Is there any pizza left for Gerry?

 Plan

I can write all the amounts as fractions. I will find a common denominator. Then I can add to find how much pizza was eaten.

 Solve

Think: I will write all the numbers as fractions. The common denominator is eighths.

$50\% = \frac{1}{2} = \frac{4}{8}$ $0.25 = \frac{1}{4} = \frac{2}{8}$ $\frac{2}{8} + \frac{4}{8} + \frac{2}{8} = 1$

There is no pizza left for Gerry.

 Look Back

Why did I represent all the numbers in the same form? To make it easier to calculate the sum.

Distribute **Math Center Card 14A** to students.

Math Center Card 14A

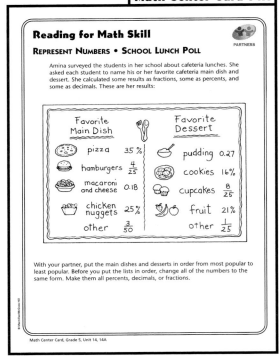

STRATEGY: Use Logical Reasoning
Model the strategy using a word problem such as:

 Read

Jesse and Paul are on the soccer team. Susan, John, and Matthew are on the softball team. Jesse also plays softball. John plays on the soccer team too. Jill plays softball. Ken and Alan are on both teams. Do more students play soccer or softball?

 Plan

I can use the information in the problem to make a Venn diagram. I can compare.

Solve

Think: I can label one circle *soccer* and the other *softball*. I can label the intersection *both*.

soccer	both	softball
Paul	Jesse	Susan
	John	Jill
	Ken	
	Alan	

5 students play soccer. 6 students play softball. More students play softball.

 Look Back

How can I check my answer? I can write addition sentences. $3 + 4 = 7$ $2 + 4 = 6$ $6 < 7$

Distribute **Math Center Card 14B** to students.

Math Center Card 14B

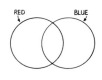

Assessment Checklist

	STUDENT NAMES									
SCHOOL:										
TEACHER: **SCHOOL YEAR:**										
Mark: + = Mastery ✓ = Satisfactory − = Needs Improvement										
LEVEL OF LANGUAGE PROFICIENCY (1–5)										
MATH OBJECTIVES										
• Change numbers between percents, decimals, and fractions.										
• Understand and interpret percent.										
• Find percent of a number										
• Find what percent one number is of another.										
• Interpret and make circle graphs.										
ESL/TESOL LISTENING/SPEAKING										
Analyze, synthesize, and infer from information.										
Explore alternative ways of saying things.										
Demonstrate knowledge through application in a variety of contexts.										
Negotiate and manage interaction to accomplish tasks.										
Select, connect, and explain information.										
ESL/TESOL READING										
Read about subject matter information.										
Apply basic reading comprehension skills.										
Follow written directions, implicit and explicit.										
ESL WRITING										
Write to demonstrate comprehension.										
Write using spelling patterns and targeted English vocabulary.										

 **by Dinah Zike**

❶ Preproduction
- Did students write the unit vocabulary?
- Did they copy the definitions?

❷ ❸ Early Production and Speech Emergence
- Did students label the tabs correctly?
- Did they write the vocabulary words?
- Did they copy the definitions?

❹ ❺ Intermediate and Advanced Fluency
- Did students write definitions for the unit vocabulary?
- Did they use correct spelling and grammar?

Using Percent

Circle Graphs

Glossary

A

acute angle An *angle* with a measure of less than 90°.

acute triangle A *triangle* with 3 *acute angles*.

addend A number that is to be added.

algebraic expression A *variable* by itself or a combination of one or more *variables*, one or more *operations*, and possibly one or more numbers.

Example: $3x + 5$

algebraic rule A mathematical *expression* that contains *variables* and describes a *pattern* or *relationship*.

angle A figure formed by two *rays* or *line segments* with the same *endpoint*.

area The number of *square units* needed to cover the inside of a figure.

array A group of objects separated into rows and columns.

Associative Property of Addition When adding three *addends*, the grouping of the *addends* does not change the sum.

Example: $16 + (14 + 89) = (16 + 14) + 89$

Associative Property of Multiplication The way *factors* are grouped does not change a *product*.

Example: $20 \times (5 \times 77) = (20 \times 5) \times 77$

axis (plural: axes) A *horizontal* or *vertical number line* on a graph.

B

bar graph A graph that compares *data* by using *vertical* or *horizontal* bars.

base a. The number that is to be raised to a given power. **b.** A polygon's side or a solid figure's face by which the figure is measured or named.

benchmark A point of reference from which other measurements may be estimated.

biased sample A *sample* that is not representative of the entire *population*.

C

capacity The amount a container can hold, measured in units of liquid measure.

Celsius (ºC) A temperature scale in which water freezes at 0˚C and boils at 100˚C.

center The *point* from which all points on a *circle* are the same distance.

central angle An *angle* formed by two *radii* in a *circle*.

certain An *outcome* or *event* is certain if it has a probability of 1.

chord A *line segment* that connects two *points* on a *circle*.

circle A *closed* figure in a *plane* that has all of its *points* the same distance from the *center*.

circle graph A graph in which *data* is represented by parts of a *circle*; also known as a pie graph or pie chart.

circumference The distance around a *circle*.

closed figure A figure in a *plane* that can be traced with the same starting and stopping *points*.

clustering A way to *estimate* a sum by changing the *addends* that are close in *value* to one common number and multiplying by the number of *addends*.

Example: $89 + 113 + 102 + 93 \approx$
$100 + 100 + 100 + 100 =$
$4 \times 100 = 400$

common denominator A common *multiple* of the *denominators* of two or more *fractions*.

common factor A *whole number* that is a *factor* of two or more numbers.

    Example: 3 is a common factor of 6 and 15.

common multiple A *whole number* that is a *multiple* of two or more numbers.

    Example: 24 is a common multiple of 4 and 6.

Commutative Property of Addition When adding, the order of the *addends* does not change the sum.

    Example: $43 + 13 = 13 + 43$

Commutative Property of Multiplication The order of the *factors* does not change a *product*.

    Example: $8 \times 11 = 11 \times 8$

compatible numbers Numbers that can be easily added, subtracted, multiplied, or divided mentally.

    Example: 7,200 and 90 are compatible
          numbers for division because
          $72 \div 9 = 8.$

compensation A mental math technique for adding or subtracting two numbers, involving doing the same *operation* or the opposite *operation* to the two numbers.

composite number A *whole number* greater than 1 that is *divisible* by more numbers than just itself and the number 1.

compound events A series of two or more simple *events*.

compound figure A shape that is made up of two or more shapes.

concrete representations of numbers Having a definite form or relating to an actual object. See place value models; see decimal models.

cone A *3-dimensional figure* that has a circular *base* and one curved surface from the base to a *vertex*.

congruent figures Figures that have the same shape and size.

congruent line segments Line segments that have the same length.

coordinate One of two numbers in an *ordered pair*.

coordinate graph or grid A network of evenly spaced, *parallel, horizontal* and *vertical lines* especially designed for locating *points*, displaying *data*, or drawing maps.

corresponding parts Matching parts of *congruent* or *similar* figures.

counting principle The number of possible *outcomes* in a *compound event* is equal to the *product* of the number of possible *outcomes* for each simple *event*.

cross product A *product* of the *numerator* of one *fraction* and the *denominator* of another *fraction*.

cube A rectangular *prism* in which every *face* is a *square*.

cubic unit a unit for measuring *volume*, such as a cubic inch or a cubic centimeter.

customary units The units of measure developed and used in the United States. See *Table of Measures*.

cylinder A *3-dimensional figure* having two *parallel congruent* circular *bases* and a curved surface connecting the two *bases*.

data Collected information.

decimal A number with one or more digits to the right of the *decimal point*, such as 8.37 or 0.05.

degree (°) **a.** A unit for measuring temperature. See *Celsius* and *Fahrenheit*. **b.** A unit for measuring *angles*.

denominator The number below the bar in a fraction; the part of the *fraction* that tells how many equal parts are in the whole.

diagonal A *line* segment, other than a *side*, that connects two *vertices* of a *polygon*.

diameter A *chord* of a *circle* that passes through the *center* of the circle.

direct measure A way to obtain the measure of an object by using measuring devices, either standard devices of the *customary* or *metric systems*, or nonstandard devices such as a paper clip or pencil.

Distributive Property of Multiplication over Addition To multiply a sum by a number, you can multiply each *addend* by the number and add the *products*.

Example: $9 \times (8 + 7) = (9 \times 8) + (9 \times 7)$

Distributive Property of Multiplication over Subtraction To multiply a difference of two numbers by a third number, you can multiply each of the first two numbers by the third and then find the difference of the *products*.

Example: $23 \times (11 - 5) = (23 \times 11) - (23 \times 5)$

dividend A number to be divided.

divisible A *whole number* is divisible by another *whole number* if the *remainder* is 0 when the first is divided by the second.

divisor The number by which a *dividend* is divided.

double-bar graph A *bar graph* that compares two related groups of *data*.

 E

edge A *line segment* where two *faces* of a *3-dimensional figure* meet.

effects of operations The results of applying an *operation* to given numbers (e.g., adding two *whole numbers* results in a number greater than or equal to the original numbers).

elapsed time The amount of time that passes from the start of an activity to the end of the activity.

empirical probability The *likelihood* of an *event* happening based on experience and observation, rather than on theory. Also called **experimental probability**.

endpoint A *point* at the end of a *line segment* or *ray*.

equally likely Two or more *outcomes* are equally likely if they have the same *probability* of occurring.

equation A mathematical statement with an equal sign in it.

equilateral triangle A *triangle* with three *congruent* sides.

equivalent forms of a number The same number expressed in different forms.

Example: $\frac{1}{2}$, 0.5, 50%

equivalent decimals *Decimals* that name the same number.

Example: 0.6 and 0.60

equivalent fractions *Fractions* that name the same number.

Example: $\frac{1}{3}$ and $\frac{12}{36}$

equivalent ratios *Ratios* that can be represented by *equivalent fractions*.

Example: 3:5 and 12:20

estimate To find a number that is close to the exact answer without calculating an exact answer.

evaluate To find the numerical *value* of an *expression* by substituting numbers for the *variables* and following the *operation* symbols.

event A set of one or more *outcomes* in a *probability* experiment.

expanded form A way of writing a number as the sum of the *values* of its digits.

Example: $638 = 600 + 30 + 8$

experimental probability See *empirical probability*.

explain in words Directions asking for a written description of method or *solution*.

exponent The number that tells how many times a *base* is used as a *factor*.

expression A collection of numbers, *variables*, and/or *operation* signs that stand for a number.

face A flat *side* of a *3-dimensional figure*.

fact family A group of related facts using the same numbers.

factor **a.** A number that is multiplied to give a *product*. **b.** A number is a factor of another *whole number* if the *remainder* is 0 when the second is divided by the first.

Example: 5 is a factor of 245 because $245 \div 5 = 49$.

factor tree A diagram used to find a prime factorization of a number.

Fahrenheit (˚F) A temperature *scale* in which water freezes at 32°F and boils at 212°F.

flip A *transformation* that produces the mirror image of a geometric figure. Also called a *reflection*.

formula An *equation* with at least two *variables*, showing how one *variable* depends on the other *variable* or *variables*.

fraction A number that names part of a whole or part of a group.

frequency The number of times a response occurs or something happens.

frequency table A way of organizing a set of *data*, showing the number of times each item or number appears.

function A *relationship* in which one quantity depends on another quantity.

glide reflection A *transformation* that is a combination of *reflection* and *translation*.

greatest common factor (GCF) The greatest common factor of two or more numbers is the greatest *whole number* that is a *common factor* of the numbers.

Example: 28 and 88 have common factors 1, 2, and 4. So their greatest common factor is 4.

grid A network of evenly spaced, *parallel*, *horizontal* and *vertical lines*.

height of a parallelogram The length of a *line segment* from one *side* of the *parallelogram* to the side *parallel* to it, drawn *perpendicular* to both of the *sides*.

height of a triangle The length of a *line segment* from a *vertex* of a *triangle* to the *side* opposite that *vertex*, drawn *perpendicular* to that *side*.

hexagon A *polygon* with six *sides*.

histogram A *bar graph* that shows *frequency* of *data* for *intervals*.

horizontal line A line that runs straight across.

I

Identity Property of Addition When a number is added to 0, the sum is that number.

Example: $8 + 0 = 8$

Identity Property of Multiplication The *product* of any *factor* and 1 is that *factor*.

Example: $8 \times 1 = 8$

impossible An *outcome* or *event* is impossible if it has a *probability* of 0.

improper fraction A fraction that has a *numerator* greater than or equal to its denominator.

independent events Two *events* where the first *event* does not affect the *probability* of the second *event*.

indirect measure The measurement of an object through the known measure of another object.

inequality A sentence that states one *expression* is greater than, greater than or equal to, less than, less than or equal to, or not equal to, another *expression*.

Examples: $a \neq 6, x < 8$.

integer A *positive* or *negative whole number* or 0.

intersecting lines *Lines* that meet or cross at a common *point*.

interval The distance between adjacent numbers on an *axis* of a graph.

inverse operations *Operations* that can undo each other.

Example: Multiplying by 6 and dividing by 6 are inverse operations.

isosceles triangle A *triangle* with at least two *sides* of the same length.

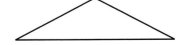

L

labels (for a graph) The titles given to a graph, the *axes* of a graph, or the *scales* on the *axes* of a graph.

leaf A ones digit in a row of a *stem-and-leaf plot*.

least common denominator (LCD) The *least common multiple* of the *denominators* of two or more *fractions*.

least common multiple (LCM) The least *whole number* greater than 0 that is a *multiple* of each of two or more numbers.

length The measurement of an object along its greatest dimension.

less likely An *event* is less likely than a second *event* if it has a smaller *probability* of happening than the second *event* has.

like denominators *Denominators* that are the same number.

likelihood The chance that something is *likely* to happen. See *probability*.

likely An *outcome* is likely if it probably will happen.

line A set of *points* that form a straight path that goes forever in both directions.

line graph A graph that uses one or more *line segments* to show changes in *data*.

line of symmetry A *line* that divides a figure into two parts that match when the figure is folded on that *line*.

line plot A graph that uses columns of Xs above a *number line*.

line segment A part of a *line* that connects two *endpoints*.

M

mass The amount of matter in an object.

mean The quantity that is found by adding the numbers in a set of numbers and dividing their sum by the number of *addends*. Sometimes called an average.

> Example: The mean of the numbers 7, 8, 9, 6, and 9 is 7.8.

median The middle number in a set of numbers arranged in order from least to greatest. If the set contains an even number of numbers, the median is the *mean* of the two middle numbers.

> Example: The median of the numbers 7, 8, 9, 6, and 9 is 8.

metric system See *metric units*.

metric units The units of measure developed in Europe and used in most of the world. Also called metric system. See *Table of Measures*.

mixed number A number that combines a *whole number* and a *fraction*.

mode The number that occurs most often in a set of numbers.

> Example: The mode of the numbers 7, 8, 9, 6, and 9 is 9.

more likely An *event* is more likely than a second *event* if it has a greater *probability* of happening than the second *event*.

multiple A multiple of a number is the *product* of that number and any *whole number*. For example, 15 is a multiple of 5 because $3 \times 5 = 15$.

N

negative number A number less than 0.

net A *2-dimensional* pattern that can be folded to make a *3-dimensional figure*.

nonstandard units of measure Objects such as blocks, paper clips, crayons, or pencils that can be used to obtain a measure.

number line A *line* on which numbers can be written or visualized.

numerator The number above the bar in a *fraction*; the part of the fraction that tells how many equal parts are being used.

O

obtuse angle An *angle* that measures greater than 90° and less than 180°.

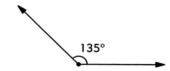

135°

obtuse triangle A *triangle* with one *obtuse angle*.

open figure A figure that starts and stops at different *points*.

operation Any mathematical process, such as addition, subtraction, multiplication, division, raising to a power, or finding the square root.

opposite integers Two different *integers* that are the same distance from 0 on a *number line*.

> Example: 5 and ⁻5

order of operations The agreed-upon order for performing *operations*.

ordered pair A pair of numbers that gives the location of a point on a *coordinate graph* or *grid*.

> Example: (4, 0)

organized data *Data* arranged in a display that is meaningful and assists in the interpretation of the data.

origin The point on a *coordinate graph* where the vertical *axis* meets the horizontal axis.

outcome A possible result in a *probability* experiment.

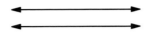

parallel lines Two or more *lines* in the same *plane* that never intersect.

parallelogram A *quadrilateral* in which both pairs of opposite *sides* are *parallel*.

pattern (relationship) A sequence of numbers, objects, etc. Also called a *relation*.

percent Per hundred, or part of a hundred.

perimeter The distance around a *closed figure*.

period Each group of three digits in a *place-value chart*.

perpendicular lines *Intersecting lines* that cross each other at *right angles*.

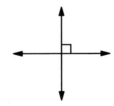

perspective drawing A drawing that shows a *3-dimensional* object in a *2-dimensional* drawing.

pictograph A graph that compares *data* by using picture symbols.

place The position of a digit in a number.

plane A flat surface that extends forever.

plane figure A *2-dimensional figure* that lies entirely within a single *plane*.

plot To graph a *point* on a *coordinate plane*.

point An exact location in space.

point of rotation A *point* around which a figure may be rotated less than 360° and still match the original figure.

polyhedron A figure with polygonal faces.

polygon A *closed plane figure* whose sides are straight *line segments* that are connected *endpoint* to *endpoint*.

population A group about which information is wanted.

positive number A number greater than 0.

power A number obtained by raising a *base* to an *exponent*.

Example: $5^2 = 25$

power of 10 A number obtained by raising 10 to a given *exponent*.

Examples: $10^1 = 10, 10^2 = 10 \times 10 = 100$

prime factorization A way of expressing a *whole number* as a *product* of its *prime factors*.

prime number Any *whole number* with only two *factors*, 1 and itself.

prism A *3-dimensional figure* formed by flat surfaces that have the shape of *polygons;* two of the *faces* must be *congruent* and *parallel,* the rest of the faces must be rectangular.

probability A number between 0 and 1 that measures the chance of an *event* happening.

product The answer in a multiplication problem.

properties of addition See *Associative, Commutative,* and *Identity* properties.

properties of multiplication See *Associative, Commutative, Distributive, Identity,* and *Zero* properties.

proportion An *equation* stating that two *ratios* are *equivalent*.

Examples: $\frac{7}{8} = \frac{28}{32}; \frac{n}{10} = \frac{12}{5}$

protractor A semicircular tool for measuring and constructing angles.

pyramid A *3-dimensional figure* formed by flat surfaces that have the shape of *polygons*. One *face*, called the *base*, may be the shape of any *polygon*; the rest of the *faces* must be *triangular* and meet at a single *point*.

Q

quadrant One of the four sections on a *coordinate graph* formed by two *axes*.

quadrilateral A *polygon* with four sides and four *angles*.

quotient The answer to a *division* problem.

R

radius (plural: radii) A *line segment* that connects the *center of a circle* to a *point* on the *circle*.

random sample A *sample* where every member is chosen by chance, and everyone in the *population* has an equal chance of being chosen.

range The difference between the greatest and the least number in a set of numbers.

> Example: The range of the numbers 7, 8, 9, 6, and 9 is 3.

rate A *ratio* that compares measurements or amounts.

> Example: 50 miles per hour

ratio A comparison of two quantities.

ray A part of a *line* that has one *endpoint* and continues in one direction without end.

reciprocal One of two numbers whose *product* is 1.

> Examples: 3 and $\frac{1}{3}$ are reciprocals since $3 \times \frac{1}{3} = 1$.

rectangle A *parallelogram* with four *right angles*.

reflection (See *flip*.) A *transformation* that creates a mirror image of a figure across a *line*.

regular polygon A *polygon* that is both *equilateral* and *equiangular*.

relation (relationship) See *pattern*.

remainder In *division*, the number left after the *quotient* is found.

> Example: When 30 is divided by 7, the remainder is 2.

repeating decimal Sometimes in division, the *quotient* does not end. This is called a repeating decimal.

> Example: $3\overline{)2.000}$ .666

representative sample A *sample* of a *population* that gives you the same answers you would get if you surveyed the whole population.

rhombus A *parallelogram* with four *congruent* sides.

right angle An *angle* with a measure of 90°.

right triangle A *triangle* with one *right angle*.

rotation (turn) A *transformation* that turns a figure around a *point*.

rotational symmetry A figure has rotational *symmetry* if, after a given number of *rotations* of the figure about a *point*, the figure returns to its original position.

round To find the nearest *value* of a number based on a given *place*.

> Example: 6.38 rounded to the nearest tenth is 6.4.

rule A mathematical *expression* that shows a *pattern* or *relationship*, or a written description of the *pattern* or *relationship*.

S

sample A part of a *population* used to get information about that population.

sample space The set of all possible *outcomes* in a *probability* experiment.

scale **a.** The numeric *values* assigned to the *axes* of a *graph*. **b.** The *ratio* of the *lengths* on a map or *scale drawing* with the actual *lengths*.

scale drawing A reduced or enlarged drawing of an actual object.

scale model A reduced or enlarged 3-dimensional model of an object.

scalene triangle A *triangle* in which no two *sides* are *congruent*.

scientific notation A number expressed as the *product* of two *factors* where the first *factor* is between 1 and 10 and the second *factor* is a *power* of 10.

sides **a.** of an *angle* are the *rays* that form the angle. **b.** of a *polygon* are *line segments* that meet at the *vertices*.

similar figures Figures that are the same shape but are not necessarily the same size or in the same position.

simplest form A *fraction* is in simplest form when 1 is the only *common factor* of the *numerator* and *denominator*.

      Example: $\frac{5}{12}$ is in simplest form because 5 and 12 have no common factor greater than 1.

slide To move along in constant contact with the surface in a *vertical, horizontal,* or *diagonal* direction. Also called a *translation*.

solution **a.** A mixture of materials that is evenly mixed. **b.** An answer that makes an equation true.

spatial relationships Relationships of figures existing in space.

sphere A *3-dimensional figure* that is the set of all *points* that are the same distance from a given point, called the *center*.

square A rectangle with four *congruent sides*.

square unit A unit for measuring *area*, such as a *square inch* or a *square centimeter*.

standard form The usual or common way to write a number.

standard units of measure Accepted measuring devices and units of the *customary* or *metric* system. See *Table of Measures*.

stem The digit or digits to the left of the ones digit of a number in a *data* set.

stem-and-leaf plot An arrangement of numerical *data* that separates the digits into columns. The digits to the left of the ones digits are called the *stems*; the ones digits for each stem are the *leaves*.

straight angle An *angle* with a measure of 180˚.

surface area The total area of the surface of a *3-dimensional figure*.

survey A method of gathering *data* that involves asking people questions or observing events.

symbolic expression A symbol or set of symbols expressing a mathematical quantity or operation (e.g., *2y* is equal to two times *y*).

symmetry about a line A figure has symmetry about a line if it can be folded along a *line* drawn through the *center* of the figure so that the two halves match exactly.

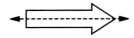

tally chart A way to keep track of data using marks to record the number of responses or occurrences.

terminating decimal In a *division* problem, when the *decimal quotient* ends evenly, the decimal *terminates*.

terms The numbers in a *ratio*.

tessellate To fit together to make a *tessellation*.

tessellation An arrangement of shapes that covers a region without any gaps or overlaps.

theoretical/expected probability The *likelihood* of an event happening based on theory rather than on experience and observation.

3-dimensional figure A figure that has *length*, width, and height.

transformation A change of position of a geometric figure.

translation (slide) A *transformation* in which a figure moves along a straight line.

trapezoid A *quadrilateral* with exactly one pair of *parallel sides*.

tree diagram A diagram in which all the possible *outcomes* of a given event are displayed.

trial A test or experiment.

turn (See *rotation*.)

unit price The cost of a single item or the cost per unit of measurement.

unit rate A *rate* in which the second measurement or amount is 1 unit.

unlikely An *outcome* is unlikely if it probably will not happen.

value The *product* of a digit multiplied by its *place*.

variable A symbol used to represent a number or numbers.

Venn diagram A diagram that uses overlapping circles to organize and show data.

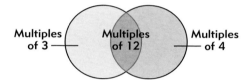

Multiples of 3 — Multiples of 12 — Multiples of 4

vertex (plural: vertices) a. The *point* where two rays meet in an *angle*. **b.** The point where three or more *edges* of a *3-dimensional* figure meet.

volume The amount of space that a *3-dimensional figure* encloses, expressed in cubic units.

weight A measure of the force of gravity that attracts an object to the center of Earth. (See *Table of Measures*)

whole number Any one of the numbers, 0, 1, 2, 3, and so on.

Z

Zero Property of Multiplication The *product* of any *factor* and 0 equals 0.

Name _____

Coins

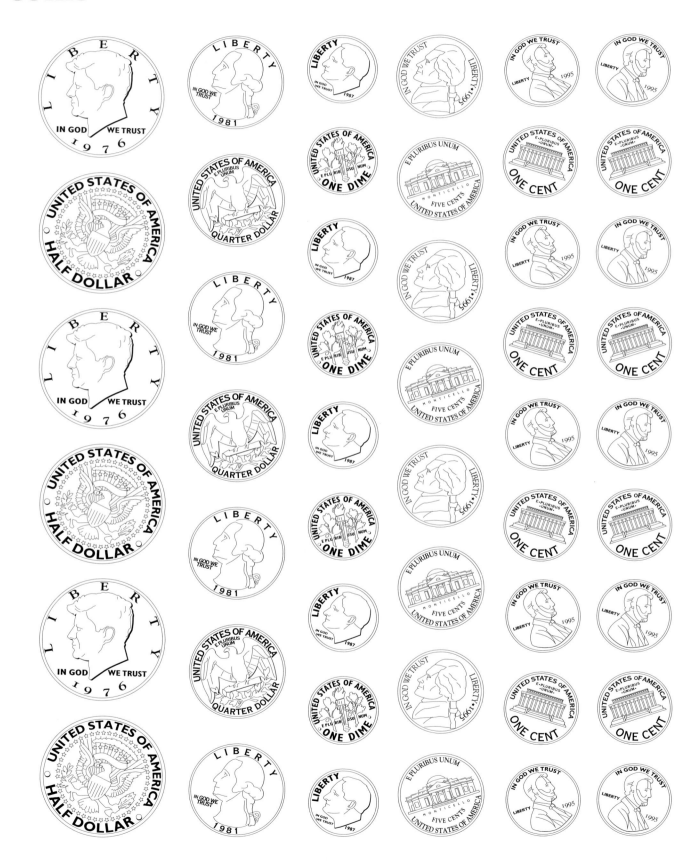

Teacher Tool

Name _____

Place-Value Charts

Millions Period			Thousands Period			Ones Period		
Hundreds	Tens	Ones	Hundreds	Tens	Ones	Hundreds	Tens	Ones

Ones	•	Tenths	Hundredths
	•		
	•		
	•		
	•		
	•		
	•		
	•		
	•		
	•		

Teacher Tool

Name

Bills

 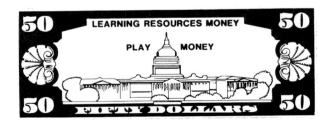

Name _____

Number Cube Patterns

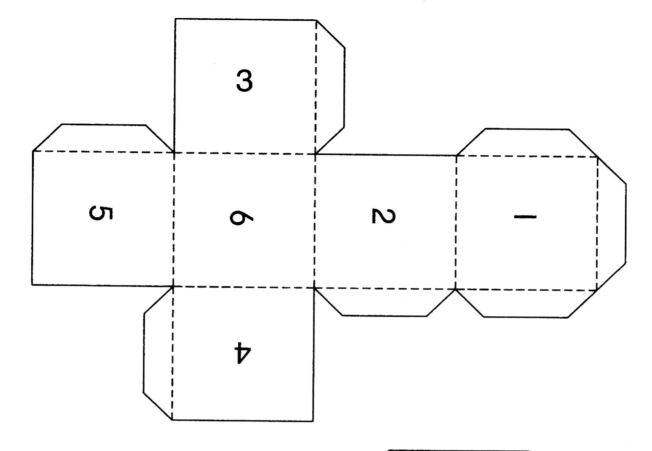

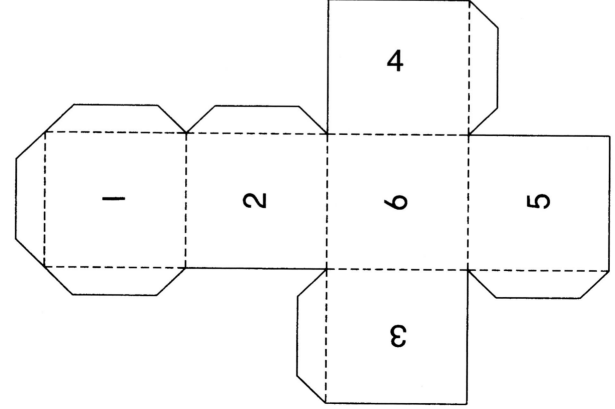

Name

Two-Color Counters

Name _____

Grid Paper

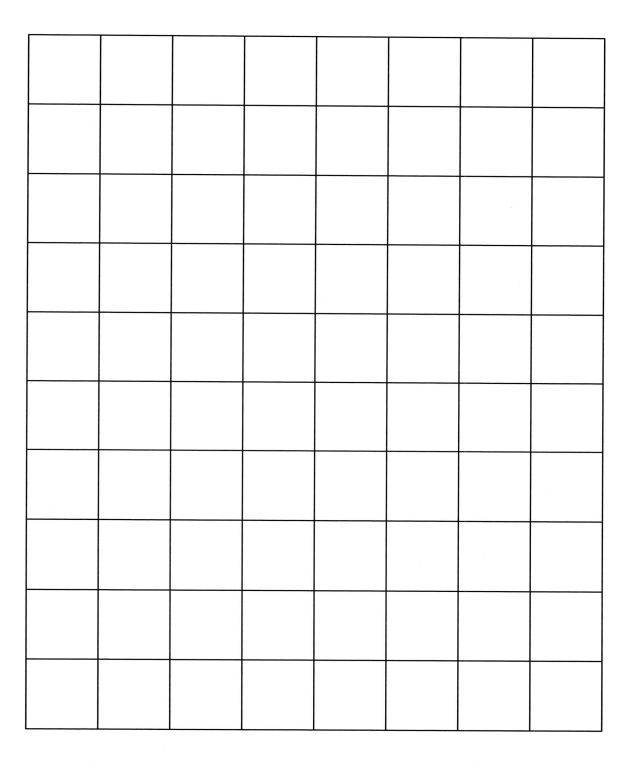

Name_____

10 x 10 Grid

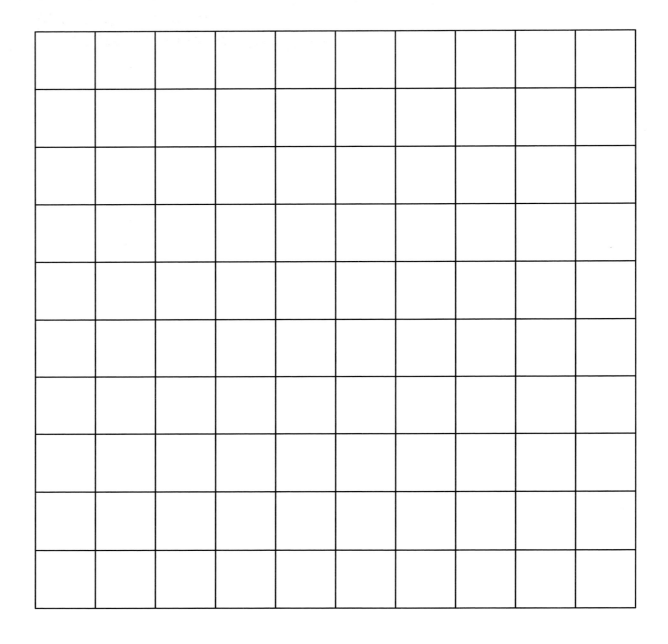

Name _____

Graph Paper

Name_____

Inch Graph Paper

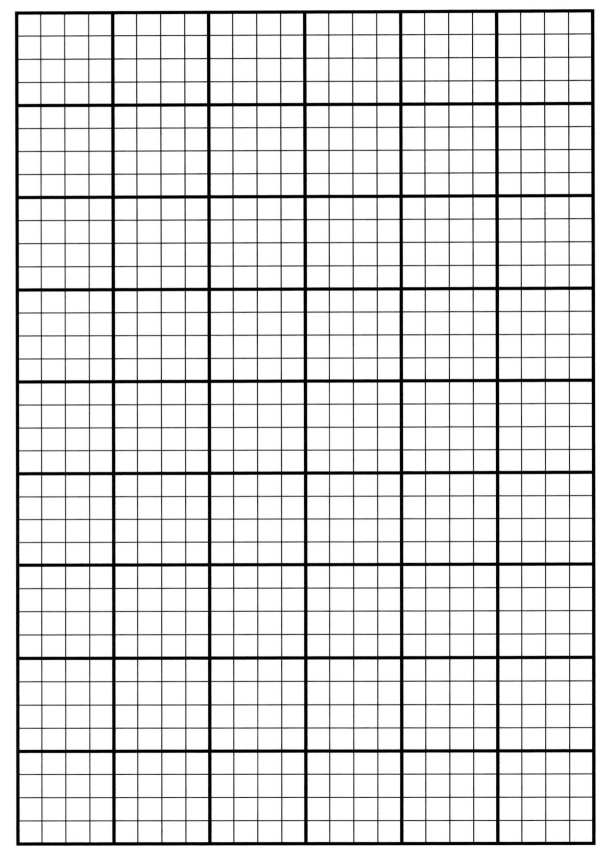

Teacher Tool

Name _____

Fraction Strips

| $\frac{1}{12}$ | $\frac{1}{12}$ | $\frac{1}{12}$ | $\frac{1}{12}$ | $\frac{1}{12}$ | $\frac{1}{12}$ | $\frac{1}{12}$ | $\frac{1}{12}$ | $\frac{1}{12}$ | $\frac{1}{12}$ | $\frac{1}{12}$ | $\frac{1}{12}$ |

| $\frac{1}{10}$ | $\frac{1}{10}$ | $\frac{1}{10}$ | $\frac{1}{10}$ | $\frac{1}{10}$ | $\frac{1}{10}$ | $\frac{1}{10}$ | $\frac{1}{10}$ | $\frac{1}{10}$ | $\frac{1}{10}$ |

| $\frac{1}{8}$ | $\frac{1}{8}$ | $\frac{1}{8}$ | $\frac{1}{8}$ | $\frac{1}{8}$ | $\frac{1}{8}$ | $\frac{1}{8}$ | $\frac{1}{8}$ |

| $\frac{1}{6}$ | $\frac{1}{6}$ | $\frac{1}{6}$ | $\frac{1}{6}$ | $\frac{1}{6}$ | $\frac{1}{6}$ |

| $\frac{1}{5}$ | $\frac{1}{5}$ | $\frac{1}{5}$ | $\frac{1}{5}$ | $\frac{1}{5}$ |

| $\frac{1}{4}$ | $\frac{1}{4}$ | $\frac{1}{4}$ | $\frac{1}{4}$ |

| $\frac{1}{3}$ | $\frac{1}{3}$ | $\frac{1}{3}$ |

| $\frac{1}{2}$ | $\frac{1}{2}$ |

| 1 |

© Macmillan/McGraw-Hill

Teacher Tool

Spinner

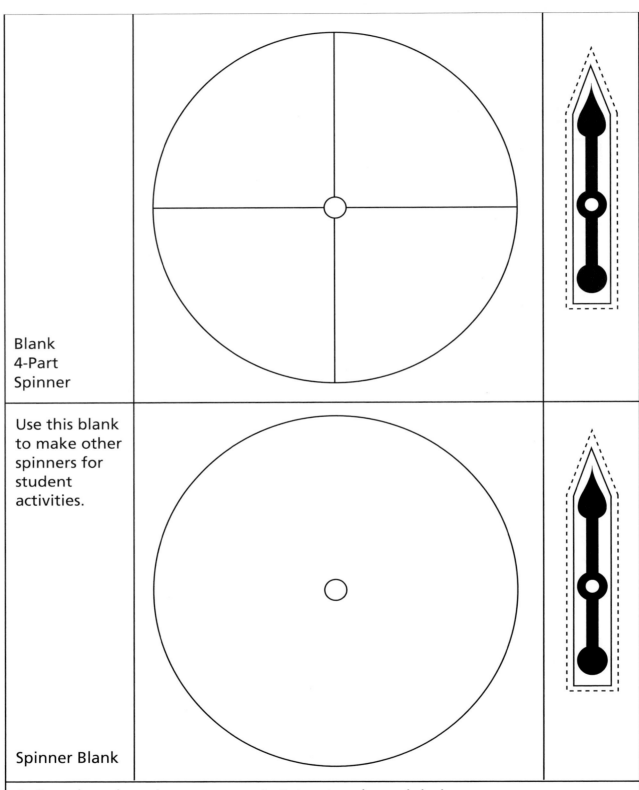

Blank
4-Part
Spinner

Use this blank to make other spinners for student activities.

Spinner Blank

1. Complete the spinner
2. Add color.
3. Mount on heavy paper.

4. Cut out and punch holes.
5. Attach spinner with a paper fastener.

Name _____

Analog Clockface

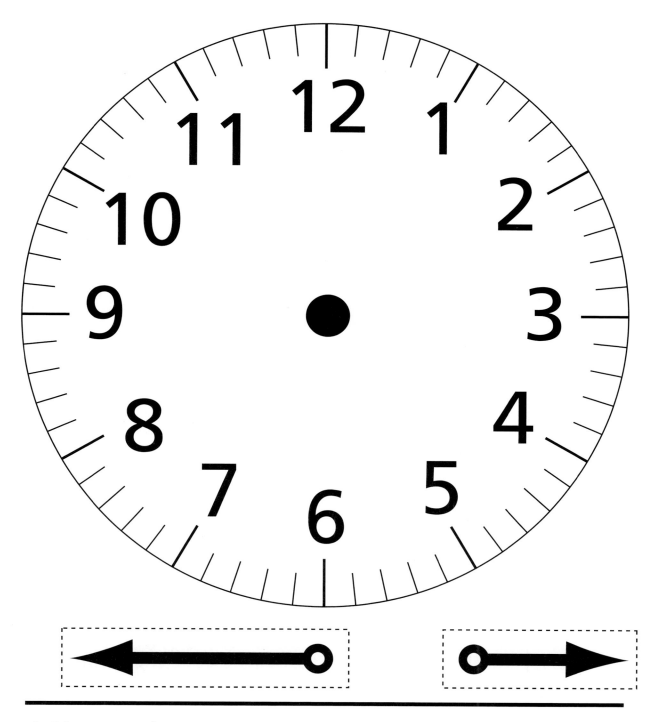

1. Mount on heavy paper.
2. Cut out the clock hands.
3. Attach them to the clock with a paper fastener.

Name _____

Ruler/Protractor

To make a 12-inch ruler:
1. Cut out ruler strips.
2. Glue the strips together to form a 12-inch ruler.

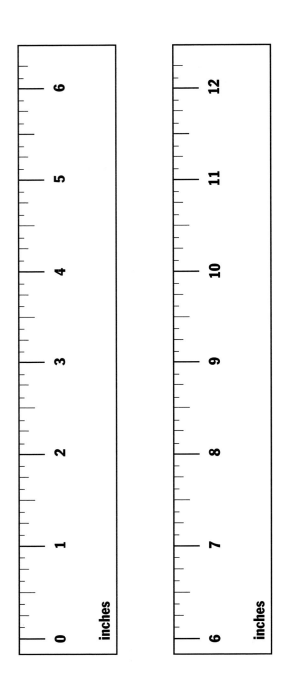

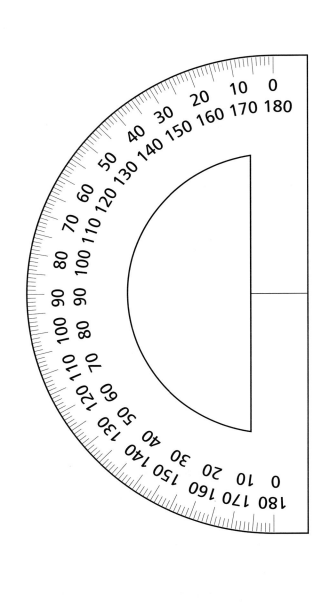

Name _____

Tangram Shapes

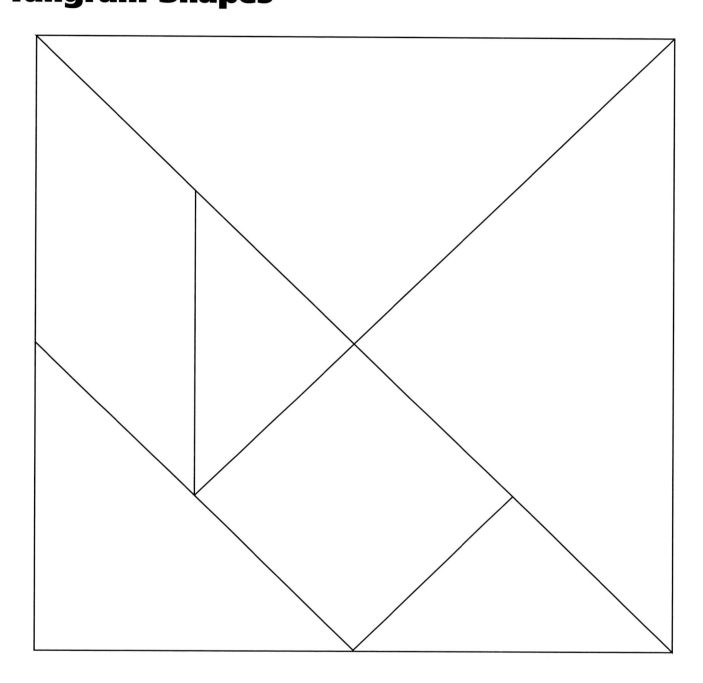

1. Cut on the lines.
2. Use the shapes to form a picture or a pattern.
3. You may wish to color the shapes before cutting.

Teacher Tool

Name _____

Metric Measuring Tape (1 Meter)

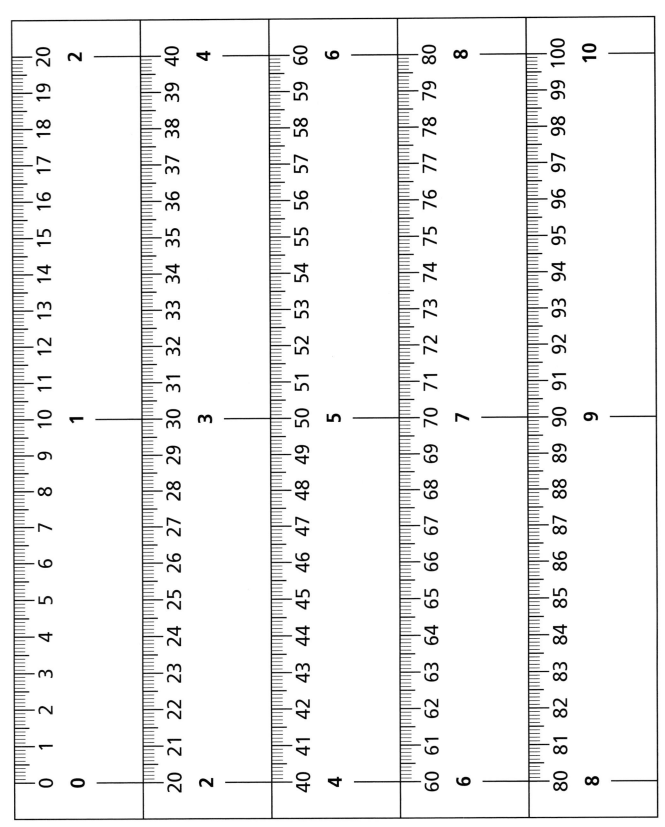

1. Cut strips apart. 2. Tape together for a metric measuring tape.

Name

Triangles

Name

2-Dimensional Shapes

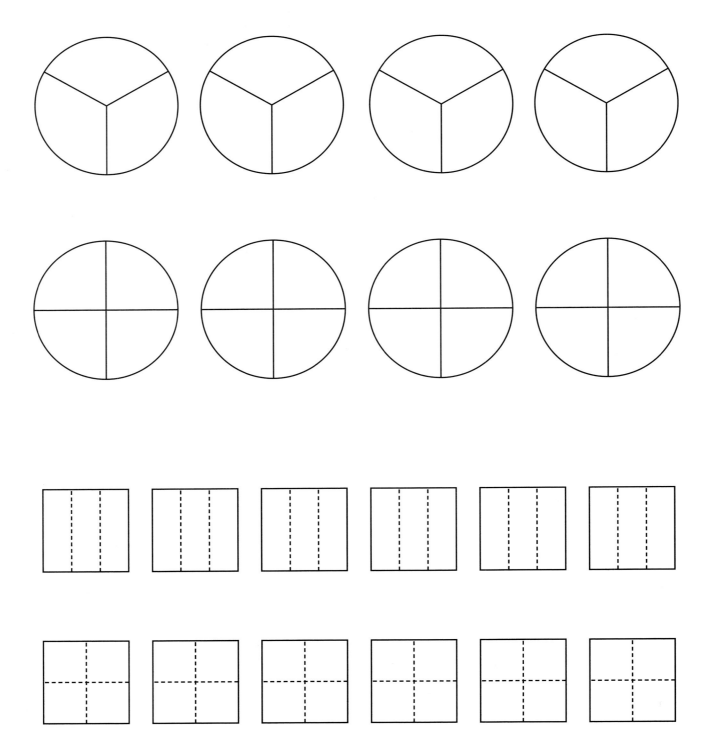

Four–Column Chart

Graphic Organizer

Word Web

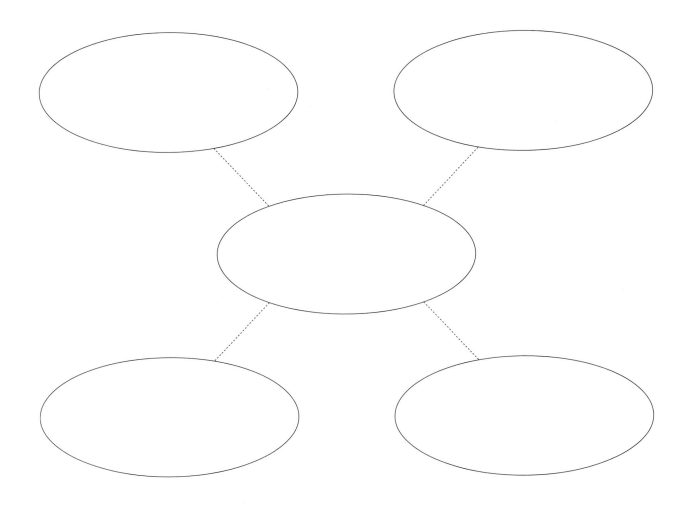

Main Idea Pyramid

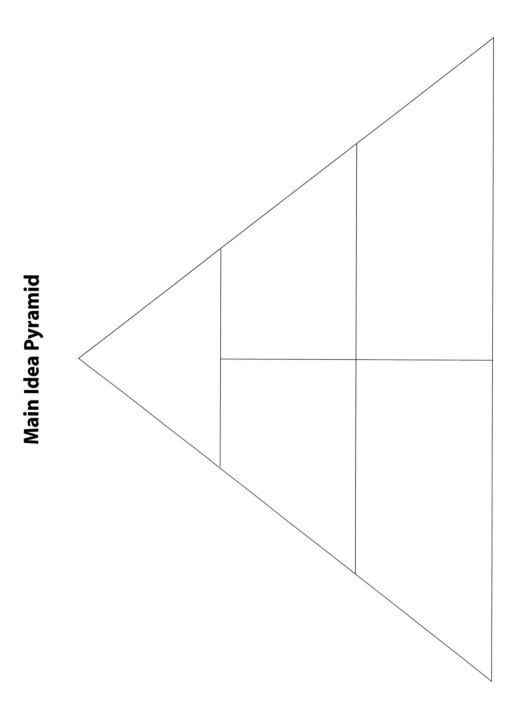

Graphic Organizer

Main Idea and Supporting Details

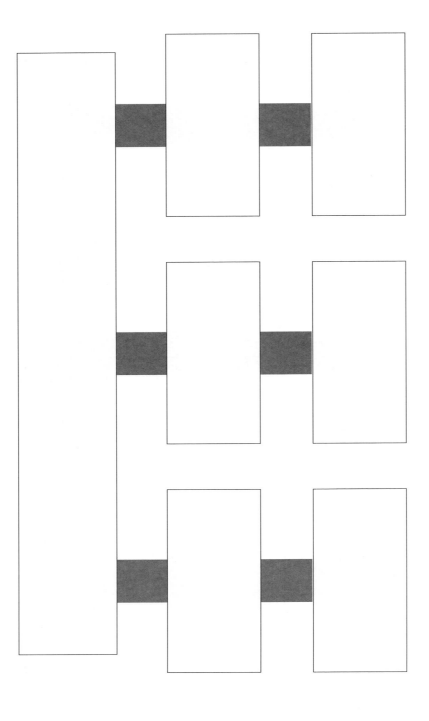

Cause and Effect Table

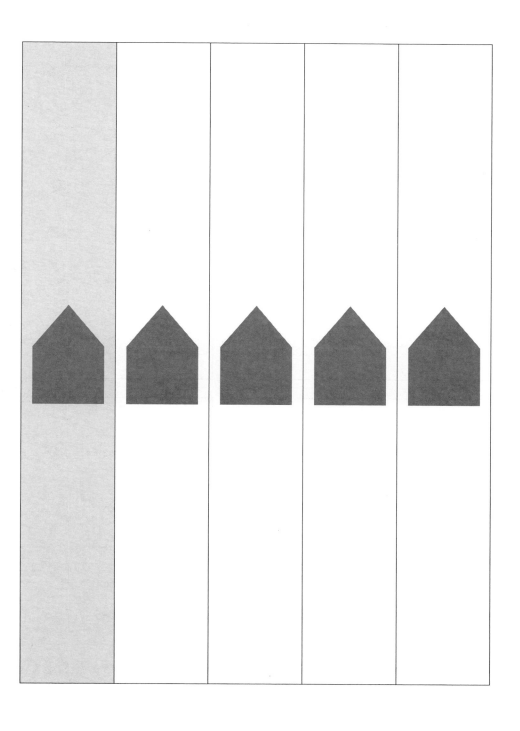

Answer Key

Language-Free Math Inventory

Name _____ **Date** _____

Math Inventory

A. Write Whole Numbers to 1,000,000

999,994	999,995	999,996	999,997	999,998	999,999	1,000,000
79,997	79,998	79,999	80,000	80,001	80,002	80,003
699,997	699,998	699,999	700,000	700,001	700,002	700,003

B. Write Decimals

63.1	63.2	63.3	63.4	63.5	63.6	63.7	63.8	63.9	64
5.42	5.43	5.44	5.45	5.46	5.47	5.48	5.49	5.5	5.51

C. Compare Whole Numbers and Decimals

$<$ $=$ $>$

$127,643 < 127,644$ $131,584 = 131,584$

$500,300 < 530,000$ $640,000 > 604,000$

$55 > 5.5$ $82.03 < 82.3$

$2.71 < 27.01$ $4.28 < 428$

Math Inventory **1**

Name _____ **Date** _____

Math Inventory

D. Order Whole Numbers, Fractions, and Mixed Numbers on a Number Line

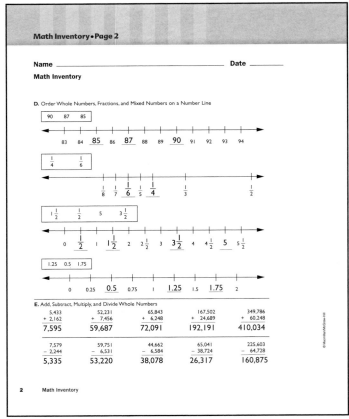

E. Add, Subtract, Multiply, and Divide Whole Numbers

5,433 + 2,162 **7,595**	52,231 + 7,456 **59,687**	65,843 + 6,248 **72,091**	167,502 + 24,689 **192,191**	349,786 + 60,248 **410,034**
7,579 − 2,244 **5,335**	59,751 − 6,531 **53,220**	44,662 − 6,584 **38,078**	65,041 − 38,724 **26,317**	225,603 − 64,728 **160,875**

2 Math Inventory

Name _____ **Date** _____

Math Inventory

513 × 23 **11,799**	323 × 52 **16,796**	42,313 × 22 **930,886**	75 × 64 **4,800**
269 × 43 **11,567**	823 × 58 **47,734**	3,595 × 65 **233,675**	25,261 × 37 **934,657**

13,232 3)39,696	**32,122** 2)64,244	**8,382** 4)33,528	**10,873** 6)65,238

F. Evaluating Expressions

$(36 − 14) − 8 = $ **14** $(25 − 10) − 6 = $ **9**

$36 − (14 − 8) = $ **30** $25 − (10 − 6) = $ **21**

$(2 × 12) − (16 ÷ 4) + 5 = $ **25** $(10 × 3) − (24 ÷ 8) + 6 = $ **33**

$(12 + 16) ÷ 7 + 8 = $ **12** $(8 + 8) ÷ 4 + 10 × 2 = $ **24**

$(22 + 11) ÷ 3 + 7 = $ **18** $(13 + 17) ÷ 6 + 5 × 3 = $ **20**

Math Inventory **3**

Name _____ **Date** _____

Math Inventory

G. Graphing Equations

$y = 2x + 3$

x	y
2	7
3	9
5	13
8	19

$x + 5 = y$

x	y
15	3
25	5
40	8
100	20

H. Solving Equations

$6 + 4 = (2 × 3) + $ **4** $8 × 2 = (4 + 4) × $ **2**

$0 + 7 = (8 − 8) + $ **7** $5 × 5 = (2 + 3) × $ **5**

$x − 3 = 5$ $7x = 35$

$x = $ **8** $x = $ **5**

I. Prime Numbers

2	3	5	7	11

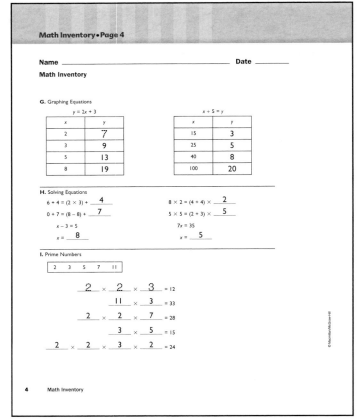

4 Math Inventory

290 Answer Key

Answer Key

Language-Free Math Inventory

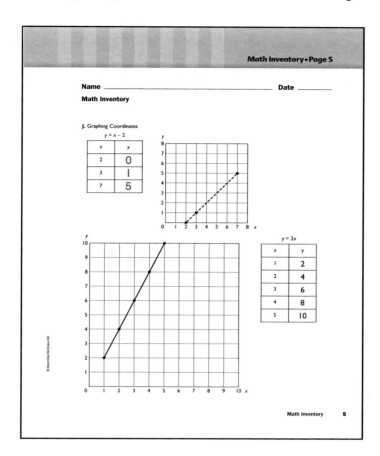

Name _____ Date _____

Math Inventory

J. Graphing Coordinates

y = x − 2

x	y
2	0
3	1
7	5

y = 2x

x	y
1	2
2	4
3	6
4	8
5	10

Math Inventory   5

UNIT 1 ACTIVITIES

1. Game
2. Results will vary.
3. Game
4. **One:** 218; **Two:** 290; **Three:** $4.47; **Four:** 260.

MATH CENTER CARDS
Card 1A

1. How many of each kind of bill are in circulation
2. Which kind of bill is most common and which is least common
3. Greatest $10; least $2
4. $10; $1; $20; $100; $5; $50; $2

Card 1B

1. How many sit-ups he plans to add on the second, third, and fourth days
2. How many sit-ups he will do on the tenth day
3. 119
4. Possible answer: No, he plans to add too many each day so that he will quickly reach more than he can possibly do.
5. Possible answer: He could add 2 sit-ups each day.

UNIT 2 ACTIVITIES

1. Answers will vary.
2. **One:** product is 12 no matter which row or column is multiplied. **Two:** product is 12,000 no matter which row or column is multiplied.
3. Game
4. **One:** 3 x 3 x 447 = 4023. **Two:** 3 x 3 x 186 = 1674. **Three:** 3 x 3 x 400 = 3600.

MATH CENTER CARDS
Card 2A

1. You can estimate, because you want an idea, not the exact cost.
2. Exact number; you don't want too many or too few tiles.
3. Estimate; a gallon covers 350 square feet. You need to know only if the walls are more or less than 350 square feet.

Card 2B

1. $(9 \times 2) + (9 \times 4) = 18 + 36 = 54$
2. $(8 \times 2) + (10 \times 4) = 16 + 40 = 56$
3. $(6 \times 2) + (12 \times 4) = 12 + 48 = 60$

UNIT 3 ACTIVITIES

1. $23.8 \div 4 = 5.95$; $28.32 \div 3 = 9.44$; $23.55 \div 5 = 4.71$; $15.12 \div 7 = 2.16$; $34.96 \div 8 = 4.37$.

2. Tomato soup: 16, 0; Tuna fish: 12, 4; Apple juice: 21, 2; Olives: 62, 2.

3. Game

4. One: $54.3 \div 2 = 27.15$; **Two:** $2.34 \div 5 = .468$; **Three:** $42.5 \div 3 = 14.17$.

MATH CENTER CARDS
Card 3A

1. $127 \div 8 = 15R7$. Because there is a remainder, you need 16 packages.

2. $127 \div 6 = 21R1$. Because there is a remainder, you need to make 22 batches.

3. 2 (cookies) $\times 127 = 254$; $254 \div 24 = 10R14$. Multiply each ingredient of the recipe by 11. The remainder of 14 means that 10 batches of cookies won't be enough.

Card 3B

1. 8 obstacles; $66 - 10 = 56$ points; $56 \div 7 = 8$

2. Answers may vary.

UNIT 4 ACTIVITIES

1. 20 (Diagram A); 27 (Diagram A); 66 (Diagram B)

2. Ari has 313 cards and Carol has 349 cards; 10, 15, 15, 15, 20.

3. Game

4. Answers will vary.

MATH CENTER CARDS
Card 4A

1.

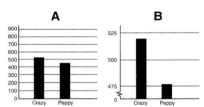

2. Graph B, because the scale is smaller and doesn't begin at zero, it appears that many more people prefer Crazy Cola.

Card 4B

1. Line graph, because it shows change over time

2. Bar graph, because it compares different quantities

3.–4. Check students' work.

UNIT 5 ACTIVITIES

1. 1. $3 + 13$; **2.** $7 + 7$; **3.** $11 + 17$; **4.** $13 + 17$; **5.** $31 + 5$ or $29 + 7$ or $17 + 19$; **6.** $3 + 39$ or $5 + 37$ or $11 + 31$ or $13 + 29$ or $19 + 23$; **7.** $3 + 53$ or $5 + 51$ or $13 + 43$ or $17 + 39$ or $19 + 37$; **8.** $3 + 59$ or $5 + 57$ or $11 + 51$ or $19 + 43$; **9.** $5 + 73$ or $7 + 71$ or $11 + 67$ or $17 + 61$ or $19 + 59$ or $31 + 47$; **10.** $3 + 97$ or $7 + 93$ or $11 + 89$ or $13 + 87$ or $17 + 83$ or $29 + 71$ or $41 + 59$ or $43 + 57$ or $47 + 53$; **11.** No. Cf. Commutative Property of Addition.

2. 1. 4 is GCF; **2.** 10 is GCF; **3.** 4 is GCF; **4.** 6 is GCF. **Word problem:** 24.

3. Game

4. Game

MATH CENTER CARDS
Card 5A

1. $\frac{13}{24}$

2. Can't answer because some students may be in both band and chorus; you need to know how many students are in both groups.

3. 15 students

4. Can't answer; you need to know the number of students who belong to more than one club.

Card 5B: Game, no answers

UNIT 6 ACTIVITIES

1. Results will vary.

2. Game

3. Game

4. 1. $16\frac{3}{4}$; **2.** $1\frac{7}{8}$; **3.** 1; **4.** $\frac{1}{8}$.

MATH CENTER CARDS
Card 6A

1. $4\frac{3}{16}$ inches; add because you need to know how long the head, tail, and body are together.

2. 4 inches; subtract because you need to know the difference between the two lengths.

3. $\frac{1}{8}$ inch; subtract because you need to know the difference between the two lengths.

Card 6B

2. $8\frac{1}{2} - 1\frac{1}{4} = 7\frac{1}{4}$ minutes

3. $15 - 7\frac{1}{2} - 1\frac{3}{4} - 5 = \frac{3}{4}$ minute or 45 seconds

UNIT 7 ACTIVITIES

1. Students use shapes and write sentences to show answers.

2. Game

3. Game

4. Students subdivide rectangles to show answers.

MATH CENTER CARDS
Card 7A

1. Possible answer: **1.** Add the fractions to find what fraction of the class was in an activity. **2.** Multiply the fraction by the total number of students in the class to find how many are in activities. **3.** Find half of this number.

2. Add the fractions: $\frac{1}{5} + \frac{2}{3} = \frac{3}{15} + \frac{10}{15} = \frac{13}{15}$ of the class were in activities. Multiply the fraction by the total number of students in the class to find how many are in activities.

3. Find half of this number.

Card 7B

1. 15

2. 6

3. 21

UNIT 8 ACTIVITIES

1. Game

2. Results will vary.

3. Game

4. Game

MATH CENTER CARDS
Card 8A

1. Olga is right. Fred divided by 3 instead of multiplying by 3.

2. 2. Fred is right. Divide 103 yd by 0.5 yd, or divide 309 ft by 1.5 ft. Olga divided 103 yd by 1.5 yd.

Card 8B

1. 6 stop signs

2. 10 stoplights

UNIT 9 ACTIVITIES

1. **1.** 11.1, 9.25, 8.4, 6.8; **2.** 5.2, 6.8; **3.** 4, 5.2, 6.8, 8.4; **4.** 8.4, 9.25.
2. Answers will vary.
3. Game
4. Answers will vary.

MATH CENTER CARDS
Card 9A

1. 1 cm
2. 4 cm
3. 19 cm
4. No, it is not likely. Possible answers: The plant may reach its maximum size; Marco may forget to water it; its growth may slow down, etc.

Card 9B

1. $16.50
2. 10 days

UNIT 10 ACTIVITIES

1. Check students' figures.
2. Game
3. Game
4. Game

MATH CENTER CARDS
Card 10A

1. No
2. Yes; 7 inches

Card 10B

Diagram Number	1	2	3	4	5	10	25
Number of Squares	1	4	9	16	25	100	625

4. You get the number of squares. The bottom numbers are squares of the diagram numbers.
5. 100 tiles; 625 tiles

UNIT 11 ACTIVITIES

1. Results will vary.
2. Area of 30: E, L, P, F, U, O, R, W. Area of 24: S, M, A, T, H, I. Sentence then becomes: "Math is powerful."
3. Game

4. **1.** Yes, the perimeter is 117 km + 230 km + 39 km + 120 km + 78 km + 350 km = 934 km.
   2. The additional fencing he needs is 39 km + 120 km = 159 km. Farmer Dell has 66 km left over from before. 159 km − 66 km = 93 additional km of fencing he will need to purchase.

MATH CENTER CARDS
Card 11A

1. **a.** area, find the length and width of floor; **b.** perimeter, measure distance around the room, not counting the door; **c.** perimeter, measure the distance around the window (or measure the length and width of window); **d.** area, measure width and height of each wall; **e.** area, measure the dimensions of the window
2. Possible answers: area, new roof; perimeter, plant flowers around outside of shed

Card 11B: Answers will vary.

UNIT 12 ACTIVITIES

1. Green (72), Red (56), Yellow (40), Blue (32), Orange (32), Purple (30).
2. Results will vary.
3. Game
4. Triangle: 3; Square: 4; Pentagon: 5; Hexagon: 6; Octagon: 8. A regular polygon will have as many lines of symmetry as it has sides.

MATH CENTER CARDS

Card 12A: Answers will vary.

Card 12B: Answers will vary. Check students' drawings to be sure there are seats for 11 students and that the 2 art supply tables have only 1 seat.

UNIT 13 ACTIVITIES

1. 136 perch, 102 halibut, 68 trout. Answers will vary, but students must find numbers between 300 and 350 that are multiples of 9.

2. Results will vary.
3. Game
4. Results will vary.

MATH CENTER CARDS
Card 13A

1. No; he will make $15 each day, so he will make $75 for the week.
2. There will be enough flour and sugar, but not enough eggs. He neds 2 eggs for each batch, so he needs 8 eggs in all.
3. Yes; $100 ÷ $5 = 20.
4. No; this will be too many muffins. Each batch makes 12 muffins, and $12 \times 6 = 72$ muffins. He only needs to make 4 batches.

Card 13B: Predictions and answers may vary.

UNIT 14 ACTIVITIES

1. **1.** 39% nonfiction.
   2. 38% dinner. Results will vary.
   3. 10% Transportation.
   4. 22% violinist.
2. $14.00. Answers will vary.
3. Game
4. Results will vary.

MATH CENTER CARDS
Card 14A

Main dish: pizza ($35\% = .35 = \frac{35}{100}$); chicken nuggets ($25\% = .25 = \frac{25}{100}$); macaroni and cheese ($18\% = .18 = \frac{18}{100}$); hamburgers ($16\% = .16 = \frac{16}{100}$); other ($6\% = .06 = \frac{6}{100}$). Desserts: cupcakes ($32\% = .32 = \frac{32}{100}$); pudding ($27\% = .27 = \frac{27}{100}$); fruit ($21\% = .21 = \frac{21}{100}$); cookies ($16\% = .16 = \frac{16}{100}$); other ($4\% = .04 = \frac{4}{100}$)

Card 14B

2. a. 4; b. 2; c. 13

© Macmillan/McGraw-Hill

Index

Acknowledgments

"Bushy-Tailed Mathematicians" from COUNTING CATERPILLARS AND OTHER MATH POEMS by Betsy Franco. Copyright © 1998 by Betsy Franco. Scholastic Professional Books.

"The Doorbell Rang" by Pat Hutchins. Copyright © 1986 by Pat Hutchins. By permission of Greenwillow Books (A Division of William Morrow & Co.).

"The Pet Graph" from POEMS TO COUNT ON by Sandra Liatsos. Copyright © 1995 by Sandra O. Liatsos. Scholastic Professional Books.

"The Birthday Party Surprise!" by Margarita Kurtz. By permission of the author.

"Mathemagician!" Sandra Liatsos. Copyright © 1993 by Sandra Liatsos. Use by permission of Marian Reiner for the author.

"Matharena — Linear Equations" Lyrics by Vicki Young from website: **http://www.mscc.cc.tn.us/webs/vyoung/songs/math.html**.

"Surprising Symmetry" from COUNTING CATERPILLARS AND OTHER MATH POEMS by Betsy Franco. Copyright © 1998 by Betsy Franco. Scholastic Professional Books.

"For Any Equation," a poem by Michael Garin. Reprinted with permission of the author.

"Shapes" from A LIGHT IN THE ATTIC by Shel Silverstein. Copyright © 1981 by Evil Eye Music, Inc. Reprinted by permission of HarperCollins Publishers, Inc.

"A Square Story," a poem by Michael Garin. Reprinted with permission of the author.

"Too Clever By Half," a poem by Michael Garin. Reprinted with permission of the author.